Geology of GRANITE

Geology of GRANITE

by

E. RAGUIN

*Professeur de Géologie appliquée
à l'Ecole des Mines de Paris, France*

with a Foreword by

C. E. WEGMANN

Translated from the second French edition by

E. H. KRANCK and P. R. EAKINS

*Department of Geological Sciences,
McGill University, Canada*

with

Jean M. EAKINS

1965

INTERSCIENCE PUBLISHERS
a division of John Wiley & Sons Ltd.
LONDON – NEW YORK – SYDNEY

First published under RAGUIN, *Géologie du Granite*, by Masson
et Cie., Paris, 1957.

Library of Congress Catalog Card Number 65–16745

Set in 12 point Bembo.
Made and printed in Great Britain by Page Bros. (Norwich) Ltd.

TRANSLATORS' ACKNOWLEDGEMENT

We wish to thank Professor James E. Gill for his careful reading of the final manuscript.

E.H.K
P.R.E
J.M.E

CONTENTS

Foreword xi

1 General Statements 1
 Definition of granite 1
 The time factor and the evolution of granite . . . 4
 Concepts and terminology 4
 Comments on the plan of study 7

2 The Composition of Granite 9
 The minerals of granite 9
 Structure and texture of granite 15
 Evolution of granite on the scale of the crystal . . . 18
 Chemical composition and classification 28

3 Granites as They Occur: Granite in Circumscribed Massifs . 30
 The batholiths 30
 The stratiform massifs 36
 Subvolcanic massifs 39
 Depth of the emplacement of granites 42
 Conclusion 43

4 Granites as They Occur: The Anatectic Granites with Suites
 of Migmatites 45
 Description of anatexis 46
 The overall structure of migmatite massifs 49
 Granites of intermediate type 53
 Petrogenesis of migmatites 54
 Experimental anatexis 56
 Chemical composition of anatectic granites . . . 57

5 Assimilation by Granite 59
 The marginal facies of granite 60
 The inclusions or enclaves 72
 Endomorphism 80
 Conclusion 84

6 The Granite Aureole 86
 The products of metamorphism 87
 The development and structures of contact metamorphism . 90
 The chemical fronts in the aureole 93
 Mechanical deformations in the aureole 106

Surfaces of discontinuity of the aureole; screens; the granitization front 108
The relationship between contact metamorphism and assimilation 110

7 The Geometric Structure of Granite Massifs . . . 112
Oriented elements of the plastic stage 113
Oriented elements in the rigid phase 114
Granite tectonics 116
Mechanical effects at the borders 118
Petrofabric analysis (*Structurologie*) 122
Conclusion 123

8 Differentiation of Granites 125
Magmatic differentiation and generalizations . . . 125
The facies of variation of granites 129
Statistical study of the variations in a granite massif . . 130
The composite massifs 131
The lithologic series 134
Conclusion 136

9 The Dyke and Vein Satellites of Granite 137
Aplites and pegmatites 139
Lamprophyres 153
Porphyries 156
Conclusion 158

10 Weathering and Crushing of Granite 160
Weathering 160
The crushing of granites 165

11 Granitization and Metamorphism 173
Definitions of the three types of metamorphism . . . 173
Factors in general metamorphism 177
Rearrangement of material during general metamorphism . 188
Connections between general metamorphism and granite . 193

12 Granite and Orogeny 195
Anatectic granites and syntectonic migmatites . . . 196
Migmatites in an immobile environment 201
Synkinematic granites 201
Post-tectonic granites 203
Atectonic granites 204
Connection between granitization and orogeny . . . 204
Conclusion 211

13 Granite and Volcanism 212
    The subvolcanic granite massifs 213
    Transition from plutonic to volcanic rocks 215
    Dyke suites of granite and their volcanic affinities . . 218
    Metallogenic volcanism 221
    Relationships between granites and older volcanic formations 223
    Conclusions concerning the relationship of volcanism and
        granitic plutonism 226

14 Granitic Metallogenesis 230
    Essential characteristics 230
    Origins of the metals of the deposits 232
    Mode of deposition 235
    Are the metallogenic granites of a special nature? . . 237
    Principal parageneses 240
    The granitic deposits in the metallogenic classification . . 241
    Conclusion 245

15 The Radioactivity of Granite 247
    Uranium deposits 247
    Thorium deposits 251
    Granite and the metallogenesis of uranium 252
    Conclusion 255

16 Granite in the Earth's Crust 257
    The notion of Earth's crust 257
    Beneath the terrestrial crust: the sima 259
    The granitized domains of the crust 267
    Conclusion 268

17 The Problem of the Formation and Emplacement of Granite 270
    Temperature of formation 271
    The physical state of granite before crystallization . . 274
    Aspects of the formation of granite 280
    Hypotheses on the mechanisms of the emplacement of granite 288
    Conclusion 296

Bibliography 299
Glossary of Terms 313

FOREWORD

The title of Eugène Raguin's work, *Geology of Granite*, encompasses a program much broader than most petrographic accounts. It in fact renders to this subject all its complexity and its fundamental importance. Covering a vast assemblage of knowledge, it touches on all the domains of the earth sciences, for the geology of granitic rocks cannot be limited to the study of phenomena pertaining to one order of magnitude, as for example the study of ore minerals or the proportions of chemical elements. It embraces a vast dimensional spectrum, for it involves atomic or molecular proportions equally as well as the crystalline species and their assemblages, and the external forms of veins and massifs and their internal structures, while not neglecting the great units of the Earth's crust, the mountain chains, the continents and the oceanic basins.

The geology of granite sorts out observations made at the present topographic surface: it records and interprets the manifestations of the displacements in the depths of the Earth's crust. It labours over completed structures without ever having seen the processes forming the structures in action. It has a historical perspective for it applies as well to the granitic rocks of ancient platforms as to those emplaced during the cycle of Alpine deformations. It takes into account, on the one hand, the results of the experimental sciences, and on the other hand the methods of kinematic reconstructions of the traces of movements in the past. It attempts to return to their place in space and in time objects of diverse magnitudes in reconstructing a series of synchronous geometric images. These more or less hypothetical images are generally bound together by a few guiding ideas which form a series of invisible channels along which the sequences travel and which they only rarely seem to leave. It is thus necessary to separate the observations from the reconstructions and the guiding ideas, a very difficult task, for what is in one domain accepted knowledge is subjected to doubt in another, a fact which this book illustrates in abundance.

The greater part of the methods of investigation are based on a few assumptions, and these assumptions strongly influence the results. One of the most interesting studies is that of the relationships between the structure of premises, the methods and the results. But studies of this genre are only possible if one is aware of the hypothetical character of the premises and their provisional nature. The history of geology reveals numerous cases where assumptions of this type have been transformed into dogma in the hands of a leader of a school, and above all in the handing on to disciples; the examples seem to show that the less an assumption is verifiable, the more easily it becomes entrenched as dogma. This transformation, once accomplished, is almost impossible to reverse and it hinders by its very nature a view of the subject from another angle.

The geology of granitic rocks is obliged to consider the same facts from very different angles and to see them in different perspectives. It must take into account the multiple significance that a single phenomenon can possess when reviewed in the context of the entire subject. Moreover one must be aware that the serial arrangements that we impose on the data are only a few of a great number of possibilities and that our solutions are only relative and provisional.

The task of setting forth such a subject intended for young researchers, of leading them through the labyrinth of theory to the limits of the unexplored, is formidable. Our gratitude is all the greater to him who offers us this invaluable guide which makes one think, not by polemics, but by throwing light on the subject from different sides, and by making apparent the many difficulties. It is a vast panorama which he unfolds before us. In comparing it to the opinions so widely held some tens of years ago, he makes us realize the ground covered: at that time one often heard the affirmation that the geologists and the tectonists could not provide valid observations and that they had to hold their tongues in the discussions concerning the genesis and emplacement of granitic rocks, for the subject was reserved for the petrochemists. The hotbeds of general interest have shifted in the course of the years. These shifts were not made without lively discussions and not without old prejudices, weighty with the prestige of a great name, being reduced to their proper character of provisional hypotheses. Each of these awakenings was followed by a rich harvest of new facts and a stirring up of new ideas. The new results have not always escaped ossification, as this is in the nature of evolution. Let us be grateful to Eugène Raguin, who throws light successively on the various sectors, and who makes us aware of the dangers of a closed and rigid science.

In comparing the different attempts to organize the great variability of phenomena, one discovers that one has applied a certain number of cipher-stencils to decode the cryptograms of Nature. Because of this fact, the answers depend in large part on the structure of the stencils used. It is thus important to compare stencils and to attempt to classify them. The answers which one obtains by employing different stencils are often contradictory. If one stops at this point, one encounters a certain number of antinomies. These antinomies merit special attention, because on their resolution depend the concepts of the future. The present work places before us a series of such antinomies and hints at solutions.

Among the numerous methods of interpretation, one group plays a particularly important role: this is that of the processes of the *reconstruction of movements*. The observations in the field provide us only with traces. This is what explains the decisive role of the methods of kinematic interpretation, permitting a reconstruction of the emplacement of granitic rocks.

Movements can take place on several orders of magnitude. The units, mobile in relation to one another, pertaining to each of these orders, have distinctive characteristics and are subjected to energy fields of different types, as for example gravitational field, lattice energies, temperature gradients, etc. The magnitudes and the nature of the mobile units, as well as their combinations, allow the classification of different theories. The principal mobile units are: atoms, ions and molecules, mobile in molten masses, in aqueous and gaseous solutions, and, in a different manner, in intergranular films, the crystalline lattices and mosaics; other movable units are crystals or fragments of crystals allowing the transport of assemblages of elementary particles. On a still greater scale one will distinguish homogeneous masses of variable magnitude, moving in relation to assemblages of different composition; these are the rock masses, assemblages of crystals, molten masses, liquids or gases which are displaced in relation to other rocks.

The combination of systems of mobile units is characteristic for the different theories for the hypotheses on the chemical differentiation as well as for the emplacement of granitic rocks. A good theory would take into account the phenomena of each rung in the ladder of magnitudes and of the relationship between them. Several hypotheses are too exclusively occupied with certain orders in neglecting multiple relations and their variations. I will cite a much discussed example: in observing veins of granitic rock it has been possible to affirm that the contents of

the vein were introduced in a liquid state. Based on the external form
one has drawn conclusions on the state of the materials at the time of
their emplacement without taking account of other possibilities. The
external form is not related in a unique manner to the state of a filling;
on the contrary one knows actually of numerous schemes, of the sort
that it is necessary to establish by more precise diagnosis.

The theories are not distinguished only by the magnitude and the
nature of the mobile units but also by the *milieu* in which these units
evolve. Since the number of possible arrangements is high, one obtains
a rich diversity. All the arrangements have not always been put to the
test. A choice is made, in such a way that most of the body of theories
is carried along as in guiding channels by a few directing ideas. The
network of these channels is always so impressive that he who would
begin the study of these problems risks losing himself in the labyrinth
of theories. A mentor who lays out a chart of the body and who guides
us through numerous straightforward ways up to the present is thus
particularly welcome.

He who would make investigations in the domain of the geology
of granitic rocks must not only know the methods and theories, but also
their relationship to the guiding ideas. Two groups of processes permit
the outlining of the natural history of generating guiding ideas. Some
demonstrate their mechanisms in laying bare the articulations and their
function, the joints, the interlockings and the spare parts, others subject
these ideas to tests in attempting to integrate them in the great trends
of geological thought.

The work of Eugène Raguin shows the functioning of different
methods of interpretation, and the reader will gratefully appreciate the
amplitude of this demonstration.

As for other procedures, the history of geology makes them evident.
It reveals that there exist some constant ideas, common to all theories.
Their number is necessarily limited. Leaving aside the details, it is possible to reduce the diverse explanations to a few outline types on which
are sketched, with the aid of points represented by physico-chemical
rules, the different outlines varying from one generation to the next,
according to the taste of the time. The point of departure of the drawing
seems in many cases to restrain the possibility of scope by the authors
in a decisive manner in making them conform to certain tracks from
which they no longer seem able to escape.

*   *   *

Before blocking out the principal canvases it is useful to mention a few ideas common to most authors, but it is not easy to find a common denominator.

Since the first geological studies, the granitic rocks have been considered as *materials formed under conditions realized at the present time nowhere on the surface of the earth*. For Werner the crystalline rocks were laid down in aqueous sheets of a special composition at high temperatures. A part of this view will be taken up later.

Hutton's theory takes its point of departure in the ideas concerning the volcanoes developed in Auvergne. According to Hutton, the molten materials rose from the depths of the Earth's crust where they were born by the fusion of rock masses. For Werner the origin was exogenic, for Hutton endogenic. The extraordinary conditions were placed by Werner in unknown periods of the past, by Hutton in unknown regions of the depths. All geologists and petrologists are today in agreement that the minerals of granitic rocks have been formed under conditions of high temperature and pressure, and nearly all relate these conditions to an endogenic origin. These are thus two points upon which present authors are in agreement. Opinions differ when it becomes a matter of defining the mechanisms of emplacement.

In considering the strong brush strokes, one recognizes two great sequences of principles which seem mutually exclusive and over which partisans are often in dispute. It is important to take this clash into account.

For Hutton, the granites were the result of fusion of rocks in the depths of the Earth's crust. These masses were then carried up to higher levels where upon cooling they would have crystallized. In this concept granite makes up part of a cycle. A first canvas type is thus represented by the idea of the *cyclic nature* of the granite rocks.

To this concept is opposed another which has also played an important role. According to this hypothesis the granite rocks are the result of a differentiation from basic rocks. They are formed at the time of each period of intrusion. Their material is thus undifferentiated and juvenile for they have never taken part in exogenic phenomena. Another consequence of this manner of conception is the augmentation of the quantity of granitic juvenile rocks in the course of geologic time.

This canvas, that of *juvenile origin*, has given rise to numerous sketches, varying in detail, depending upon the importance attributed to the sequence of different physico-chemical rules. These are the drawings represented by the various hypotheses of magmatic differentiation, from the theory of immiscible magmas (theory of liquation) to that of the gravity separation of crystallized products and Bowen's rules.

One sees without difficulty that Werner's primitive idea has been revived by one of these theories, but the sedimentation is no longer made on the surface as in the past hypothesis, but in inaccessible intratelluric basins.

The common basis of this group of hypotheses is the aspect of temperature. Every differentiation takes place simultaneously and proportionately to dropping temperature. This aspect is rendered understandable by the assumption that the original materials have conserved *grosso modo* their heat since the formation of the globe. Differentiation is, in this concept, a consequence of cooling, for the subcrustal masses can only lose heat either in their ensemble or in moving to higher parts of the crust. This group of theories influences the outlooks in numerous domains, from geochemistry to oceanography.

The elements, formerly hidden in the depths of the Earth, are exposed in the course of geologic history by the activity of exogenic phenomena. The balance sheet of these elements in the external circulation changes with juvenile influxes and its composition varies in an irreversible way. Among the substances thus introduced in the course of time, water plays a leading role. The augmentation of water on the Earth's surface was recognized by Suess (1909); the hypothesis was revived by Rubey (1951) and other oceanographers and geochemists. In this form it is bound up with the evolution of the crust from the standpoint of stratigraphic history.

The hypotheses involving a juvenile origin of granites involve the gradient between the intratelluric temperatures and those of the surface. All the mechanisms invoked by these hypotheses appear to depend on the ascent of intratelluric magmas. Masses coming from the depths are necessarily *intrusive*.

The canvas of the *cyclic evolution* of granitic rocks groups the phenomena in another way. Rocks are not only subjected to diminutions of temperature but also to increases. Variations are not only related to the lowerings of temperature but also to heating. The actions of the two aspects of temperature are not symmetrical views, as people would represent them. An increase in temperature can render one or more components of a rock more mobile, either on the scale of ions, atoms or molecules, by melting or by an increased deformability and may in this manner cause a more or less marked separation.

Many authors maintain that there was originally one sole sort of rock or molten mass and the various species encountered at the present time derive from original materials by differentiation. It is not recognizable in every case whether the author has chosen this assumption to be able to initiate an ingenious mechanism of differentiation, or whether this hypothesis is the result of the natural bias of man to maintain that the unknown beginnings of all things must necessarily be simple. This is an axiom: it is thus possible to establish another hypothesis basing it on a contrary affirmation, which has also its degree of likelihood, for the oldest known formations are complex. Although this question is of great interest in the natural history of the geological theories, I do not wish to discuss it here, but to admit provisionally the existence of a unique initial rock of basic character.

On the canvas of cyclic evolution the rearrangements of chemical compounds and minerals can be made in several ways: they can be the result of exogenous phenomena (weathering, erosion, sedimentation, as in the persedimentary hypothesis of Nieuwenkamp); they can accompany the heating in the interior of the Earth's crust or the cooling time of the active or passive ascent towards the surface. These three groups of processes are superimposed and related to one another in a variable and complicated manner. According to this concept the rocks we observe are not the result of a linear evolution, but the outcome of a complicated superposition of phenomena whose beginnings are lost in the unknown. Such a superposition involves of necessity also the possibility of *phenomena of convergence*. In this manner of conception, the species of rocks are not individualities—a little like the biological species —but states of passage corresponding to different rearrangements of terrestrial material.

The study and interpretation of the crystalline rocks in the canvas of cyclic evolution is still further complicated by the following phenomena: the diversification is followed at certain moments and in certain places by a homogenization at times on a grand scale, as in some granitic massifs. In this case the course of geologic history is not only a differentiation, but a redistribution of elements corresponding to a greater dispersion. This dispersion is as important from the general and geochemical point of view as the concentrations of some elements which until now have been the centre of attention.

Homogenizations have often destroyed the traces of earlier structures, but this disappearance is not an indication of the juvenile origin of the rock. The methods existing to disclose the pre-existing structures and to establish their correlation are particularly important, because they allow the deciphering of the remains of documents in large part lost, and to follow the history beyond the moment of emplacement, that has been so long considered as the beginning. J. J. Sederholm has compared the ghosts of these older structures to palimpsests. The canvas of cyclic evolution thus reveals a vast spectrum of possibilities and combinations. An examination much more profound on all scales is necessary to discern the movement history of rocks.

The theory of juvenile magmas knows only emplacement by intrusion. In using the canvas of cycles it is necessary to distinguish among several principal possibilities and a series of mechanisms. It is thus necessary to know the distinctive characteristics and the methods of observation and coordination to cover a vast gamut of terrains from the migmatites on one hand and the granitic diapirs on the other, showing very diverse contact phenomena.

The granitized masses can arise as well from sedimentary and metamorphic rocks as from granitic or basic rocks of an earlier cycle. Rocks which have formed at a certain moment the upper level can be plunged to the depths of the Earth's crust. Ancient structural surfaces of first order can, in some sectors, disappear under the influence of homogenization. Facts of this type explain the difficulties encountered in the stratigraphic coordination within profoundly eroded deformed segments. Since the depth to which a particular cross-section has extended is not the same throughout, evolution varies a great deal within a deformed segment, as well as from one segment to another.

The evolution of magmas according to the canons of the juvenile origin occurs for the most part in the unknown and inaccessible depths. The series of eruptive rocks are considered as a sampling sent from time to time from the subcrustal basins to inform the upper levels about the stage attained by differentiation. Even the granites, which are so to speak the cream of the magma, are assembled, according to some authors, under the solid crust before occurring as intrusions.

The observations take on a different significance on the canvas of cyclic evolution. The transformations take place in the interior of the crust and the products fixed at all the stages of their evolution are preserved and become accessible in many migmatic and granitic terrains. It was the greatness of J. J. Sederholm that he recognized in 1907 (*Om granit och gneisa*, p. 35) that the islands polished by ice in southern Finland allow us to catch a glimpse of the "fabrics" where the granite masses have been recirculated anew. The relations between the "granite fabrics" and the upper levels of the Earth's crust appear under several forms: the mobilized granitic masses can rise in the form of diapirs in the upper levels where they are generally relatively quickly exposed by erosion, or else the crust can rise as a whole; the phenomena of granitization are fixed and are laid bare by erosion. The tectonic significance of the two processes is different. Since the parts formerly superficial can plunge to different levels, variable in time and space, the cycles have not the same amplitude throughout. The series of events recorded by the different elements of the same segment will not be the same. Certain traces can be effaced anew. It is thus necessary to establish the evolution in many places, and then to coordinate the different records. These methods of coordination constitute an important part of the equipment of the geologist concerned with the granitic rocks. Using them he will be able to reconstruct the intracrustal part of the cycle of rocks. Such a history completes, in a happy manner, the stratigraphic records and the paleogeographic reconstructions. In this way, each geologist comes in contact, from near or far, with the problems of the geology of granitic rocks.

The point of departure in the canvas of juvenile magmas is a molten mass, homogeneous and isotropic at high temperature. The other canvas recognized nearly as many points of departure as there are rocks in the Earth's crust. The components of these rocks undergo several sortings above all at the time of crustal breaking in. A stable fraction will be separated from the migratory elements. These last can appear in several states: gases, liquids or solids if they are concentrated, or on the other hand in the form of ions, of atoms or of molecules crossing other environments. The percentage of the migratory factors can be low, as in the major part of the superstructure, or high, as in the rocks of the infrastructure; the way traversed by the components can be small as in recrystallization, or large as in the deep levels.

The rocks resulting from the rearrangements are thus composed of a part left in place, the residual fraction, and of substances come from elsewhere, or influxes. In comparing the residual fraction with the original rock, one realizes that there has been a removal of certain components. The residual substances can appear, either in their original form, or as products of reaction with the influxes. The aspect of a rock species depends thus on its proper mineral composition, on that of the rocks which accompany it, on the depth that it has attained, and on the length of time of arrest at different stages. If this time is sufficiently long, physico-chemical equilibrium can be established; if it is short, the reactions, scarcely initiated, must follow another way. The canvas of juvenile origin of magmas allows the determination in a fashion fairly simple, of the place of a particular rock in the evolution; one finds it by seeking the point representing the chemical composition on the diagram corresponding to the standard evolution. As a rule, such a determination is not possible by following the other concept. To determine the place of a rock it is necessary to determine the history in fixing a certain number of successive images in time and in space. Chemical composition remains an important factor, but it alone no longers plays a determining role. It is the geological investigation in the broadest sense of the word which will reconstitute the evolution. The "geology of granite" is thus a basic understanding permitting us to tackle these fundamental problems.

*   *   *

It would still be possible to show a series of common and dissimilar points between the two canvases. That which we have sketched will suffice to make clear that discussions at times have been lively, and that certain propositions seem to be mutually exclusive. In fact the most fervent partisans of juvenile magmas have long battled every concept against their way of seeing things. One finds this in many vestiges in the nomenclature. Such an evolution will appear today perhaps to be a detour; but at the stage of the science in the first half of the century, it was probably necessary to develop the two bodies of doctrine with all their varieties; a consequence of this parallel development was the circumstance that the discussions seemed at times to have forgotten the long-term goals of the science, which are to reunite on a higher plane the opposed ideas. Even though the two points of view had been developed to certain extreme consequences, a synthesis seems possible, and some traits of this synthesis can be hinted at at present. A certain number of parts and articulations will serve in the new broader framework. It is thus that Bowen's rules, for example, adapted to cooling will serve every time that such a case appears; but it is necessary to complete them by rules which can guide us in the various cases of heating and by a certain number of principles of coordination.

It is probable that terrestrial materials do not follow only cyclic paths in the Earth's crust, but that juvenile materials are added in every cycle. The task of the future will not be to justify one or the other of the two opinions but to create methods to distinguish the cyclic materials from the juvenile influxes. *It is probable that geochemistry will be able to establish the characteristics to separate the fractions.* Until now the geochemists have on the whole employed one or the other canvas to interpret their facts. It would probably be useful in the development of their science if they could abandon these frameworks, which are a little too narrow for the future, and favour a broader synthesis even if this synthesis is only provisional like all those of the past.

The canvases which I have outlined have been developed from a certain number of observations. Several affirmations, at first sight contradictory, become compatible if one takes into account tectonic levels. The partisans of opposing opinions often base their arguments on correct and respectable observations, but the objects upon which they are made do not pertain at all to the same tectonic level, and often only have in common their more or less vague name. It is thus important to place the phenomena in their tectonic levels. The vision of synchronous movements in several levels, each having its own style and mutually influencing each other, is still little accepted. A certain number of methods permitting the establishment of this synchronism exist; others have only been roughed out and need finishing touches. The endogenous rocks relating the levels in several ways play an important role in this research. In this way, the problems of the granitic rocks form part of the fundamental questions of geology and geophysics.

A guide who leads us readily after having shown us the roads to travel, and who furnishes us with the necessary mental equipment merits the gratitude of all researchers. It is in this that I salute the second edition of the *Geology of Granite*.

C. E. WEGMANN

Chapter 1

GENERAL STATEMENTS

DEFINITION OF GRANITE

Granite is a rock formed essentially of an assemblage of crystalline grains of feldspars and quartz with a small proportion of mica flakes and occasionally hornblende. The name granite signifies that the rock consists of grains. They are randomly distributed and distinguishable because of their different lustres and colours. Except in special cases, the grains are more or less uniform in size and proportions within the compass of an outcrop, a quarry, a cliff face, or even a mass of greater extent. Microscopic examination reveals that no glassy material exists between the grains. The individual grains have an outer shape which is either limited by their own crystal faces, i.e., idiomorphic or automorphic form, or more often by random faces, i.e., allotriomorphic form, which may be the crystal faces of adjoining grains, or irregular faces formed by the competition of growing adjacent grains. The minerals in the rock are not arranged in such a way as to produce zoning or schistosity in a marked or regular manner over vast areas, such as characteristically found in the crystallophyllian[1] rocks (*roches cristallophylliennes*) of metamorphism. Furthermore, as granite often forms homogeneous bodies cutting like wedges through neighbouring sedimentary or crystallophyllian rocks, on the scale of an outcrop or on greater dimensions, all the foregoing properties including the last are the properties of "plutonic" rocks, as opposed to the properties of the other

[1] Translators' note: the crystallophyllian series of metamorphism comprises the whole range of regional metamorphic rocks, from the phyllites to the granite gneisses, and includes the two main divisions of French petrology, the ectinites or crystalline schists in the true sense of the word, and the migmatites, or as they are sometimes called the granitized gneisses. These rocks are characterized notably by being at the same time finely foliated and largely crystalline. Hence the name, from *cristallon*—crystal, and *phyllon*—leaf (J. Jung, 1958).

rock types: sedimentary, volcanic and metamorphic. Granite is thus a plutonic rock.

In virtue of the associations found in Nature, the term granite is used in a rather broad sense, which may include other kindred plutonic rocks such as syenite, with the decrease or the disappearance of quartz, and quartz diorite, through an increase in the basicity of the feldspars.

Contrasts and Transitions

Granite has never consolidated upon the Earth's surface. The wide gamut of volcanic flows, the emission of which we can witness in nature today, and which comprises magmas of the same chemical composition as granite, do not produce it. Granites have crystallized beneath generally important thicknesses of other formations which today have disappeared, but whose existence nonetheless can often definitely be proved, although they have subsequently been removed, thanks to erosion. In some doubtless unusual cases referred to as *subvolcanic massifs* (chapter 3), granite has consolidated only a few hundred meters beneath the surface of the Earth. Granite is, however, essentially a deep-seated rock, similar to the other plutonic rocks, such as the diorites or the gabbros.

Another essential property is that the grain of the rock is coarse, ranging from several millimeters to several centimeters, i.e., granular rock. Lastly the effect upon the surrounding formations during the emplacement (*mise en place*) of a granite is frequently marked by chemical changes and recrystallizations.

In complete contrast is the physical aspect of a volcanic flow, particularly a rhyolitic lava, which has about the same chemical composition as a granite. Lavas are crystalline aggregates of a very fine grain, which is often invisible to the naked eye; they may furthermore consist entirely of glassy material. Bigger crystals may float in the ground mass or mesostase[1] forming porphyritic rocks. The texture is often fluidal, with a dense pattern of microscopic streaks like those of congealed currents. These rocks frequently contain small cavities due to entrapped gas bubbles, or cavities of the same origin (lithophyses) which have been subsequently filled with crystals. Lastly, lavas upon extrusion have only a very slight effect on the pre-existing rocks; at the most only a local baking takes place. They are often associated with tuffs, the fragmental debris thrown out during volcanic explosions.

[1] The groundmass (mesostase) is the material of a rock apart from inclusions or isolated elements found "drowned" in it.

In partly crystalline varieties of rhyolite, spheroidal forms may originate which are generally microscopic in size but sometimes larger and easily visible to the naked eye, e.g., the pyromerides. These are fibro-radial spherolites consisting of orthoclase fibres more or less impregnated with quartz or with fibres of chalcedony. They indicate an incipient crystallization of a magma which has passed through a glassy state. In other cases one sees globules or arborescences of micro-pegmatite, an association of quartz and feldspar with an intimate inter-growth of the crystals, one mineral forming a "skeleton" for the other. As for "globular quartz", small sponges of quartz with sectors showing the same crystallographic orientation, they are the effects of devitrification a long time after the consolidation of the rock. Contrary to this, the spherolites mentioned above are connected with the consolidation of the magma, with the undoubted exception of those of chalcedony which are late.

In contrast to these properties of lavas, granites are formed of an aggregate of crystals which are molded together without any inter-space between them, or which enclose one another. *The magnificent crystallinity of granite and similar rocks is a striking characteristic.*

The contrast between the plutonic and volcanic rocks is marked in nature; one sees large massifs of the former and important sheets of the latter, independent of one another. It is, however, possible to collect rocks of intermediate type and to demonstrate "a perfect gradation of textures from completely glassy lavas like obsidian to completely crystalline granite, ranging through rhyolites and porphyritic granite" (Shand, 1927). But these intermediate rocks rarely appear under the conditions of natural occurrence corresponding to the above-mentioned transition. More frequently no transition is seen and the contrast remains, from the point of view of geological occurrence, if not from the point of view of the petrographic collection. There are exceptions, however, and we will return to the relationships between granite and volcanism in chapter 13.

The contrast between granite and the metamorphic rocks which have a regular zoning and schistosity over vast areas has already been emphasized, but there are schistose or banded granites particularly in the realms of the migmatites, and as a consequence transitions which are extremely common. As H. and G. Termier (1953) write:

There are all gradations between rhyolite, a rock of magmatic origin, and granite, and one sees no way of establishing a sharp limit within the intermediary series; moreover it is easy to find all the transitions between the schists (solid rocks) and granite through increasing metamorphism (phyllites, mica schists, gneiss). Granite thus appears as a point of convergence, as the realization of an equilibrium.

The Time Factor and the Evolution of Granite

Many observations indicate that granite, where we now see it, is the outcome of a very long evolution reckoned in human terms, or, for that matter, on the time scale of volcanism. In most cases this evolution is related to successive cycles of orogeny. The same is probably true for the development of metamorphism. If a better comprehension of the formation of granite is desired, it is of paramount importance to muse upon its chronology, and to follow on different scales the indications of the successions of events, from dimensions of the crystal under the microscope to those of the great granite complexes in the field. It is a difficult task, requiring great patience, but a very suggestive one for the elucidation of the "life" of granite. I will stress this point whenever possible throughout the whole of this book.

One such study is based mainly on the indications of displacement of material on different scales: there, where movements are inscribed, a chronology is outlined. C. E. Wegmann's *structural analysis* of granitized complexes and the rocks of their settings is the basis of such research. A piece of granite produced by laboratory synthesis, while admittedly a "perfect marriage" and difficult to distinguish from a piece of natural granite, will never be more than a schematic model, and not a real granite which can look back on a whole history. The same difference exists between an immobile robot and an Egyptian mummy. "Rocks are things with a history which may be read by the study of their present characters. Geology is a science of time, studying the succession of events. It is not applied physics or chemistry, although these sciences may give an important aid to geology" (Sederholm, 1926).

Concepts and Terminology

Because of the emphasis placed upon the evolutionary point of view one is obliged to depict, in a more or less approximate and moreover vague fashion, the state of the material before the conclusion of the phenomenon. Objectively one indeed only knows the finished granite. Thus, anticipating later chapters, I will immediately definite *the mobilized environment* (*milieu mobilise*), the physical state of which is a *mixed state* in the course of granitization, as well as the significance which I will give to the word *granitization* itself.

The mobilized environment

The first question concerning the evolution of granite is whether the material comes from elsewhere or whether it has been rearranged in place, whether or not there has been a massive or partial *influx* of substances. Three different lines of thought are apparent in this regard:

A. Granite is created essentially *elsewhere* at depth and moves upwards like liquid volcanic magma. Granite is an igneous rock in the manner of lavas, the difference in the final result arising from consolidation at greater depth in the Earth's crust. This is the point of view of the pure magmatist. It is scarcely defensible in such an extreme form any more, except perhaps in cases of some very special granitic varieties.

B. Granites are created in place or almost in place with quantitatively important chemical influxes of material, influxes according to the authors either in the form of more or less subtle injections of magma, in the form of impregnating solutions, or as ionic diffusions along the interfaces of the pre-existing crystals or across their crystal lattices (Perrin and Roubault, 1939).

C. Granites are created in place or almost in place without important chemical influx (Nieuwenkamp, 1949). One concept of the mechanism is that of the *differential anatexis* of P. Eskola (1933). It implies a partial fusion followed by an expulsion of the most fusible materials in the rock, giving rise to fluids of granitic composition, capable of some migrations and permeations of other rocks at varying distances. Other concepts envisage processes of rearrangement of minerals, recrystallization similar to metamorphism in the solid state.

These diverse points of view seem to me too cut and dried: reality is more complex. Granite probably has a composite origin to a variable degree depending on different granite, and depending upon the particular stage of development of any one granite. The milieu evolving towards granite reflects the effects of transports of material in various concentrations and of various spatial amplitudes. Such an environment is called the *mobilized environment*. Its mobility may be of different degrees, more or less chemical and more or less mechanical.

For a large part of their material, many granites are formed in place, with greater or lesser additions of migrated material. Anticipating what follows, I will say that this *in situ* condition is indicated by the alignment of inclusions (*enclaves*) or endomorphic zones, or by nebulitic patterns in the rock mass. Such alignments and such patterns may sometimes be caused by deformations of the mobilized environment or by mineralogical segregations. In many cases, however, careful observation shows that these phantoms often correspond to a coherent stratigraphy of pre-existing geological layers. C. E. Wegmann's *structural analysis* has shown to what extent these layers have been deformed and which parts are segregations connected with the deformation.

Rheomorphism, or the local massive movement of nearly completed granite under the influence of tectonic forces or by the increase in volume during granitization may obliterate the traces of the formation in place, and this is probably often the case. The term *rheomorphism* was created by H. G. Backlund (1937) to designate "all the effects of thermal fluidification (*Verflüssigung*), partial or total, in a pre-existing rock under the influx of greater or lesser quantities of new material, brought in by diffusion". He also states (1938): "The increase in volume in a given space leads to a mobilization of the product of granitization in a measure all the greater as the increase in volume becomes more important. The mobilization determines the flow, the differential movements, the eruptions (*Durchbrüche*), and the intrusions in the direction of least resistance." I believe that the volume increase by addition of material is not necessary in producing rheomorphism, but that a local or general exaggeration of stresses can also produce this effect.

Mixed state

Another matter for discussion is the physical state of the environment in the course of its evolution towards granite—either the amorphous state (liquid, glassy) or the crystallized state. This second question is independent of the first, i.e., the formation in place or with introduction of material. Thus in case B above one may presume that the added material might bring about a eutectic composition and that the milieu would melt *en masse* (P. Termier, 1910). One might also think that everything happened by metasomatism[1] in an environment at all times crystalline; this is the point of view of the *pure metasomatist* on the matter of granitization.

We will take it for granted, in conformity with the detailed observations presented in the following chapters, that during the course of granitization this environment is generally in a *mixed state* (*état mixte*), in other words, formed of crystals swimming in amorphous material.

---

[1] *Metasomatism* (*métasomatose*) is the transformation of rocks in the solid state by recrystallization, generally without important changes in the total volume. It is very often accompanied by a chemical migration in two directions: the influx of some chemical substances and the elimination of others. The physico-chemical mechanism of metasomatism is obscure.

It would be analogous to a suspension of crystals, if these occupy only a small proportion of the environment; or to a vesicular aggregate, in which the vacant spaces are filled with liquid, if the proportion is the opposite. Very probably the proportions would vary during the development of a particular granite, and would be very different during various phases of the evolution of different granites. In any case, and regardless of how the process starts, it is certain that the granites have concluded their development in the crystalline state, because they have undergone the strong imprint of final metasomatism revealed by many peculiarities in their petrography, as we will see later.

The term *magma* will retain its classic significance of a liquid or glassy silicate mixture, possibly containing in suspension a small quantity of crystals or of crystalline enclaves. A mixed environment very rich in liquid material passes to a magma.

All too commonly everyday experience of phenomena under atmospheric pressure leads to the idea that an easy deformability of material is only possible in the liquid state, whereas the crystalline state implies solidity, rigidity, and undeformability. Tectonic geology reveals that this is not strictly true. The crystallized material of rocks can undergo very important deformations at high pressures provided that the applied force acts during a long enough time. It is therefore impossible to use the effects of deformation no matter how important, to distinguish the relative proportions of crystallized and amorphous material in a mixed environment.

Granitization

This word is often employed to designate the formation of granite *in situ* by metasomation. I do not accept this definition, which is far too specific; it would probably hold good only for a moment in the evolution of a given granite. It would be impossible in a particular case to define the interval where this concept would be valid. In this book the term granitization will adhere to its most general meaning. It will designate the evolution of a portion of the crust which has at a given point in time become a granite mass, regardless of what process took place, whether in place or in connection with some displacements of more or less important parts of the material.

Comments on the Plan of the Study

It may at first seem somewhat artificial to describe in a series of chapters the phenomena of several orders and of varied scales displayed in granite and its setting, and I apologize for it. Because of the diversity of granites, it follows that all phenomena can scarcely occur in the same massif of granite. Sometimes some, sometimes others, imprint their influence on the particular granite body. But it would be conceited, or at least premature, to attempt a precise classification of granites based upon the assemblages of observable phenomena. One can nonetheless take a stand on the elementary, and moreover classic, distinction of two categories: granites in *circumscribed massifs* (*massifs circonscrits*) and *anatectic granites* (*granites d'anatexie*) with migmatites. This distinction, however, is far from absolute and intermediate aspects will be noted later.

Chapter 2 treats the petrographic make-up of granite. On the scale of a piece of granite examined with the naked eye or under the microscope it is possible to review its mode of occurrence, and its variations. Chapters 3 and 4 establish the distinction on the basis of the mode of occurrence, which defines the two categories mentioned above. The chapters following bear on the relations between granite and its immediate setting (chapter 5, Assimilation of formations in contact with granite; chapter 6, Aureole of metamorphism), then on the internal structure of massifs from the geometrical point of view (chapter 7) and from the point of view of the facies of variation (chapter 8, Differentiation). These chapters, as well as the following one (chapter 9, Vein satellites of granite), are mainly concerned with the circumscribed massifs, in which to different degrees and in varying proportions, the phenomena studied are likely to be well-developed. In the anatectic granites, effects of the same order seem to take place, but they are much less well-defined and nearly always difficult to comprehend. The destruction of granite by alteration or crushing is treated in chapter 10.

Proceeding to broader points of view, we will view the position of granites in their geological settings. Comparisons of granite with the three great phenomena of metamorphism, orogeny and volcanism form the material of chapters 11, 12 and 13. The metallogenesis of granites and the radioactivity of granite in chapters 14 and 15 conclude this survey. Chapter 16 fits granite into the framework of the Earth's crust, and finally in chapter 17 we will return to the problem of the formation of granites.

Chapter 2

THE COMPOSITION OF GRANITE

THE MINERALS OF GRANITE

The essential minerals of granite, constituting among themselves almost the whole of the rock, are: feldspars, quartz, and micas. In some granites hornblende is associated with black mica; more rarely other silicates are also present: enstatite or hypersthene, diopside, aegirine or riebeckite. The accessory minerals are principally magnetite, specular hematite, pyrite, ilmenite, apatite, sphene, rutile, zircon, tourmaline, garnet, cordierite, andalusite, sillimanite, spinel, corundum, epidote, zoisite and allanite. In addition, minerals formed by weathering may be present, of which the most common are: kaolinite, sericite, chlorite, quartz, calcite, epidote, zoisite, hematite and rutile.

Feldspars

Every granite contains an alkali feldspar: orthoclase, microcline, or a plagioclase close to the composition of albite. In general a soda-lime plagioclase is also present, either oligoclase or andesine, or exceptionally, labradorite.

Orthoclase and microcline have the formula $KAlSi_3O_8$. The plagioclases, on the other hand, form a remarkable isomorphic soda-lime series ranging from albite, $NaAlSi_3O_8$, to anorthite, $CaAl_2Si_2O_8$.

Traditionally the plagioclase series is divided arbitrarily in the following manner, according to the proportions of the mixture of albite and anorthite:

	Per cent anorthite
Albite:	0–10
Oligoclase:	10–30
Andesine:	30–50
Labradorite:	50–70
Bytownite:	70–90
Anorthite:	90–100

When the soda-lime plagioclase dominates quantitatively over the alkali feldspar, the granite passes into a quartz diorite. When it is absent the rock is an alkaline granite. The predominance of either potash feldspar or alkaline plagioclase distinguishes the potash granites and the soda granites.

Potash feldspar. The potash feldspar of granites is either orthoclase or microcline, or both. Recent mineralogical investigations show among these minerals the existence of several varieties related to conditions of formation, either at moderate temperature or at high temperature. To separate them, the determination of the lattice structure by X-ray analysis is necessary. These studies still leave some points obscure, and having not yet been used systematically in the study of granites of different regions it is not possible to take advantage of them at the present time in the general geology of granite. The names orthoclase and microcline will therefore be still used to designate the potash feldspars apparently monoclinic and apparently triclinic respectively under the microscope.

Orthoclase and microcline occur together in a systematic way in a particular granite mass. For instance, a certain proportion of microcline occurs with orthoclase, and this proportion is then fairly constant throughout the entire massif. Similarly large phenocrysts[1] will consist of orthoclase in one massif and microcline in another. Microcline appears to be, all other things being equal, a lower temperature form (W. T. Schaller, 1933) from its common occurrence in metamorphic rocks and its absence in lavas; or perhaps it is a form crystallized under pressure. This does not preclude crystallizations of orthoclase at low temperature in some other rocks, or even in metalliferous epithermal veins, e.g., the variety adularia. It should be noted that microcline now and then crystallizes in granite after orthoclase.

The orthoclase of granites is often sodic, containing, in molecular proportions, albite up to 40%, but generally in the range of 15–20%. Its axial angle, 2V, increases from 35°–70° as the content of albite varies from 0–40%. Sodic microclines of similar composition also exist but their axial angles remain between 80° and 90° (Tuttle, 1952a; Mackenzie and Smith, 1955). The anorthoclases, which are potassic albites, form an isomorphic series combining high temperature albite and sanidine, or high temperature orthoclase. It is doubtful whether these anorthoclases are found in granites.

[1] See page 17.

The potash feldspars of the granite are often of the *perthite* facies[1], namely, impregnated with albite or with oligoclase in the form of very fine, irregular, more or less parallel zones, or as microveinlets, or even as irregular or diversely arranged facula. The perthite is either original or due to a later modification of a granite already formed. It is attributed, depending on the case, to an unmixing of either a sodic microcline or orthoclase which was homogeneous at high temperature (Tuttle, 1952 b), or else to a partial pseudomorphism of orthoclase or microcline by microsolutions around the crystals. X-ray diagrams, moreover, sometimes reveal the existence of *cryptoperthite* in material which under the microscope appears to be homogeneous but which on an extremely small scale shows the complex structure of a perthite.

In granites the potash feldspars generally do not exhibit any crystal form, unlike the plagioclases, which tend to have a form of their own. The granites with a *plagidiomorphic* texture have some well-formed plagioclases calling to mind those of monzonites. Nevertheless, in the porphyritic granites with potash feldspars of greater size than in the ambiant rock (1–15 cm. in length), these feldspars are better formed than the same feldspars of the groundmass, and are often strongly idiomorphic with Carlsbad twinning (p. 17).

Plagioclases. The plagioclase of granites is sometimes zoned with a border more alkaline than the core of the crystal. The phenomenon is less pronounced than in the volcanic rocks. It is nevertheless well developed in the granite facies of endomorphism, or in dioritic rocks of a granitic differentiation series. In the latter case, the zones show recurrences of higher anorthite content during the successive growth of the plagioclase. Elsewhere the absence of zoning results from a slow crystallization, or recrystallization, under stable conditions allowing the crystals already formed to adapt themselves to the slowly changing chemical conditions in the immediate environment.

We know today that each plagioclase has two varieties with different optical properties, one a *high temperature* form typical of volcanic rocks, the other a *low temperature* variety of the metamorphic rocks (A. Köhler, 1941). It has been verified that the plagioclase in many granites is the low temperature variety. Some authors, like O. F. Tuttle (1952 b), interpret this as a terminal recrystallization of the feldspar originally crystallized in the high temperature form; others, such as R. Perrin and M. Roubault (1951), see it as the proof of a mode of formation of granitic rock radically different from the magmatic crystallization of

---

[1] Translators' note: in French the term *faciès* has retained its broad useful meaning denoting the overall aspects, including the genetic, of a group of any related phenomena.

B

volcanic rocks. Further study seems necessary in order to clarify this point.

Statistical studies have revealed that the plagioclase of granitic rocks often has Carlsbad twinning or a combination of Carlsbad with albite twinning, but rarely albite or pericline twinning alone, or an absence of twinning (M. Goraï, 1950; F. J. Turner, 1951). This fact relates the feldspars of granites to those of volcanic rocks and sets them apart from metamorphic rocks. However, according to M. Goraï, certain migmatites of Japan are in this respect similar to metamorphic rocks.

Colour. The granite feldspars are rarely transparent. Their milky aspect comes from inclusions produced by a slight alteration and giving rise to a partial reflection, or else it is due to reflections on cleavage lamellae. The colour of the alkali feldspars varies with the granite: rose, yellow, reddish, gray, or milky white. The first of these tints is due to microscopic inclusions of hematite, either original as schillerization, as in the rose granite of Piana, Corsica, or due to weathering. The others result from alteration through the formation of small lamellae of sericite. A schillerization of microcline sometimes is observed giving rise to a blue opalescent effect recalling the oligoclase of the laurvikite of Norway; it is the result of very fine inclusions of magnetite or ilmenite distributed through the crystals along crystallographic planes. The green colour of certain microclines of pegmatites, e.g. amazonite, has been explained by E. Elisséeff (Jérémine, Lelubre and Sandréa, 1951) as due to the presence of ferrous iron in their lattices.

The plagioclases are generally less colourful: white to dark gray. They become greenish by incipient alteration with the formation of microscopic chlorite or epidote (saussuritization). They may also become sericitized.

Quartz

Quartz alone forms 25–40% of the rock, depending on the variety. Generally its form is molded by the other minerals, that is to say, is bounded by the crystal faces of other minerals. It may also be without any regular form at all, limited by irregular surfaces or forming aggregates of grains without well-defined shape. It is thus in general allotriomorphic. Sometimes it shows a tendency towards the bipyramidal form, particularly in granites containing white mica and pneumatolytic minerals. Bipyramidal quartz is typical of rapakivis. Aside from its normal development in grains corresponding in size to the grain of the rock, quartz also exists in very small inclusions in feldspar.

Its colour is gray, bluish or yellowish.

Under the microscope cavities can be seen, some microns in size, lined up approximately along one or two systems of planes. The alignment sometimes shows parallelism from one grain to another. These cavities may contain small isolated crystals, or a liquid with sometimes a mobile gas bubble. The liquid is an aqueous solution of alkali chlorides or compressed carbon dioxide. The gas may be carbon dioxide. These substances thus were found free in the mobilized milieu at the moment of crystallization of the quartz (Deicha, 1955).

O. F. Tuttle (1952 b) has shown that the transformation point of quartz, in the neighbourhood of 573° at ordinary pressure, is invariably a little higher for the quartz of granites than it is for the quartz of rhyolites, the difference being of the order of 38°. This is attributed to a lower crystallization temperature of the quartz in granite. Probably the quartz which crystallized at a higher temperature has been able to incorporate in its lattice traces of certain elements whose presence lowers the transformation point. In any case he interprets the fact as a recrystallization of granitic quartz at a temperature lower than that at which it would have first crystallized. It should be noted that as for the low temperature albites discussed earlier, one may assume that quartz has here crystallized directly at a lower temperature than that of rhyolitic magmas.

The quartz in granite is often twisted, as if it had been strained, which is often revealed by undulatory extinction in polarized light under the microscope. Such extinction can be observed not only in mylonitic granites but in any granite. The end of the crystallization seems to have taken place under stress (Protoclasis, p. 170).

The *myrmekite* of some granites is a microscopic association of quartz and feldspar appearing upon orthoclases or microclines where these are in contact with a plagioclase, and forming buds with convex limits against the potassium feldspars (Sederholm, 1916). The buds can be over 1 mm in diameter. The quartz of the myrmekite is in fine worm-like shapes, engulfed in a plagioclastic substance which is slightly more alkaline than the neighbouring plagioclase to which it is welded. Myrmekite results from a reaction between potash feldspar and soda-lime feldspar (p. 23). Some migmatites, however, contain autonomous myrmekites, and are not related to such a contact.

Micropegmatite is an association of quartz and potash feldspar, not as fine but still microscopic, which is sometimes found in small quantities in granite, as well as in the granitic porphyries known as granophyres. It consists, as already mentioned, of a mutual intergrowth of the two minerals, similar to the texture of large-scale pegmatites. It seems to denote a corrosion of feldspar by quartz, as will be shown later.

Micas

The micas are quantitatively the third most important minerals of the granites, and may represent 3–10% of the assemblage, according to S. J. Shand. Biotite is more common than muscovite, the two micas coexisting in many granites. When the white mica dominates, the granite is labelled "granulite" on French geological maps; this term should not be confused with that designating, in international geological literature, a fine-grained gneiss with little mica of deep facies, i.e. the metamorphic "granulite[1] facies" of Eskola, which will be discussed in chapter 11. The micas form small tablets with irregular boundaries, some millimeters in diameter, scattered throughout the rock.

The formula of biotite is $K(Fe,Mg)_3((OH,F)_2Si_3AlO_{10})$ and of muscovite $KAl_2((OH,F)_2Si_3AlO_{10})$. Actually these are two components of a very complex mineral family, where metallic atoms of very different kinds can enter the structure of the silicon–aluminum–oxygen tetrahedral frameworks. This accounts for the ferromagnesian character of biotite. Some micas in pegmatites contain lithium and fluorine, as for instance lepidolite and zinnwaldite, whereas others are titaniferous. In all of them the hydroxyl ion is contained in the formula; thus the micas are pneumatogenic (p. 98), that is, they are formed in the presence of water vapour and possibly other mineralizers, e.g., fluorine.

The granitic biotite often contains very small inclusions of certain of the accessory minerals of granite: apatite, zircon, rutile, etc. These inclusions are responsible for the pleochroic halos in this black mica, particularly in the case of zircon, allanite, monazite or possibly other minerals containing lanthanides and traces of actinides.

Amphiboles and pyroxenes

A hornblende, black to the naked eye, green or brownish-green and strongly pleochroic under the microscope, accompanies biotite in amphibolitic granites. It forms prismatic crystals without basal planes. Some diopside, enstatite or hypersthene is found in certain granites, as for instance in the charnockites. Aegirine and riebeckite occur in hyperalkaline granites.

Tourmaline, topaz, fluorite, garnet and sphene

Tourmaline, essentially an aluminium borosilicate, is occasionally an

[1] In the French text, *granulit* without the terminal "e".

important constituent. It crystallizes late and forms at the expense of feldspar and biotite, perhaps by pneumatolysis (p. 98). It readily gives rise to micropegmatitic structures with quartz or feldspar. Generally it is of the black iron-rich variety called schorl. Topaz and fluorite are also found, although more rarely, in tin-bearing granites. These minerals are sometimes concentrated in small miarolitic pockets. The rapakivi granite is remarkable for its fluorite.

Garnets are not common in ordinary granites. They are found, above all, in aplitic types. The variety present is almandite or spessartite. In the migmatites, they are often found in the myriad of small granite veinlets characteristic of these rocks. Sphene is sometimes in small poorly-shaped crystals associated with biotite or hornblende.

Andalusite, sillimanite and cordierite

Andalusite and sillimanite, aluminum silicates of identical formula, and cordierite, at the same time a magnesian and aluminous silicate, are minerals not normally found in granites. Where they are found, assimilation of aluminous material may be suspected. Sillimanite forms a felt of fibres or microscopic rods associated with biotite. The cordierite is of the colourless variety and almost always highly altered to sericite.

Epidote, allanite and zoisite

Whereas allanite, or orthite, which is an epidote containing lanthanides found in certain granites, is a primary mineral, ordinary epidote is either primary, or a product of the weathering of granite. In the first case, it is allotriomorphic in habit, and is present only in small quantities. In the second case, it occurs in aggregates of minute ill-formed grains associated with other minerals in the granite. The same holds true for zoisite, which is usually secondary.

Alteration minerals

These will be dealt with in chapter 10.

STRUCTURE AND TEXTURE OF GRANITE

In conformity with the terminology of A. Lacroix (1933), *structure* refers to the disposition and mutual relationships of the minerals constituting a rock. It is not revealed completely except under the microscope. *Texture* "consists essentially in the variations in the continuity of the rock", in a way that is ordinarily visible to the naked eye,[1] *Grain* refers to the average size of the particles that form the rock.

The texture (i.e. Fr. *structure*) of granites is granular, i.e., composed of united crystalline hypidiomorphic grains. The term hypidiomorphic means that some of the minerals of the rock (idiomorphic minerals) have well-defined crystal forms, although the forms are seldom complete, while others have formed in the available spaces without being able to produce boundaries controlled by their own geometric faces (allotriomorphic minerals). This seems to express the successions during crystallization, the minerals formed first having hindered the development of later minerals. On the other hand, younger minerals which are "stronger" may impose their form by corroding their predecessors. We will return later to these considerations.

The following individual textures (Fr. *structures*) have been defined by J. Jung and M. Roques (1952):

> *Automorphic plagioclase texture*, also called plagidiomorphic, in which potash feldspar and quartz occupy the spaces between often zoned tabular plagioclases.
> *Partition texture* (*structure coilsonnée*), in which quartz and feldspar are separated by more or less developed partitions of minerals of finer grain. It develops mainly in granites associated with migmatites.
> *Sutured texture* (*structure engrenée*), in which quartz and feldspar form lacy intergrowths, grains of one fitting into the grains of the other mineral. This texture seems to represent a variety developed from the preceding one.

The grain, which is generally about the same for all the principal mineral constituents (quartz, feldspar, mica, hornblende) if the granite is not porphyritic, varies notably from one granite to another, from some millimeters to some centimeters. The rock has thus a fixed grain. The following subdivisions are generally accepted:

> Coarse-grained: over 1 cm.
> Medium-grained: 0·5–1 cm.
> Fine-grained: less than 0·5 cm.

---

[1] Translators' note: this usage of the terms is common throughout continental Europe, but is almost the reverse of the English meaning of the terms, as understood in the United Kingdom and North America. Throughout the text the English terms have replaced their French "opposites" in almost all cases, except for instance, in the above statement.

The grain observed by the naked eye can be overestimated, if it is composed of several crystals, the association of which can only be resolved under the microscope.

The distinct, comparatively coarse, grain of the normal granite contrasts markedly with the fine, often very fine, grain of neighbouring sedimentary, metamorphic, or volcanic rocks. It has thus a characteristic "stamp" for the granites as for the other plutonic rocks such as the syenites, gabbros, etc., which are sometimes called the "granular rocks" because of this property.

The porphyritic texture (Fr. *structure*) of some granites, where the potash feldspar, and more rarely quartz crystals, are here and there much larger than the grain of the rest of the rock, has already been mentioned. Their dimensions, depending on the granite, vary from 1–15 cm, whereas the grain of the groundmass may be of the order of a centimeter or much less. These big crystals may be scattered at great intervals (decimeters) or else they may be so numerous that the distance between them is of the same order as their dimensions. Mechanical movements with related deformation seem to play a role in the formation of porphyritic granites, for the synkinematic granites, migmatites and border types of granite massifs are often porphyritic. Deformations favour the influx and diffusion of mineralizers. A phase of subsequent tension allows the regular crystallization of large feldspars with an idiomorphic tendency. According to Drescher-Kaden (1948):

W. Schmidt thinks that the formation of porphyroblasts takes place in parts of the very strongly mechanically deformed fabric along shear planes, or at the intersection of swarms of such planes. H. Backlund holds that the holoblasts (phenoblasts) originate because of a heterogeneous distribution of the stresses in the fabric, an idea which seems promising.

The *structure* (Fr. *texture*) of granite, which is nearly massive, presents at the same time more or less pronounced stratiform orientation, although sometimes almost invisible or nonexistent. The minerals, particularly the micas, show a tendency to parallel orientation. This property can be very pronounced in some granites (gneissic or planar structure). On the other hand, a careful study often shows a linear orientation of elongated crystals, following a direction in the plane of the gneissic structure. In every respect these orientations represent, apart from exceptional cases, a tendency rather than a rule. Part of the mineral constituents do not follow it at all or only imperfectly.

Oriented structure may result from flow before the termination of crystallization, a flow due to pressures in a semi-fluid phase. Otherwise it may reflect old, stratified-rock structures granitized in place or almost in place. It grades in this case into *palingenetic* structure of the anatectic granites (chapter 4). Then one sees in the granite streaks and diffuse veins along which the grains are slightly different or the density of distribution of the different minerals is not the same as within the body as a whole. The granite looks as if covered by strange arabesques which indistinctly reflect the old structure of tectonized sediments.

Miarolitic structure refers to granites containing small spots, some centimeters in diameter, in which crystallization is coarser, sometimes geodic (vuggy) with the development of pneumatolytic minerals: muscovite, sometimes tourmaline or cassiterite, and better formed quartz and feldspar crystals which are possibly idiomorphic.

Orbicular structure is an exceptional case in which granitic minerals are distributed in such a way as to form rounded aggregates, some centimeters to some decimeters in diameter. "The spheroids formed by alternating crusts of biotite and colourless material are combined with granular granite which occupies the centre of each spheroidal mass" (J. de Lapparent, 1923). The *rapakivi* granite is a very special case. Such structures are enigmatic. They will be discussed in connection with the border facies of granite massifs in chapter 5.

EVOLUTION OF GRANITE ON THE SCALE OF THE CRYSTAL

Consider for a moment a piece of granite. Many features indicate that it took a long time for this granite to achieve its definite crystalline aspect. In fact, these reveal a succession of events which will be analyzed. Having started to form at temperatures above 600°–700° and involving enormous masses, the duration of cooling of granite by thermal conductivity is certainly very long, and the susceptibility of minerals to mutual reactions took a long time to become negligible. Lastly the pegmatites, which are the most important satellites of granite massifs, go through numerous successive phases in their formation, phases made classic by the work of A. Fersman (1931) and others, as we will see in chapter 9.

As F. K. Drescher-Kaden (1948) writes:

None of the components of granite has remained with the exterior form which it had when it originated. Each one shows obvious traces of attack by later solutions. This attack may result from an instability of the crystals formed relative to a modification of the mother liquid by the progress of crystallization, or else from the action of new solutions introduced from the surroundings as a consequence of the evolution of the deformation in the milieu.

Rosenbusch's order

According to H. Rosenbusch (1910):
the order of succession of the formation of the essential and accessory constituents of normal granites is:

      1. apatite, zircon and ore minerals;
      2. mica, amphibole and pyroxene;
      3. plagioclase and alkaline feldspar;
      4. quartz.

In this order the periods of formation of 1 and 2, and 2 and 3 only overlap a little. The separation of plagioclase begins well before that of alkaline feldspars, proceeds for a considerable time contemporaneously with it, and is still in progress when quartz begins to form.

Rosenbusch indicates that dynamic phenomena sometimes disturb this succession. He notes the existence of late pneumatolytic aegirine in miarolitic cavities of alkaline granite, and pneumatolytic muscovite at the end of the consolidation of some normal granites.

This order of succession arises from the form and disposition of the crystals: an older mineral being molded by a younger one, or occurring as inclusions in the younger. These criteria would hold strictly true if the rock mass had crystallized entirely by fractional crystallization from a molten magma. They become more uncertain in the light of indications obtained from the study of metamorphic rocks. As in the metamorphic rock, so too in the granites, indications of *blastesis*, that is, growth of crystals which have already been formed for a more or less long time, exist; and one can expect a possible idiomorphic development of "strong" minerals at the expense of other minerals already crystallized.

In particular, some of the tiny accessory minerals, such as tourmaline, zircon, apatite and sphene, may be formed late. In analogy with the crystallization of pegmatites, A. E. Fersman (1931) classes in the ultimate phases of consolidation of granite and in the order indicated, the following minerals which are accessory in some granites, except for terminal albite which is sometimes an essential mineral: schorl, muscovite, beryl, topaz, cassiterite, albite, lepidolite and epidote.

B*

Among the obvious exceptions to Rosenbusch's order, the late albite which surrounds all other minerals in some alkaline granites should be noted, as well as the early quartz occurring as small rounded inclusions which contrast with the large mosaics of late quartz. The potash feldspar ovoids surrounded by zones of plagioclase in rapakivi granite may readily be mentioned in this connection. We will return to the particular interpretation of rapakivi in chapter 5. However, the exceptions concern special types of granite that form very small masses compared to the enormous volume of ordinary granites. Many of them are connected with late pneumatolytic effects, concentrated in the small miarolitic or intergranular domains in the heart of the rock.

Rosenbusch's order has its value, but it appears to concern mainly the end of the crystallization of different minerals, the beginnings of which may have been more or less simultaneous. There is a striking similarity, as R. Perrin and M. Roubault have strongly emphasized in different publications, between the large feldspars in porphyritic granite and those frequently developed in schists within the aureole of the same granite or in its inclusions. It is not unusual to see the big feldspars à cheval[1] along the boundary between an inclusion and the surrounding granite and "biting" both sides. This type of feldspar appears late in the crystallization of the granite, whereas those of the aureole are forerunners, and consequently early; the favourable conditions for the crystallization of such feldspars have thus been quasi-permanent during the development of the granite. A similar comment arises from the observation of the marginal facies of granite. For example, the Ment porphyritic granite, Morocco (p. 65), grades towards its margins into a microgranite with large feldspars, which are apparently earlier than the crystallization of the groundmass of the rock, whereas the same feldspars are late in the groundmass of the granite itself. An important time lag must exist between the formation of the big feldspars of the two extreme types of rocks with a gradual transition between both rocks over a short distance. These facts reconcile the existence of earlier pegmatites and later pegmatites commonly met with in the peripheral portions of granite batholis.

Obviously this does not mean that all mineral species of a granite had started to crystallize together in all cases. The beginnings are, however, hard to define, being more or less obscured by later crystallizations.

An analogy might be found between Rosenbusch's order and

[1] Translators' note: an allusion to the position of a rider with one leg on each side of the horse.

Bowen's "reaction series" (1933). These specify the series of crystals deposited during the fractional crystallization of silicate melts in the laboratory. There are essentially two series. One is made up of olivine, pyroxene, amphibole, biotite, potash feldspar with muscovite and quartz. The other consists of the plagioclases from more calcic to more sodic and ending in the same potash feldspar with muscovite and quartz. It is possible that the metasomatism in the interior of crystal aggregates tends to follow the same succession as the crystallization starting in a liquid, and Bowen's series, so far as they can be observed in granites, do not necessarily imply passage through the molten state. We know that in the complicated metallogenetic series of the metallic minerals, the crystallizations from solutions in cavities have counterparts in similar metasomatic crystallizations, following the same successions, in the solid material of the neighbouring rock.

Perhaps Bowen's series also involve the amorphous, intergranular fluid of "the granitic mobilized milieu" during the course of consolidation, and perhaps the evolution of this fluid controls the surrounding metasomatisms.

Other Indications of a Succession of States of Equilibrium

A first category concerns residual or partly resorbed minerals: broken and corroded garnets and andalusites, and sericitized cordierites. These minerals perhaps are remnants of incompletely assimilated inclusions (chapter 5). The effects of the corrosion by feldspar of early quartz, which was a part of sediments existing before the granite, gives rise to pseudo-granophyric textures, in other words, resembling some micropegmatites. This case is cited by Drescher-Kaden (1948) and by P. Ljunggren (1954). Such quartz can also be seen corroded by muscovite. Thus, pebbles of quartz from an ancient puddingstone (conglomerate) in a granitoid migmatite (Peyregrand gneiss, Ariège, Pyrenees) furnish a typical example (Raguin, 1955).

A second category of observations deals with zoned minerals: allanite with a girdle of epidote, some amphiboles, but above all the zoned feldspars. Plagioclases with normal zoning with more alkaline material on the outside are common. Plagioclase with recurrent zoning is found in more basic granites contaminated by assimilation. G. Frasl (1954) has described peculiar zoned microcline in gneiss and granites from Tauern and the old massif of Austria. Their oscillatory zoning seems to derive from chemical fluctuations in the milieu during the crystallization, this milieu being liquid. He actually indicates that three hypotheses are conceivable for an interpretation of this observation:

1. growth of a crystal in zones from molten material;
2. growth by means of replacement of surrounding solid material;
3. rhythmic exsolution from a crystal of an originally homogeneous sodium–potassium feldspar.

He objects to the third hypothesis because the zones are of different thicknesses; each zone represents a complex crystallographic form and the form is slightly different from one zone to another, as if they represent the outlines of a crystal at different moments in its growth. The objection to the second hypothesis is based upon the fact that each zone has a sharp rectilinear border, whereas the border of the crystal as a whole is ameboid: it is hardly possible that the zone boundaries could have been straightened to rectilinear forms after their formation, for small inclusions of quartz and plagioclase mark out some of these linear zones in the feldspar and it seems very unlikely that they would be transported into their positions in the solid material. There remains only the first hypothesis, which he accepts.

Finally a succession of states of equilibrium is related to the terminal stages of the evolution of granites in an environment almost completely crystallized. Naturally the later phases can be better studied than earlier ones, because they are not obliterated by their own evolution. The studies of O. H. Erdmannsdörfer have emphasized the importance of the phenomena which relate the final crystallization of granites to crystal-loblastesis, that is to say with metamorphism, and which he has grouped under the term *endometasomatism*.

Endometasomatism

The exsolution of perthite, the late albitization of some granites, the myrmekites, and the micropegmatites belong to this domain.

The *microperthites* have already been mentioned (p. 11), attributable, depending on the case, to the splitting up of a soda-potash feldspar or to the action of sodic solutions coming from without and altering the pre-existing potash feldspar. The importance of exsolution has been shown by O. F. Tuttle (1952 b), who even suggests the possibility that all the existing albite may depend on such a division in alkaline granites.

Final albitization of alkaline granites is a striking phenomenon. For example, in the bearing granites of Aïr in the southern Sahara, albite is mainly formed from orthoclase and microcline by replacement. This calls to mind the metasomatic albitization of pegmatites (chapter 9).

The *myrmekites*, which quite often form in granites and above all in migmatites, have been studied by numerous authors. Myrmekite consists of small buds penetrated by microscopic curving vermicules of quartz and is generally found at the border of a plagioclase crystal in contact with a crystal of potash feldspar. The material of the buds forms a direct continuation of the plagioclase with a slight change to a more sodic chemical composition. Towards the potash feldspar the buds, in contrast, are separated by a sharp contact, convex towards this feldspar. The dimensions of this form are always very small, of the order of less than a millimeter.

It has long been accepted, particularly since the studies of J. J. Sederholm (1916), that myrmekite is the result of a reaction at the contact of the two feldspars. Among the older generation of authors who were concerned with this problem, F. Becke and J. J. Sederholm thought that the potash feldspar was older than the myrmekite and had been corroded by it. In contrast, according to F. K. Drescher-Kaden (1948), who supported his argument by remarkable photomicrographs, the development of potash feldspar, later than that of the plagioclase, provokes corrosion and modification of the outer part of the plagioclase through the action of microsolutions which are the source of the potash feldspar. After this corrosion, the vermicular quartz crystallizes along minute channels and there finally the potash feldspar is formed.

Eventually myrmekitization is more intense under the influence of more mobile solutions and it forms in the cores of plagioclases of the rock away from any contact with a potash feldspar. The microsolutions were without doubt of the same character as in the normal case, but did not end in the formation of crystals of potash feldspar. The migmatites in the south-eastern part of the French Massif Central show this peculiarity, according to M. Roques (1941); and Drescher-Kaden also mentions it for granoblastic rocks without potash feldspar. Every now and then a later phase of myrmekite is found formed in microfissures between microline crystals or between microcline and quartz grains (the second type of myrmekite of Drescher-Kaden).

According to M. Roques (1955) the myrmekite in the same migmatites of the Massif Central is formed most often at the expense of both plagioclase and microcline. On the basis of quantitative studies which he carried out, the phenomenon would depend upon an addition of silica and a removal of alumina, lime and a little potash. It would represent essentially a siliceous metasomatism.

The *micropegmatites*, which are much more localized than the myrmekites, but very characteristically developed in the facies of granite passing over into granophyre (chapter 9), result, according to Drescher-Kaden (1948), from a corrosion of potash feldspar by quartz. The quartz of the micropegmatites shows a common crystallographic orientation giving rise to the well-known "graphic quartz" of pegmatites in general. Drescher-Kaden shows that there are transitions between this type of quartz and the ordinary quartz grains in the rock. This observation is important in that it suggests, for the quartz of this granite, a formation later than the potash feldspar by a process of corrosion of grains of feldspar already formed and by intergranular films probably occupied by microsolutions. This would be a *crystalloblastesis in the solid environment* for all grains of quartz in the rock.

It must be noted, however, that P. Ljunggren (1954) attributes some granophyric microstructures, in his "Barktorp gneiss" of Dalecarlia, Central Sweden, to a corrosion of quartz grains by the birth of feldspathic porphyroblasts. The unity of orientation of small quartz groups indicates that they originally belonged to a single grain of quartz in the groundmass. It is possible that both processes take place in granophyres, depending on the case.

The different phenomena described in some detail reveal clearly how both delicate and efficient is granitic endometasomatism.

It would naturally be necessary to delimit the domain of endometasomatism *vis à vis* that of a metamorphism affecting a granite very much later. Often such a metamorphism is revealed by the crushing of the grains, producing a characteristic schistosity accompanied by recrystallization: development of chlorite and muscovite and the granulation of the quartz and feldspar crystals. However, less obvious cases also occur. A. Schüller (1951) has described the Dessau granite, southeast of Magdeburg, Germany, which is of Precambrian age but which is affected by Hercynian metamorphism. Whereas its alkali feldspars and micas are stretched and crushed, its plagioclases have been recrystallized after deformation. They have attained the "glomeroblastic" facies, by the agglomeration of several individual crystals in one large plagioclase and they show an inverse zoning with a kernel of 20% An and borders of 25% An. These singular circumstances differ from those which could be regarded as normal for the evolution of a granitic crystallization taking place in only one cycle.

Change in the Physical and Chemical Conditions during the Course of Formation of Granite

Biotite of granites develops for the most part in a mobilized environment, which is still nevertheless essentially solid. Approaching the boundary of a granite from the outside, clusters of biotite may be seen becoming bigger and thicker following the stratification of the rock. In some inclusions in the marginal parts of a granite one readily discerns the moment when the phantoms of the inclusions, in which the large streaks of biotite still reflect the original stratification, become dispersed and grade into homogeneous granite. The biotite grains are spread out, and become randomly oriented, or are arranged according to numerous orientations with an average direction, but are freed from the original orientation of the stratification. This gives the impression of a rather sudden appearance of a dominating hydrostatic pressure regime and suggests an environment rich in impregnating solutions. This process has also been pointed out by B. C. King and A. M. J. de Swardt (1949): the biotite, forming a fine mosaic which existed before the development of the prinipal granite of Osi, Nigeria, in fine-grained gneisses, is reorganized in the coarse granitic crystallization.

Later on, the moment of the final crystallization of the normal plagioclase, excluding the terminal albitization, corresponds to a maximum of mobility of the environment, or perhaps a maximum of fluidity. The plagioclases, sometimes idiomorphic and zoned, actually recall strongly those of the volcanic magmas, as has been pointed out by Turner and Verhoogen (1951). This is striking in the granites of plagidiomorphic texture, such as those of the Birrimien in West Africa (L. Bodin, 1951), but it has some universality of a less obvious degree.

In contrast the termination of the crystallization of alkali feldspars and quartz gives the impression of metasomatism with the formation of poecilitic crystals and corrosion of the edges of crystals. In some cases, late stage crystallization fills small spaces rich in residual fluids giving a miarolitic structure.

However, it would be too simple to assign to the granite an evolution in a "mixed environment", at first impregnated with a small quantity of solutions, then very rich in solutions containing crystals in suspension, and finally anew almost holocrystalline with residual liquid vesicules which in the last stage crystallize in their turn. One can sense rather multiple variations of the quantitative relations between crystals and solutions, variations in extent and rhythm different in different types of granite. The foregoing observations in fact may lead us to conceive of at least three phases of quartz. First there is that of the primitive quartz of the sedimentary rock before granitization, quartz doubtless more or less modified. Then that of the myrmekitic quartz of an age close to that of the potash feldspar is formed; this quartz, which is often absent in the final rock, may be transitory. Finally, there is the terminal granoblastic quartz formed by crystalloblastesis. L. J. G. Schermerhorn (1956) even distinguishes six different types of quartz representing two or three generations in a granite in Portugal. There are also in most granites several phases of plagioclase: the main plagioclase of the rock fabric; that of perthite in the interior of potash feldspars, subdivided into several stages from the exsolution perthites to the replacement perthites; finally the interstitial albite along the edges of crystals, possibly with myrmekite of the two types described earlier.

Against the idea of a single process confined entirely to a solid crystalline environment in crystalloblastesis, Drescher-Kaden (1948) has remarked on the possibility that sometimes the plagioclase crystals rotate small included minerals to orient them along the crystallographic directions of the large crystal, a phenomenon which is better explained in a viscous fluid. However, the marginal repulsion and mechanical orientation at the border of the crystal during its growth could also produce such an arrangement.

G. Frasl (1954) has presented similar observations for large zoned microclines rich in inclusions of plagioclase aligned along the borders of the zones. As he has indicated, one can hardly assume an ameboid growth of microcline in a solid aggregate containing unorientated grains of plagioclase, grains which would only be orientated in the finished microcline along the imaginary growth-surfaces of the great feldspar. Why should they choose to be orientated along certain directions of faces and ignore others equally important crystallographically? Furthermore, it cannot be accepted that the plagioclases were developed only after the microcline had already crystallized, for these plagioclases differ in form, size and chemical composition in the same microcline. Finally it cannot be accepted that the plagioclases have developed at the same time as the microcline, at the moment when the edge of the large feldspar has reached their present position in the course of its growth. They would, in such a case, have a flared out form and would not show independent zoning starting from their respective centres, Frasl thus concludes that the microcline has developed in a liquid milieu, and has oriented pre-existing plagioclase crystals along its edges, and engulfed them during its growth, which is ended by an ameboid crystalloblastesis. The size of the inclusions, often of several millimeters, gives some idea of the minimum size of the free space occupied by the fluid, in order that the plagioclase could rotate on itself to be placed alongside the face of the large feldspar. He adds that in some cases the proportions of large microclines reaches 25–40% of the total volume of the rock; consequently the proportion of fluid material was great and did not constitute only a sort of residue in the pores of the rock.

Indications of Movement of Material during Crystallization

Movements affecting the granitic material during crystallization are indicated by deformations of the rocks of the aureole, very marked in the scale of "small tectonics" (chapter 6). In the granite itself, however, the completion of its slow crystallization, including metasomatic phases, obliterates the deformations in reorganizing the grain. Vestiges of possible twisting of micas, and undulose deformation and granulation of quartz are observed. More or less healed microfractures in feldspar crystals are not rare.

It is probable that some of the features of Cloos's Granite Tectonics (chapter 7)—schlieren, alignment of crystals, planar or linear orientation of crystals—may represent phantoms of these deformations, when they do not coincide with the old stratification of the pre-granitic rocks. B. C. King and A. M. J. de Swardt (1949) think that the development of crystallizations in fine-grained mosaics is characteristic of moments of stress, and that more coarse crystallization represents moments of release. In some granites of irregular grain (border facies, facies grading into migmatites), the effect of cycles of stress mechanics and release mechanics should be recognizable, if the original nature of the material before granitization does not have a preponderant influence.

In the synkinematic granites (chapter 12), the traces of movement become more prominent, in a very different manner, moreover, from one zone to another in the mass. The tectonic movements contemporaneous with the emplacement and the crystallization of a sykinematic granite are manifestly much more important than those conducted with the emplacement of a batholithic homogeneous granite; they continue until much later than the principal crystallization at least in some parts of the massif. The effects of stretching, the breaking of feldspar crystals and gliding along mica plates, are commonly present without internal crushing of these minerals, which have not completed their crystallization at this time. Finally, mylonitic foliation is found occasionally distributed through the rock and later than the crystallization of the main minerals. Identical effects are found in some migmatites. The feldspathic lenses of the classic embrechites of the Gorges d'Heric, Massif Central (Jung and Roques, 1952), show a peculiar stretching and shearing having sometimes made each "eyed" feldspar into the shape of two or three almonds closely squeezed together and separated by slip planes. The sketches of embrechites of the Saint-Etienne region of France given by A. Demay (1942) illustrate some similar observations.

CHEMICAL COMPOSITION AND CLASSIFICATION

The granites are composed essentially of quartz and feldspar, mica being less abundant and other possible minerals often reduced to insignificant amounts. The most important elements in the chemical composition are consequently silica, alumina, lime, potash and soda, and it is on their proportions that the classification of granites is based. The scarcely coloured minerals (coupholites) give the rock its character, whereas the coloured minerals (barylites) serve only to define varieties.

R. A. Daly (1933) has calculated the averages of analyses of a great number of granites: 47 Precambrian granites, 184 post-Cambrian granites, 20 calc-alkaline granites, and 12 alkaline granites. The range of variations in percentages of the average figures he gives are: 69–73% for silica, 12–15% for alumina, 0.5–2.2% for lime, 3.2–4.5% for soda, and 2.7–4.5% for potash.

The variations are greater if individual granite massifs are considered. According to analyses quoted by F. Rinne (1949), variations in the order of 64–76% for silica, 8–16.5% for alumina, 0.1–3% for lime, 2–6% for soda, 2.7–6.5% for potash were found. He even mentions one range for silica of 61–82%. Overall the sum of soda and potash does not vary more than from 8–10%. Finally the sum of ferrous and ferric oxides may vary from 1.7–13%, and magnesia from 0–4.7%.

The chemical composition is relatively constant within a given granite mass, apart from its borders and zones rich in inclusions. In contrast there is chemical diversity from one massif to another, and one may speak of a "Pelvoux granite" or of a "Mont Blanc granite" and quote their individual chemical compositions.

In the classification of granites, I will follow A. Lacroix (1933). The two main categories, *alkaline* granites and *calc-alkaline* granites, can be distinguished by the exclusive presence of alkaline feldspars (orthoclase, microcline, albite) in the former, and by additional calcic plagioclases in the latter.

Chemical analyses of alkaline granites reveal no feldspathic lime, although there may be some in a barylite, or else very small quantities of it. Amongst these granites, the *hyperalkaline* granites contain less Al_2O_3 molecules than $Na_2O + K_2O$ molecules, which results in the appearance of alkaline amphiboles or pyroxenes in the rock. More alumina produces simply an alkaline granite, which may possibly contain lime-magnesia amphiboles or pyroxenes along with mica.

Among the calc-alkaline granites, granites can be first distinguished which are more potassic than sodic, in which the coefficient s of Lacroix (the ratio of the molecules K_2O to Na_2O) is greater than 3 : 5. These can be divided into two species: in the *perorthoclasic* granites, this ratio is greater than 5 : 3; in the *monzonitic* granites the ratio ranges between 5 : 3 and 3 : 5. It can be seen that in these there may be almost as much potash feldspar as plagioclase. Amphibole may possibly be present.

The second category of calc-alkaline granite comprises granites more sodic than potassic. The ratio s is less than 3 : 5. These granites may also contain amphibole. *Akeritic* granites are defined as those with plagioclase in the range of composition of oligoclase. The ratio of alkali molecules to feldspathic lime molecules (the ratio r of Lacroix) is greater than 5 : 3. Finally there are the *granodiorites*, in which the plagioclase component is more calcic (andesine). The ratio r is less than 5 : 3. The rock is generally more melanocratic, that is, darker and richer in barylites.

Chapter 3

GRANITES AS THEY OCCUR: GRANITES IN CIRCUMSCRIBED MASSIFS

The two main categories in the classification of granites have already been mentioned. The first, which will be studied in this chapter, comprises granites with well-defined borders. I call them *granites in circumscribed massifs (granites en massifs circonscrits)*. They may be emplaced in any kind of country rock by dissolving it or by more or less replacing it, and sometimes by deforming it as if by intrusion of material under pressure. The second category, the *anatectic granites (granites d'anatexie)*, will be the subject of the next chapter.

The granites with which we are concerned here form individualized massifs, relatively homogeneous and strongly contrasting with the enclosing rocks, both in mineralogy and in general aspect. Their emplacement is an enigmatic phenomenon to which I will return later. Often the border of the massif is sharp and well-defined: within a few meters one may pass from granite to little-changed country rock. The massifs are referred to as concordant or discordant relative to the enclosing rock, depending on whether they conform to the layering of the country rock or cut across it.

According to form, dimensions, and relations to neighbouring formations, one may distinguish between 1. *batholiths* and *stocks*; 2. *stratiform massifs* with the varieties known as *phacoliths* and *chonoliths*; 3. *subvolcanic massifs*.

THE BATHOLITHS

The term batholith, conforming to R. A. Daly's usage, signifies a plutonic rock mass for which no floor (substratum) can be seen or inferred, which seems to enlarge downwards, and which is exposed over an area of at least 100 sq. km. Such masses were emplaced under a "roof" consisting of older rocks. Similar but smaller bodies are called *stocks*. Instead of the term batholith, the term *pluton* may be used, following the practice of H. Cloos.

The outcrops of batholiths often have the form of vast, depressed domes, on top of which pendants of the roof "float", preserved as large inclusions in the granite after the erosion of the roof. Where erosion has been less deep and where most of the roof is preserved, protuberances of the dome can outcrop (fig. 44). Many stocks are only protuberances of an invisible batholith.

It is evident that stratiform massifs, i.e. large concordant sheets which are more or less parallel to the topographic surface, will display similarities to an uncovered batholith in outcrop. The two forms may be distinguished, however, by geophysical investigations: the lower gravity of a batholithic massif compared to the surrounding geological formations shows that the granite continues to great depth. R. Bollo and J. Goguel (1950) state that in Brittany:

> the negative anomalies correspond to two zones of granite massifs, and in detail, the curves which limit the anomalies often seem to mark the contacts of the granites with a precision in accord with the density of the stations. This is particularly evident in the circumscribed massifs of the Côtes-du-Nord and Finistère, at Quintin and in Montagne d'Arrée.

The largest known batholith is that of the Coast Ranges of Alaska and British Columbia, which measures 2,000 km in length with a maximum width of 200 km. The Pelvoux granite in the Dauphinois Alps arises in several large outcroppings, which undoubtedly belong to the same Hercynian batholith, in view of the somewhat special composition which is characteristic of this granite (Pierre Termier, 1897). The series of post-Alpine granite batholiths of Adamello, Bergell, etc., are of Tertiary age. The Hercynian granites of the Pyrenes are distributed along the chain; they all have very different properties and represent autonomous batholiths.

Annex Cupolas and Apophyses of Batholiths

Small granite massifs are sometimes attached to batholiths or are exposed above their upper surfaces. Even if the granite of these small massifs is slightly different they are manifestly dependencies of the main mass.

The Oulmes batholith, in Central Morocco, with an area of 10 km by 5 km, has a concordant structure under Palaeozoic shales and sandstones. It is bordered along its periphery or its upper surfaces by several small cupolas of an aplitic muscovite granite and apophyses reaching lengths of tens or hundreds of meters. One of these is cut by numerous veins of tin-bearing quartz (H. Termier, B. Owodenko and J. Agard, 1950). The Ment batholith, with a diameter of about twenty kilometers, is structurally discordant within a folded series in the same region. It has border cupolas of the same type, containing veins of tourmaline and scheelite-bearing pegmatites.

Elsewhere cupolas of this kind emerge at some distance from batholiths, but with the same rocks as in these. These are simply local swellings, more or less well-defined, from the upper surfaces of the batholiths. Such is the case in the Kalima region, Maniema, Congo, where an important tin mineralization is connected with the cupolas (Varlamoff, 1948).

In the case of differentiated cupolas, they seem to cut the large massif and emanate from its interior, even if no access vents are visible in the eroded mass. They must probably be regarded as rising chemical migrations of late origin, rich in pneumatolytic material, and not as "bubbles" of magma. Their location may have tectonic causes related to points in the roof of less rigidity or lesser impermeability. There are certain similarities between these annex cupolas and late-migmatic granite masses (p. 54).

The Borders of Batholiths

The study of the borders of massifs leads to interesting observations which may throw light on the mechanics of the emplacement of granite. As I have indicated, this border is often sharp and well-defined; elsewhere a few meters may take us from pure granite to little-modified country rock. The transitional zone is in such cases intersected by numerous veins of quartz or granite, or is finely gneissified by contact metamorphism (chapter 6). It thus has the aspect of an anatectic granite on a small scale, with the impregnation of the country rock for some distance by granitic material.

Even in the case of a sharp contact, the marginal granite in general differs from the normal granite by a heterogeneity due to irregularly distributed mineral constituents: clusters of mica and concentrations of feldspar. Furthermore, there may be a schistosity in the granite, anything from well-pronounced to microscopic, corresponding more or

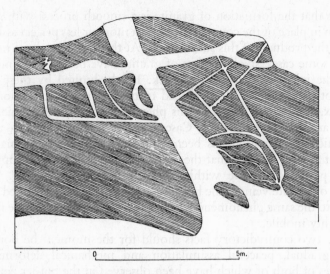

Fig. 1. Granite veins in gneiss (after A. Heikel, in V. Hackman, Geol. Kom. Finland, 1931).

less to the trend in the country rock. Finally, minor inclusions of country rock may be observed, captured in the granite, and recrystallized.

In the concordant massifs, the injection of granite seems to have been guided by layering in the enclosing rock. In the discordant massifs the country rock layers are cleanly cut by granite. Many massifs are concordant in one section of their border and discordant in another, as if they had had some degree of freedom in this respect. When the layers have been cut, one may observe occasionally strung out in the granite strings of small or large inclusions, corresponding to the layering, or else zones where the granite has an abnormal chemical and mineralogical composition approaching that of the intersected layers.

A classic example, described by Ch. Barrois (1894), is revealed by layers of Palaeozoic sandstone which can be followed for a considerable distance in the Bécherel granite massif of Brittany. They have been preserved in the interior of the granite, where they appear as pseudo-veinlets of crystalline quartz, white or rose in colour and measuring up to ten meters in thickness. In contrast, the schist layers which contained these ledges of sandstone have disappeared completely, assimilated by the granite.

These facts, as well as the microscopic peculiarities such as fine-grained schistosity and small recrystallized remnants described above, indicate that the formation of granite is a smooth process with a substitution in place of the country rock and a more or less perfect assimilation of the products of this substitution. At the border itself, as may be seen in some cases, small veinlets of granite have been readily injected along the joints of the intruded rock. Blocks limited by these veins have not been appreciably displaced from their original positions (A. Cailleux, 1946). The marks of this phenomenon are its extreme tranquility and its great slowness. Cases are also found, however, where mechanical deformation has been quite strong along these margins. Grids of fissures indicate that the already solid granite was compressed to the point of rupture within its countryrock framework. Tight folding of granite veins at the border and of the injected stratified rocks belong to the same phenomenon, but at an earlier stage when the milieu was highly mobile.

These two contradictory facts should for the moment be borne in mind: gradual, peaceful assimilation and mechanical deformation, evidences of both of which have been observed in the border zones of granites.

Aureoles and Satellitic Dykes of Batholiths

In the vicinity of granite massifs, the injected rock shows a more or less pronounced recrystallization with the development of new minerals of many kinds. This phenomenon is *contact metamorphism*, and the zone of rocks affected constitutes the *aureole* of the granite. An aureole may reach a thickness of several hundred meters outwards from the granite, the intensity of the transformations decreasing with the distance (chapter 6). In some cases the aureole may be almost non-existent.

A dyke suite often accompanies batholiths in the fractures in granite, in the aureole, and often well away from it. These veins radiate around cupolas (fig. 44) or occupy large fractures far away from them. Their importance and size varies considerably. They may be of *pegmatites*, i.e., the most mobile differentiates in the granitic material, emanated as forerunners of the ascending batholith, or as residues which have remained mobile long after the batholith crystallized. Moreover, dykes of *lamprophyres* occur, which are another facies of the final differentiation; dark rocks rich in mica flakes and amphibole. Dykes of *granite porphyry* (microgranites, microdiorites) are among the last manifestations of this evolution. The porphyritic texture of these rocks suggests the emplacement of fluid magma in an already cooled environment, occasioning an even more sudden crystallization in the manner of lavas.

Composite Batholiths

Some batholiths show a large scale zoning with the central rocks of the massif differing from the rocks of roughly concentric outer zones. The case seems common in the Sierra Nevada batholiths of California. In the region of Yosemite Park, west of Mount Lyell, the granite mass of the Sierra is divided into twin bodies measuring respectively fifteen and thirty kilometers in a transverse E–W direction, separated by a septum of metamorphic rocks (E. Cloos, 1933). The western massif is made up from the periphery inwards of successive formations of diorite, then of granodiorite, of three at least in number and such that each one dislocates and engulfs blocks of the preceding. The eastern massif consists of a mantle of granodiorite rich in basic inclusions and with a younger core of porphyritic granite containing at its centre an even younger microgranite. In these examples a centripetal evolution of the massif is manifest, as the most central rocks affect those of the peripheral portions. This represents, on an immensely greater scale, an evolution resembling that of a body of complex pegmatites (chapter 9).

However, some forerunners of the main batholith west of the Sierra Nevada do not show this chronological succession at all, although they show the same composite structure. According to R. R. Compton (1955), for instance, the Bidwell-Bar batholith, with zones from the periphery inward of tonalite, granodiorite, trondhjemite and leuco-trondhjemite, may have attained these variations through the effects of marginal assimilation or migmatization without any marked succession in the rock types.

Diapiric Batholiths

According to C. E. Wegmann (1930), some granite massifs show the indications of a mechanism of ascent similar to that of the domes of salt diapirs. As there are circular diapirs (Germany and Texas) and the tongue-shaped diapirs (Roumania), so there are similar dispositions on a grand scale of granite massifs of this type. Wegmann notes that salt diapirs arise from a plastic bed loaded by overlying thick, more rigid layers, and that conditions are analagous, but on a much grander scale, in the mobilized domains of the crust or orogenic infrastructure where the granites of the depths are formed. Mapping in the ancient shields of Fennoscandia and Greenland shows him the transition of structures of different tectonic levels, and the geometric and kinematic adaptations of geological strata to the granite masses which they harbour.

The fact is that around some batholiths a statistical study indicates that the intruded strata are shoved upwards along the border of the mass. For some of them the shoving aside is only a matter of some degrees, for others it is very much more violent and obvious.

An example of the first variety occurs in the Mont Aigoual granite, Cévennes, in the south of France, where the shoving aside of the schist layers is on the average only about ten degrees (D. de Waard, 1949). A similar situation exists around the Maniema granite massifs, in the eastern part of the former Belgian Congo (N. Varlamoff, 1949). The massifs which cause a brutal disruption of the formations, or even systems of tight peripheral folds, will be discussed in chapter 7, along with the mechanical effects of the border in conjunction with the structures of the granite massifs themselves. There I will deal with the problem of the amplitude of displacements which cannot be derived directly from geometric criteria, and which are not necessarily very great in all cases. In all ways, according to Wegmann, blocks can be observed which have ascended with the diapiric granites and which in the ascent form "intrusion breccias", as, for instance, in the Onas massif of Finland.

THE STRATIFORM MASSIFS

The stratiform massifs have the form of large concordant sheets within the layering of the surrounding rocks. Even though the term is descriptive, and even if some of these massifs could have been formed statically by metasomatism of favourable layers, I believe that they should be interpreted for the most part as synkinematic (chapter 12). They are localized along major structures of the regional tectonic plan: folds, faults, or thrust surfaces. They show diversification of their material with regard to structure and to mineralogical composition, following layers or lenticular masses in harmony with the structural pattern of the assemblage as a whole. Effects of mylonitic crushing can be seen along some layers. The texture of the rock often resembles that of anatectic granites (partition texture), but sometimes also resembles that of ordinary granite massifs. Such massive granites can be differentiated in the stratiform complexes, forming bodies of any shape but in size subordinate to other types. The material of the stratiform granites seems to have been drawn out and displaced along swarms of surfaces of tectonic lamination or thrust zones, or else squeezed into anticlinal folds in the structure. It seems as if movements and crystallization had alternated over a long period of time in successive episodes.

An example of such bodies can be seen in the Lys-Caillaouas granite, in the Central Pyrenees. Here laminae of granite, of thicknesses of meters to hectometers, are intercalated between septa of metamorphosed schists and outline a kind of fan of granite participating in the system of folding of the region (fig. 2).

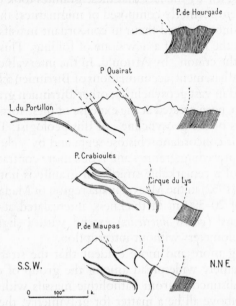

Fig. 2. Granite in sheets. The Lys massif near Luchon, Haute-Garonne. Hatched: schists; uncoloured: granite.

The granites with white mica and associated migmatites of Millevaches, in the Massif Central of France, are almost 150 km in length and several tens of kilometers in width (fig. 32). The same type of rocks can be followed *en echelon* with interruptions as far as Point du Raz in Brittany, altogether a distance of nearly 700 km.

The "heterogeneous" granites of the Birrimien of West Africa are remarkable because of two contradictory characteristics: strict concordance of boundaries and enclosed panels of migmatites in the interior of the granite (M. Roques, 1948). Their heterogeneity consists in a variation of texture (normal granitic texture, fluidal structure, schistose texture), and variations in the material (coarse and fine grained granite, fine leucocratic, or pegmatitic), and finally through abundance of inclusions at different points of development which are often migmatized. M. Roques regards them as similar to those of Millevaches and the hybrid Devonian-Dinantian granites in the southern

Black Forest of Germany. He also considers them as syntectonic. The nature of the stratiform occurrence of this type of granite in the zone of the folded Birrimien in the Ivory Coast has been revealed by M. Arnould (1961). He has shown that their contradictory characteristics can be accounted for by the fact that these granites took over the zones of an old basement formerly composed of migmatites: they reactivated these zones and incorporated them in concordant massifs for hundreds of kilometers in the heart of a new zone of folding. This type is called the "granite of the craton" by Arnould. In the intervals of the regranitized zones of the basement, accumulations of Birrimien schists and greywackes are found in vast geosynclines; other Birrimien granites, equally syntectonic, have been created at the expense of these formations. These are the "granites of the geosyncline" of this geologist. They are characterized by their concordant schistose septa and by a chemistry which differs from the preceding granites and is of a more contrasted character.

An example of a remarkable stratiform granite is noted by J. Jung and M. Roques (1952) in the Maevatanana region of Madagascar, where granite sheets of 20–500 m in thickness, intercalated at several levels with lower gneiss[1] (*gneiss inférieurs*) extend with a slight inclination for a hundred kilometers without interruption.

It is becoming more and more evident that the stratiform granite massifs are extremely widespread among the group of circumscribed granites. Their distinction from batholithic massifs with deep vertical extensions will above all be a matter for gravimetry, the latter giving rise to gravimetric minima.

Phacoliths and Chonoliths

These types of massifs, which have been defined by R. A. Daly (1914), form a transition between the stratiform synkinematic massifs and the batholiths. A *phacolith* has the form of a concordant sheet localized in the axial zone of an anticlinal or synclinal fold. A *chonolith* resembles an "intrusion" of irregular form in dislocated beds, its form being due to tectonic or poorly defined factors. Chonoliths seem to be rather common and generally confused with batholiths. The latter are actually very often localized along orogenic zones and are of "late tectonic" rather than a "post-tectonic" age; some of them have actually adopted the complicated form of chonoliths.

The Quérigut granite, in the Ariège Pyrenees, which has a length of

---

[1] Translators' footnote: the rocks of the deepest zone of these authors' metamorphic "stratigraphy".

about 60 km, contains an important migmatite facies zone all along its southern border, although its central and northern portions are of a homogeneous facies. The northern contact shows rounded extensions of some kilometers in radius, enclosed by the folds of the Palaeozoic formations and imposing aberrant directions on these folds in relation to the general plan of folding. This arrangement indicates an evolution in several phases. A zone of the birth of granite, of the migmatite facies, extending all along the southern margin, was created during an active phase of Hercynian folding, with synkinematic stretching of the migmatite and the rocks of its setting. Later the granite was forced out northwards and upwards, contorting and folding the enclosing formations, as well as cutting the folds already formed.

The Néouvielle granite, in the Hautes-Pyrénées, has been interpreted by P. Hupé (1949) as a chonolithic massif, because it has a floor revealed by fragments of Gothlandian schists brought from depth in dykes of lamprophyres from the interior of the massif. Furthermore tectonic factors have affected many parts of the margins.

Recent studies have shown that sheetlike granites, whose localization bears some relationship to tectonic factors, are common in the Pyrenees. Several of them are situated a short distance from the gneissification front, either in the gneiss or in the overlying mica schists. Later than the formation of the gneisses and migmatites and connected with the end of the main folding, their localization seems related to structural disharmonies of the overall tectonic plan. The granites of Costabona, Batère, Saint-Arnac, Ax-les-Thermes and Trois-Seigneurs are examples. Others bear no obvious relationship to the gneiss massifs and are found within Palaeozoic formations. They are partly discordant and partly concordant with the Hercynian folding.

SUBVOLCANIC MASSIFS

These granites, related to systems of volcanic flows and labelled "Vulkanplutone" by H. Cloos, represent a particular case, known from the Tertiary and the Devonian of Scotland, in the Karoo series (Erongo, Brandberg) of Southwest Africa, in the Permian of southern Norway, in Nigeria (Younger Granites, according to Jacobson, 1952), and from some other regions (Hoggar;). The Precambrian granites of J. J. Sederholm's third group in southern Finland and the Åland Islands seem to be of this category, at least in part, as C. E. Wegmann has pointed out to me.

These are small batholiths, some kilometers in diameter (up to 25 km), which pierce volcanic flows or are emplaced in the important emission centres of certain flows. These granites are in general true granites capable of a strong contact metamorphism. Those of Nigeria are tinbearing. In Scotland granophyres instead of granites are often present in the Tertiary complexes.

The shape of the massifs is approximately circular or oval. They may show a composite batholithic structure with concentric zones of two or more granitic rocks, differing in texture or chemical composition (fig. 3).

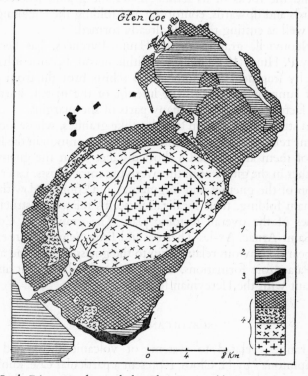

Fig. 3. Loch Etive complex and the Glen Coe cauldron subsidence. Simplified drawing from: *Grampian Highlands, Brit. Reg. Geol.* (Geological Survey, 1948). 1. Old schists; 2. volcanic rocks; 3. diorites; 4. successive granites.

The concentric structure is sometimes emphasized by circular dykes at the outer side of the massif (ring dykes) formed of the same rocks as the massif itself or more often of corresponding microgranular porphyries. In some of the complexes of this nature connected with Tertiary volcanism in Scotland, two or three circular systems composed of a central plutonic rock massif and porphyritic ring dykes succeed one another with displacements of some kilometers, the more recent truncating the older (figure 4).

Composite batholiths and ring dykes bear witness to a very accentuated differentiation which may extend from granite to gabbro. Rocks of these complexes, particularly well studied in Scotland, exhibit

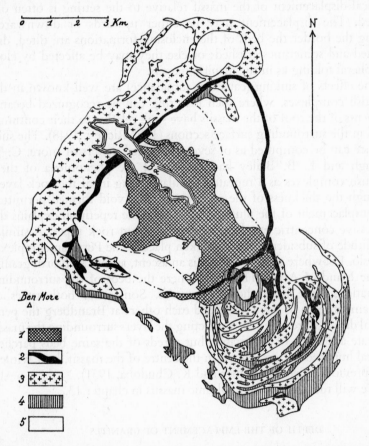

Fig. 4. Map of the central part of the eruptive complex of Mull. Ring dykes and central intrusion. Simplified drawing from: *The Tertiary Volcanic District. Brit. Reg. Geo.*, (Geological Survey, 1948).

1. Central intrusions (granophyres and felsites). 2. felsites of ring dykes. 3. granophyres. 4. dolerites and gabbros. 5. volcanic formations and various grannular rocks.

Note the juxtaposition of the two successive eruptive centres, the second to the northwest truncating the first.

all varieties of granites, gabbros and diorites, as well as the corresponding porphyries. In Norway alkaline rocks, syenites and essexites
are associated in ring complexes (O. Holtedahl, 1943). It is probable that
the granular alkaline rocks in environments of basic rocks, known in
several districts (the Canaries, some Pacific islands), are related to similar
phenomena.

Around the subvolcanic granite massifs, indications of an important
vertical displacement of the massif relative to the setting is often observed. The displacement may be either upwards or downwards.
Along the border the beds of the enclosing formations are tilted, dislocated and sometimes crushed; or else they may be affected by close
peripheral folding as in the diapiric massifs.

The effects of sinking (cauldron subsidence) are well known in the
Scottish complexes, where such lowering can be recognized because
elements of the roof of the massifs have sunk relative to their continua-
tions in the surrounding surface sections (J. E. Richey, 1948). The subsidence can be computed as of several hundred meters or more. C. T.
Clough and E. B. Bailey have explained the phenomena of these
Scottish complexes as a repeated circular caving in of the rock layers
through the thickness of the substratum. The void formed permitted
the emplacement of the plutonic rocks, and the repetition explains the
successive concentric emplacements of different rock types. A similar
amplitude of subsidence has also taken place in the Permian complexes
of Oslo. Elsewhere the movement is an ascent, as for the North granite
of the Island of Arran, Hebrides, where the beds of the surrounding
formations have been shoved upwards. Sometimes both types of
movement seem to have succeeded each other: at Brandberg the peripheral dips towards the centre affecting the layers surrounding the massif
indicate a descent of the massif, but shreds of the same beds perched
several hundred meters higher, in the centre of the massif, bear witness
to a previous ascent (H. Cloos and K. Chudoba, 1931).

We will return to the subvolcanic massifs in chapter 13.

DEPTH OF THE EMPLACEMENT OF GRANITES

R. A. Daly admits that granites may reach the earth's surface, covered
there only by the corresponding effusive facies in the form of thick
rhyolites. Even if this opinion may seem debatable it is manifest that in
the case of subvolcanic massifs, the top of the granite has reached to
within only some hundred meters of the surface of the earth's crust
at the time of the intrusion. But sobvolcanic massifs are rather rare and

of an exceptional character compared to the vast granite masses of the earth. For a dozen examples cited by Daly (1933) from the works of different authors, the estimated thickness of the roofs of the batholiths at the time of formation of the granite varies from 600–6000 m.

Although one generally knows the thickness of the geologic formations in a particular region, and consequently the extent of erosion which has subsequently stripped them to a specific level of stratigraphy, the calculation of the thickness of batholithic rocks is difficult. In many cases the rocks of the countryside are folded and the reconstruction of the structure of the upper parts, which have been destroyed by erosion, is of doubtful value. In other cases, where the structure is less disturbed, one is ignorant of the precise age of the granite, and consequently the age of the most recent stratigraphic layers *at the moment of granitization* in the accumulation of formations overlying the batholith. Examples must therefore be sought in regions of undisturbed structures and for granitizations exactly dated. Those of the Basin and Range zone of the U.S.A. are perhaps the best. C. F. Loughlin (quoted by Daly) gives 1000 meters as the maximum in the district of Tintic, Utah. It must be noted that the cupolas of the batholiths in that region often show a porphyritic facies of the micromonzonites, probably because of the thinness of the roof. J. Barrel (in Shand, 1927) has shown that the Marysville batholith in Montana was originally 1300 meters below the surface. The subvolcanic plutons of the Oslo region were probably not more than at the most 1000–1200 m below the original cover. According to P. Despuljols and H. Termier (1946) the depth of cover would be 5000 m for the Oulmès granite in Central Morocco. Some authors envision 15–30 km of cover for other granites. The latter figure would be very exaggerated, according to the opinion which C. E. Wegmann was good enough to convey to me.

CONCLUSION

In the foregoing chapter we have seen that the mineral constituents of granite lend themselves to different combinations by their mineralogical properties, by their proportions and by their arrangements. If the diversification of granites is very significant on the scale of a hand specimen, it is still greater on the scale of a granite massif. We have just now seen the principal details which the anatomy of a massif may reveal. These views will be clarified and completed in the later chapters on the assimilation of rocks, the aureole, the internal geometric structure of massifs, the differentiation of granite, and on the dyke satellites.

c

At this stage, it is already apparent that the emplacement of granites is a phenomenon with a multiplicity of aspects, of which the details are still largely conjectural, and in which the mechanisms recall to mind some of the characteristic properties of living beings: the choice, the digestion of foreign substances, and the transformation of part of the outside milieu into themselves.

Chapter 4

GRANITES AS THEY OCCUR:
THE ANATECTIC GRANITES WITH
SUITES OF MIGMATITES

The anatectic granites with their suite of migmatites are vast diffuse granites which impregnate immense volumes of the earth's crust. They do not form homogeneous delimited masses, but mingle intimately throughout the greater part of their extent with the substance of the pre-existing rocks, penetrating it, insinuating themselves in all ways, modifying the rock without destroying it, or more or less effacing it here and there. These diffuse granites are the result of a very advanced mobilization of deep-seated zones, a mobilization which resembles a partial fusion. It is referred to as *anatexis*, which signifies a fusion, in accordance with J. J. Sederholm's terminology. Where the structures of pre-existing layers are more or less preserved in a partial granitization, an intimate mixture of granitic material and of recrystallized sedimentary remnants is observed; the resulting mixed rocks have been called *migmatites* (*Mischgesteine*). Broadly speaking, the migmatites surround and enclose on all sides the anatectic granites with transitions between the granite and the migmatites. The upper limit of the migmatites situated within metamorphic formations, which may be only feebly metamorphosed, has been called the *migmatite front* by C. E. Wegmann.

The characteristics of these rocks which will be described lie essentially in the particular structures of the different types of migmatites, structures which are very obvious in the heterogeneous facies of these rocks. Where the rock passes over into an anatectic granite, which may be just as homogeneous as any other type of granite, the anatectic can only be distinguished from other granites by a study of relationships *in the field*. Some peculiarities in the microscopic texture are, however, noteworthy: the frequency of partition and sutured textures (*structures cloisonée et engrenée*) and the abundance of myrmekites in the granite and the migmatites.

Anatexis has invaded enormous volumes, and there can be no doubt that it plays a grand role in the earth's crust. The old basements, the "shields" of Eduard Suess, are formed in large part by diffuse granites and migmatites, as for example in Finland and the greater part of Sweden, the Canadian Shield, Central and West Africa and, closer to home, most of the terrain classified in France as "gneiss".

DESCRIPTION OF ANATEXIS

Only when viewed on a large scale is the full significance of this phenomenon realized. In fact anatexis was only first profoundly studied in the Nordic regions, where Quaternary glaciers have cleaned, polished and removed the weathered portions of the rock exposures and, one might say, prepared them for the most detailed of observations. This circumstance facilitated the admirable work of the great Finnish geologist, J. J. Sederholm, who first cast light on the problem of anatexis. The phenomena of anatexis are very common, however, and today are recognized in different countries where erosion has been deep enough to uncover the deep-seated geological levels.

Fig. 5. Arterite or migmatite of injection gneiss facies (drawn after a photograph by C. E. Wegmann).

The migmatite terrains of Finland have an extent of several hundred kilometers. They display an irregular penetration of Precambrian rock, of diverse origin and already more or less metamorphosed before this phenomenon, by veinlets and masses of capricious outline composed of granitic material. This mixture occurs on different scales, of millimeters, meters and decameters. The granitic material may grade from one point to another from the pegmatite facies, to the aplite facies, or to real granite. Sederholm calls it *ichor*, which means serum.

Sometimes the ichor insinuates itself *lit-par-lit*, diffusing in the schists and forming foliated gneisses called *arterites* by Sederholm; or else it disperses itself in distinctly concordant parallel veinlets, producing the banded gneisses called *epibolites*[1] by Jung and Roques. Sometimes it forms a network of bizarrely intersecting veinlets, in other words breccias, referred to as *agmatites*. Sometimes the ichor disperses itself so finely in the skein of the pre-existing rock that it forms a variety of heterogeneous granite, in which the complex folded patterns of the older rocks show up half effaced and nebulous: this is the *nebulite* of Sederholm. All these facies are varieties of the migmatites.

This basic list is descriptive, and the penetration of ichors does not necessarily imply the invasion of the environment by outside material. One might imagine it derived from the rock itself, created in place or almost in place, in some anatectic regions. Whereas according to the concepts of Sederholm the arterites are injection gneisses, Holmquist (1916) regards them as "venites", in which the microscopic layers of granite are considered to be autochthonous.

Where the migmatization is regular and diffuse on a fine grained scale, it corresponds to a general feldspathization, and produces the varieties which Jung and Roques (1952) call *homogeneous migmatites*. Among these they distinguish the *embrechites*[2], in which the crystallophyllian zoning has been preserved and even accentuated, and where the dominating facies is that of the arterites; and on the other hand, the *anatexites*, of a more advanced development, where fading meandriformed folds are outlined[3].

Every conceivable transition exists between the varieties of migmatites, either because of the original nature of the pre-existing rocks, or because the phenomenon has occurred in several stages. For example, an arterite is broken up and brecciated at the end of the same phase of

[1] Translators' note: from the Greek *epibolos*—bed or couch (M. Roques 1961).

[2] Translators' note: from the Greek word meaning to impregnate (M. Roques 1961).

[3] Among the descriptive terms used by some authors are the following: *Phlebites:* veined gneiss. This term covers Sederholm's arterites and Holmquist's venites; it is more or less equivalent to the *epibolite* of Jung and Roques. *Ophthalmites:* "eyed" gneiss or augengneiss. *Stromatites:* alternately thick and thin veinlets in parallel beds.

granitization and grades into an agmatite. The debris of the rock framework form kinds of partitions or *septa*, between the granitic veinlets of migmatites. These partitions become stretched, frayed and twisted in the mobilization of the rock mass. The granitic veinlets show a foliation resembling a fluidity. This foliation becomes discordant in separated parts of the migmatite within short distances, and very often even angular folds of septa are found in abrupt disharmony with other portions in the immediate neighbourhood (fig. 7).

Fig. 6. Agmatite (drawn from a photograph by J. J. Sederholm). The picture covers a length of about 1 m.

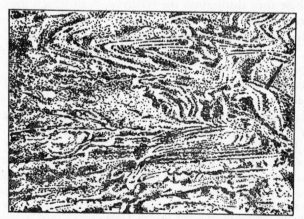

Fig. 7. Nebulite (drawn from a photograph by C. E. Wegmann).

This type of folding is called *symmigmatic* folding by M. Roques (1941). In some cases, veinlets of aplite or pegmatite, distinctively set in a schistose or finer grained groundmass, have been folded in autonomous fashion before the definitive crystallization and form the unique *ptygmatic folds* (chapter 12, figs. 34 and 35). These modes of deformation, which are much freer than those of the elastic and plastic portions of non-granitized and unmetamorphosed zones of folding, indicate a more mobile environment. The picture is similar to the effect of viscous liquid matter profusely impregnating the stratified framework of the rocks and becoming distorted during a long evolution, with shocks which separate and render discordant the elaborate structures of small tectonics. But this is nothing more than a picture.

Such mobilization appears more or less clearly throughout the domain of anatexis. One can follow the phases because it is locally fixed in a more or less advanced state at the moment of definitive crystallization. In the early phases, the matter breaks up along irregular and discontinuous fractures, following blind cracks immediately filled with granite veins. In subsequent phases, the mobilization grows stronger: nebulosity forms and, here and there, important accumulations of granite. It is this heterogeneous state of the material before definitive crystallization that M. Reinhard (1936) calls *migma*. For him it is a question of a partial fusion. In the end, the structures and textures —for a long time phantom-like, at least on the tall cliffs which give an overall view of the whole—are completely obliterated and the result is homogeneous anatectic granite.

THE OVERALL STRUCTURE OF MIGMATITE MASSIFS

Depth of the Migmatite Front

J. Jung and M. Roques (1938) have shown that the migmatite front rises more or less high depending on the region in the supposedly unfolded series of crystallophyllian formations of general metamorphism.[1] In the northern part of the French Massif Central and the Vosges, the front does not rise higher than the *gneiss inférieurs*[2]. Farther sough and in the Pyrenees, it reaches the "upper mica schists"

[1] Translators' note: for reasons given later (chapter 11), the author prefers the term "general metamorphism" to the term "regional metamorphism".

[2] Translators' note: in French geology the following depth zones of metamorphism are recognized, in descending order: *micaschistes supérieurs* (epizone, chlorite zone); *micaschistes inférieurs* (mesozone, biotite, garnet, staurolite zone); *gneiss supérieurs* katazone, sillimanite zone); *gneiss inférieurs*. See chapter 11.

(*micaschistes supérieurs*) with white mica. The front is particularly sharp when it is located in levels of weak general metamorphism; in the opposite case it is blurred.

If the Pyrenean migmatites were actually formed, as seems the case, in the epoch of Hercynian orogeny, a little before the folding, it may be assumed that they rose to a level in the Central Pyrenees whose depth might be only of the order of 3,000 m below the topographic surface, a figure representing the cumulative thickness of the Gothlandian, Devonian and Culm. This value represents perhaps a minimum depth for the important widespread migmatization. Elsewhere the probable figures seem greater, if indeed they can be estimated. According to G. Guitard (1953): "the migmatites appear beneath a Paleozoic sedimentary cover not exceeding 4,400 m" at Mount Canigou, in the eastern Pyrenees.

In many cases, the migmatites appear to be synkinematic (chapter 12) and it becomes almost impossible to estimate their depth of formation under the Earth's surface, for want of precise knowledge of the tectonic under the earth's surface, for want of precise knowledge of the tectonic structure of the environment, a structure in the process of development at the moment of formation of the migmatites.

Zoning of Migmatites

By analogy with the zoning in general metamorphism, J. Jung and M. Roques (1938) show that it is possible to map facies zones in migmatites, with from top to bottom: the embrechite series, the anatexite series, and granite at the base. They write:

> Often it must be noted that this typical section may elsewhere exhibit notable variations. In some regions only anatexites exist, as in the Sioule valley of Auvergne. In other places only the embrechites are found, as in the Kabylie of Algeria. Lastly, embrechites and anatexites inextricably intermixed may be encountered, as in the gneisses of Saint-Malo, Brittany.

In some cases, the anatectic granites are lacking in the cores of important migmatite complexes, as for instance in the gneisses of the Pyrenees of Ariège and in the gneisses from orogenic zones of different ages. Thus in the Aston massif, in Ariège, a thickness of several thousand meters of intensely symmigmatically folded embrechites is seen, with eyed structure in which the large feldspars are stretched, rotated and deformed. It seems as if the tectonic movements, contemporaneously

with the migmatization, have counteracted the formation of homogeneous anatectic granite (Gleditsch, 1950).

Returning, however, to the case of the superposition: embrechites,
anatexites, anatectic granite. The *zone of embrechites*, comprising great
thicknesses of feldspathic gneisses, is characterized by the preservation of
planar structures and layered zones of the pre-existing sedimentary
rocks. They nonetheless present several different facies: lenticular,
"eyed" with large stretched feldspars and striped. Their structure shows
in places symmigmatic deformations, or more exceptionally, nebulitic
structures. Where heterogeneities intervene in the series, such as compact layers (of leptynites, cipolins[1], amphibolites), typical structures are
striking: agmatites, epibolites, ptygmatic veinlets. The *zone of anatexites*
is the domain of nebulitic structures, where the tendency towards
homogenization is obvious, and where one senses that the anatectic
granite is not far away—if not in space at least as to matter.

Above the migmatite front a more or less metamorphic series of
general metamorphism is usually present. The influence of the underlying migmatites is occasionally expressed by the development of
minerals resembling those of an aureole of intensity weak compared to
those of batholiths (chapter 6): an association of microscopic feldspar,
tourmaline, staurolite, sillimanite and andalusite in aluminous rocks;
actinolite in lime schists. This aureole, which is not always very obvious,
has been called by Jung and Roques (1952) the *transition zone*.

The embrechite series is sometimes difficult to characterize because
of its relative homogeneity, where the idea of "mixture" inherent in the
concept of "migmatite" is not marked. It is above all the observation of
the associations of rock formations on a large scale which allows
characterization. Possible confusion with granites with oriented texture
like synkinematic granites may exist, and with orthogneisses of general
metamorphism, which are bodies of old granitic rocks which have been
affected by a metamorphic recrystallization of a much younger cycle.
With regard to the synkinematic granites, their relationship with
more homogeneous granite bodies, their contacts of "circumscribed
granite" types, their possible suites of pegmatites and their general
tectonics may demonstrate their origin. For the orthogneisses, certain
microscopic structures of general metamorphism (chapter 11) may

---

[1] Translators' note: "cipolin" (from the Italian *cipolla*, onion) is defined in the *Petit
Larousse* as a white marble containing sheets of black mica. "*Cipolin* is a beautiful marble
veined with serpentinous green streaks. By extension cipolin is sometimes used for all the
metamorphic calcic rocks, whatever they may be. This double usage may be the cause
of confusion" (Jung, 1958, *Précis de Pétrographie*). See also p. 88.

C*

facilitate the determination: remnants of primary rocks, pseudo-morph and minerals which are typical of the zoning of the extinites[1]. However, it cannot be denied that the convergent petrographic aspect of the three categories is probably in accordance with the nature of things: the different types of granitization and of metamorphism are in many respects controlled by the same common factors.

Stratiform Migmatites

The stratiform migmatites are interstratified between a "floor"and a "roof", with the form of lenses or beds which have an extent and regularity sometimes startling. Cases are known where they have been followed for tens of kilometers (Jung and Roques, 1952).

Such migmatites occur on several scales. On a small scale these may be less important lenses above the migmatite front and preceding it at some distance. On the other hand, along the margins of great massifs of migmatites lateral prolongations may be found which show in profile the shape of interstratified digitations. This may result on the one hand from diapiric effects (chapter 12), but on the other hand, a certain kind of selectivity may have favoured the migmatization along certain preferred layers, either because of their original lithological properties, or following surfaces of tectonic overthrusting. Conversely one may observe the *screening effect* of other layers which counteract the granitiza-tion, especially in metamorphism. Particularly compact layers, such as quartzites or amphibolites, are more resistant and only evolve in a slower or less complete fashion. Siliceous rocks mixed with certain aluminous, calcic or alkaline "impurities", such as arkose and certain gravels, how-ever, are likely to react readily.

The western extremity of the great migmatite massif of Aston, in the Ariègeois Pyrenees shows massive embrechites formed by granitization of schistose and slightly calcareous gravel of lower Palaeozoic age. These embrechites are superposed on a shaly series which only shows a contact metamorphism to biotite and large crystals of andalusite. The superposition, with a gentle inclination, extends for about one kilo-meter until the schists themselves become migmatized as the centre of the massif is approached (Destombes and Raguin, 1955).

The Permian migmatites of Modane, in the Alpes de Maurienne,

[1]Translators' note: the term *ectinites*, familiar to continental geologists, was proposed by Jung and Roques as one of the two great divisions of the metamorphic rocks, the other being the migmatites. They consider the ectinites to arise during geosynclinal burial and away from granitic activity.

form a stratified pseudo-layer, intercalated in the Permo-Carboniferous shales and arkoses, with a maximum thickness of some hundreds of meters and an extent of some fifty kilometers along the direction of folding. The important tectonic scar bordering the Vanoise-Mont Pourri zone prevents one from seeing the connection of this stratiform migmatite with a more important massif which one might suspect further to the east in depth (F. Ellenberger, 1954).

Of quite another order of magnitude is the phenomenon observed in some large masses of migmatite, which show, to all appearances beneath their entire extent, a substratum of non-migmatized rocks or rocks migmatized in a different way. A. Noe-Nygaard and A. Berthelsen (1952) have described, in the Precambrian chain of the Nagssugtoqides on the west coast of Greenland to the south of Christianshaab, a basement of fine grained gneiss of the "granulite" facies (see p. 191 of this book), scarcely deformed and moderately folded, and a superposed zone formed of strongly-developed granitic migmatites which had been intensely folded. These observations cover several tens of kilometers, but the phenomenon could have a much greater extent in this orogenic chain.

According to G. Guitard (1953), Mount Canigou, in the eastern Pyrenees, shows an anticline creating in the centre of the massif the emergence of a series of andalusite mica schists comprised of various rocks, locally granitized and migmatized. A thick formation of embrechites, attaining a thickness of about 3,000 m, is superposed on these mica schists and envelops the anticlinal "buttonhole", whose diameter is about 6 km.

GRANITES OF INTERMEDIATE TYPE

In spite of the somewhat academic distinction between the two categories of granite: the granites in circumscribed massifs and the anatectic granites, there exist granites of an intermediate type. These are the homogeneous massifs with clear boundaries without migmatites but almost directly related to large regions of anatexis. J. Jung and M. Roques (1938) have distinguished such granites by the term granites congeneric[1] with migmatites (granites congénères des migmatites). The effects of diapirism are sometimes visible in these granites, in accordance with the views of C. E. Wegmann (1930).

The famous granite massif of Quérigut, in the Ariègeois Pyrenees, shows along its southern border a long zone, one or two kilometers in

[1] Or cognate with.

thickness, having the character of migmatites with agmatitic structure. To the north the granite becomes homogeneous and pushes broadly out against the surrounding folded Palaeozoic formations (Raguin, 1949).

In the Pyrenean migmatites, and particularly along their borders, small massifs, stocks, or stratiform sheets can often be observed, of a generally leucocratic granite, cutting the embrechites or linked with them by transitions. I have called them *late-migmatic granites* (*tardi-migmatique*). Sometimes their structure, planar and differentiated layers, relates them more closely to the embrechites. Sometimes they are more massive, with schlieren of pegmatite and enrichments of tourmaline.

PETROGENESIS OF MIGMATITES

The structure and the large-scale arrangement of migmatites conjures up intense and widespread deformations of the environment, a physical and chemical mobility capable of producing combinations of various forms, regroupings or new assemblages of minerals.

J. J. Sederholm has described these phenomena with precision and illustrated his descriptions with impressive figures. He thus draws attention to a dyke of basalt which cuts an old granite in the Barösunds-fjörd region; a more recent anatexis, following a great period of erosion and sedimentation, reactivated this old granite, enabling it to reinject new fissures in the basalt dyke. Paradoxically this granite is at the same time much older and much younger than the basalt (Sederholm, 1926).

Thus anatexis can mean a renaissance of old rocks which take on new life. This phenomenon is called palingenesis (rebirth) by Sederholm. Through palingenesis, the distinctive features of the old rocks are more or less replaced by the new face of the rejuvenated rocks. Sometimes one can distinguish the old, almost obliterated features, very much as one can decipher in a palimpsest the old script hidden on the manuscript parchment by script added in a more recent age. All these aspects are visible on rocky surfaces, providing that the surfaces are observed over several meters or tens of meters. It is by this broad view that palimpsests can be traced. In a hand specimen of a collection it is scarcely possible to discern them. Thus Sederholm photographed surfaces, previously cleaned and brushed to remove lichens, and he has given in his publications an admirable series of plates and drawings of the infinitely diversified aspects of anatexis.

Veins of the granitic material, the ichor of Sederholm, give the impression of being introduced from elsewhere, injected from under-lying zones of granite. However, P. J. Holmquist (1916) thought that the material of the veinlets was exuded over a very short distance from the neighbouring beds. This train of thought of a mobilization almost in place by ichors thanks to the addition of a limited quantity of chemical elements, has found many adherents in recent years: most of the geologists referred to as "transformists" or "metasomatists" in the matter of granitization.

K. R. Mehnert (1953), while studying the migmatites in the old formations of the Black Forest, carried out a statistical study of the chemical composition and mutual proportion of the pegmatite veins and the septa. He came to the conclusion that the overall chemical composition of the rock has not been changed by the migmatization. The feldspar is the same in the veins and in the septa; these veins seem due to a segregation from the rock, with chemical migration in the order of decimeters as the veins attained a maximum thickness of some decimeters.

Such observations are in agreement with the *differential anatexis* theory of P. Eskola (1933). He states that the quartz-feldspar association must be the first to melt in the heart of silicate rocks in deep zones, because of the fact that it was the last to crystallize in a silicate melt in the laboratory (the fractional crystallization of the series of N. L. Bowen). An intergranular liquid would be formed, which would be injected along the shear planes of the rocks and would migrate over more or less great distances. In this mobilized zone, developed at the expense of argillaceous sediments, of arkoses or of plutonic rocks, with the exception of the most basic rocks, there would thus exist an intergranular silicate liquid, of a granitic composition almost saturated with water. It would be driven out of the pores of the rock, collected along fissures and planes of least resistance and would migrate over considerable distances. The residual parts of the rocks would be impoverished in the corresponding chemical elements, but the constant afflux of migrating material would re-establish equilibria and would produce the banded structures or the classic breccias of migmatites, taking into account the earlier heterogeneities of the rock and the mechanical deformations in process in the environment. P. Eskola goes further; he thinks that the mobilized material can move about and give rise not only to thin lamellae of pegmatite and aplite, but to great masses of granite of batholithic dimensions.

If the theory is not extended to this extreme conclusion, which opposes the formation nearly in place ascertained for many of the great massifs, it seems to give a satisfying approximation for the explanation of many aspects of anatexis, above all if one is willing to admit that the observed mobilization is not necessarily due to a "magma-generating fusion".

EXPERIMENTAL ANATEXIS

However, laboratory experiments establish the likelihood of the process of rock fusion in place. The remarkable work of H. G. F. Winkler (1958, 1960) has given evidence in favour of it. He has brought argillaceous rocks, whose composition corresponded to that of the most abundant sedimentary rocks in the Earth's crust, to temperatures varying from 600°–810°, in the presence of water, and maintaining a pressure of 2,000 atmospheres.

This pressure corresponds to that which could exist at depths of 7–8 km in the Earth's crust. The temperatures are, however, higher than those which an ordinary geothermal gradient indicates at that depth, even taking into account the increase in the gradient with depth (Tuttle, 1955).

Under these conditions Winkler obtained, within a small range of temperature, the mineralogical paragenesis of a sillimanite and cordierite gneiss. Then he brought about a progressive fusion which gave rise to a silico-alkaline melt corresponding approximately to the quartz-orthoclase-albite eutectic of Bowen and Tuttle. The solid residue, which contained from 20–55% of the material used, depending on its chemical composition, was made up of cordierite, sillimanite, biotite, ore, and a little quartz and plagioclase. When graywacke or paragneiss were used instead of clay, the course of the experiment was the same. It is worth noting that the liquid obtained had the composition of some granites (alkalic, leucocratic) but not of all granite.

One of Winkler's interesting observations is that this liquid is super-heated and consequently should tend to be displaced under the influence of tectonic movements before crystallization. Actually the anatectic fusion takes place at higher temperatures if the ratio An/Ab of the material used is higher. But the liquid obtained will have a much lower value of this ratio than that of the material before fusion; it thus will crystallize at a temperature lower than that of the fusion. The difference can attain 140°.

Similar results have been obtained by J. Wyart and G. Sabatier (1959) on pelitic sediments heated to 800° under a water pressure of 1,800 bars. The essential phenomenon is a concentration of the ferromagnesian elements in the crystals (biotite, cordierite, spinel), which are in equilibrium with the liquid phase of quartz-feldspar composition where the silica and alkalis are concentrated.

CHEMICAL COMPOSITION OF ANATECTIC GRANITES

The anatectic granites and migmatites often tend to be more sodic than batholithic granites, and are essentially granodioritic. Such rocks probably represent the normal equilibrium at a sufficient depth in the Earth's crust (chapter 14). In migmatite complexes, basic rocks occupy a minor place if at all; they are found there only by accident.

However, an anatexis of a chemistry very different from the common place granodiorites exists, no doubt as an exception. Large systems of alkaline rocks, on the one hand, and the charnockite series on the other, seem to have been formed by migmatization.

In the fjords near Julianehaab, southern Greenland, the detrital and volcanic Gardar series, probably of Late Precambrian (*anté-cambrien*) age, has been subjected to very active phases of mobilization. Its supra-crustal volcanic formations with their dykes of essexite and arfved-sonite granite have been migmatized. By fixing influxes of pneumatoly-tic material, they have led to the remarkable nepheline syenites (lujaur-ites, naujaites), strangely striped, zoned, boudinaged and agmatized, of the hyperalkaline massif of Ilimausak. Parts of this complex have been reinjected as sills and dykes, and the final products of this mobilization behave like magmas (C. E. Wegmann, 1938).

The *charnockite*[1] series comprises an association of rocks: granites, syenites, diorites, norites and anorthosites, where hypersthene and garnet are characteristic constituents and mica is of subordinate import-ance or of secondary origin. To be sure, all the members of the series are not always present. The structure is often banded, the texture grano-blastic or porphyroblastic. Sometimes the facies are strictly plutonic, sometimes they are metamorphic; the paragneisses of the settings of the massif may themselves show the same mineralogical associations. These rocks are in equilibrium with the *granulite facies* of deep metamorphism (chapter 11). There is some indication of a certain chronological evolu-tion from norite to granite. The granites formed later tend to have the ordinary facies, which indicates a diminution of the metamorphic level, or an increase of water vapour under lower pressure. The corrosion of minerals in the form of coronas of garnet or augite around hypersthene and the development of new biotite, express the changes of equilibrium. The high initial temperature is shown by the frequency of exsolution of plagioclase in the soda-potash feldspars.

Depending on the region, the authors describe the charnockites

[1] Strictly speaking the term charnockite should be reserved for the granitic facies of the series.

according to the dominant characteristics observed, either as batholiths with sharp contacts with progressive magmatic differentiation, or as metamorphic rocks. The character of the migmatites of these formations explains these disagreements. A migmatitic origin has been assumed by several authors: Groves (1935) in Uganda, Legoux (1939) in the Ivory Coast, Bugge (1945) in Norway, Hietanen (1947) in Finland, and by Michot (1955) for the anorthosites of southern Norway. According to Wegmann the rocks of the granulite facies are probably situated beneath the zone of granites and have been dehydrated; they would have developed in several stages, having first gone through the stage of normal migmatites.

These rocks are Precambrian and probably formed under conditions of stress and high temperature. They represent a type of migmatization in particularly deep zones, or perhaps in zones where locally the properties are equivalent to those at depth, because they occasionally arise in fairly weakly metamorphosed surroundings, as for example the granulites of Saxony. Even though they are not rare, they seem to be incomparably less developed than the ordinary granodioritic migmatites.

Chapter 5

ASSIMILATION BY GRANITE

A granite mass incorporates within itself the enclosing rocks during its development and advance. This phenomenon, which is called the *assimilation of rocks by the granite*, resembles a progressive dissolution in a liquid environment, or else a metasomatism in a crystalline state or in a "mixed" state in the sense indicated in chapter 1. Observations made at the margins of a granite and of *inclusions* of the country rock drowned in the granite some distance from the margins clearly indicate this assimilation.

Granite is said to be modified by *endomorphism* when it can be shown that it has been enriched in the chemical constituents of the surrounding rocks along its contacts. Assimilation is merely the homogenization of the endomorphosed portions of the granite mass and the obliteration of inclusions.

The rocks surrounding a massif are subjected to chemical-mineralogical modifications within a zone which is called the *aureole* of the massif. The study of aureoles will be the subject of the next chapter (6). Assimilation takes place in the part of the aureole nearest the granite. It is tempting to imagine that the process of the beginnings of granite is revealed by the phenomena observed in this inner fringe of the aureole, in the adjoining marginal granite, and within the inclusions. This view, which was maintained by A. Michel-Lévy and A. Lacroix, is certainly on the whole correct, although somewhat marred by its inability to take into exact account the chronology of events. For the state of affairs at present fixed in the aureole and inclusions, on the one hand, and the marginal neighbouring granite, on the other, result from a crystallization which took place simultaneously on both sides of the contact. The crystallization of the aureoles did not integrally precede that of the neighbouring granite. The aureole, as I see it, does not represent the milieu as it was at the moment of transformation into granite; but it approaches it, as we will see.

After discussing the marginal facies of granite, the inclusions which represent the remnants of an incomplete assimilation will be studied. As might well be expected, their evolution is analogous to that of the aureole closest to the granite mass.

THE MARGINAL FACIES OF GRANITE

The aspect of a granite close to its margins varies, and reflects the extreme diversity of the conditions of formation of this rock. An attempt to analyze the motifs of this diversity encounters the *duality* often witnessed in granite phenomena: mechanical movements possibly connected with the bulk transport of material, versus diffuse chemical migrations with metasomatism. The relative importance of these two processes is still unknown, as is the more important matter of the chronology of the evolution of each process, and much obscurity thus remains in the interpretation of the observations.

Aspects of Border Granites

The border granites are frequently rich in inclusions, sometimes to a monumental extent. They pass into "eruptive breccias" if there are many blocks and little granite. Other border granites are remarkable for a grid of veins of aplite, pegmatite or lamprophyre which radiates towards the periphery within the border zone. Often there are both inclusions and veins present together, the inclusions being cut by the veins. Elsewhere injection veinlets which extend into the surrounding rocks have the form of an irregular but very dense network, sometimes with veins intersecting each other, sometimes in a diffuse *lit-par-lit* manner: this is the migmatite facies. This facies, local and strictly marginal in the case of the granites in circumscribed massifs, takes on a thickness of several hundreds or thousands of meters around the granites of anatexis.

Independently of the inclusions and networks of veinlets, the marginal granite often shows a heterogeneous texture across widths that may vary from some millimeters to some meters. The constituent crystals are unequal, and abnormally distributed. Certain parts of the rock are very fine grained, of aplitic texture. Elsewhere the grain is very coarse or pegmatitic. At times the rock resembles a porphyry (micro-granite), a singular fact which we will return to below.

On the microscopic scale these observations are confirmed: the porphyritic facies, sometimes microlithic in the manner of a volcanic rock is striking. The same holds true for the heterogeneities: one can distinguish for example more or less delimited micro-inclusions, analogous, except in scale, to the inclusions just mentioned. Frequently the granite has a marked schistosity, sometimes pronounced enough and fine enough to be seen clearly under the microscope.

The southern border of the Mayenne granite of France presents an example of just such a heterogeneous facies exposed along the valley of the River Mayenne. Near Montcoustans in the Pyrenees, along the border of the Foix granite, curious specimens of finely-bedded granite are to be found. The Lys granite, near Luchon, also in the Pyrenees, has a marginal migmatite facies of a thickness of one to two meters.

The textural and structural irregularity of the border granites bears witness to a lively and irregular reaction of the granite on its envelope, a reaction that has not been followed by the usual homogenization achieved by the granites of the interior of the mass. This bounding granite may be dislocated by pressures of the internal granite, consolidated later and having undergone differentiation. The phenomena have been fixed by the arrest of the granite development or advance. But it is not always thus, for some margins are uniform and composed of homogeneous rocks. We will examine the different kinds of contacts from the chemical and the mechanical points of view.

The Chemistry of Border Granite

As S. R. Nockolds[1] notes, the contamination of a granite in contact with a limestone results either in a basified granite with the formation of calcic plagioclase, amphibole or pyroxene, or more rarely a granite modified by the loss of one or more constituents. Similar changes have been observed at the contacts of other rocks when the granite shows the variation facies: sometimes it is darkened, in other words charged with ferromagnesian and calcic elements; sometimes it shows a lighter facies where some of the same components seem to have been subtracted from the normal granite of the centre of the mass. The chemical migrations which lead to these modifications might be of two types: either centrifugal or centripetal relative to the granite mass. The former will be shown to be apparently the more effective.

In the course of the formation of a granite its border moves, whereas the observations that we can make concern a stage of arrest of the

[1] Quoted by I. D. Muir (1953).

phenomena frozen at that stage. Can it not be admitted, nevertheless, that these observations create a picture of what has taken place during the course of the evolution of the granite? It appears that the progressive advance of the granite must have been extremely slow in the great majority of cases. The physico-chemical conditions and the relationships of equilibrium with the external milieu were thus the same during the course of movement of the granite and at the moment when the outer contact was arrested. Then the conditions changed during the gradual solidification. Essentially, however, the crystallizations in the aureole and within the granite neighbouring the contact indicate high temperatures of formation, or more precisely, of the same order as for the normal granite far from the contact. They date therefore right from the start of the phase of arrest so that the crystallizations have fixed in place the chemical constituents which are found there. The observations that we can make of the stage of arrest thus create a tableau of the chemical substances which existed at each instant along the contact during the slow advance of the granite, without revealing, however, the physical state of the environment. It is possible that a part of the chemical constituents, related to what will be called "late pneumatolysis" (chapter 6), which has given rise to some crystallizations at lower temperatures, may be peculiar to the state of arrest, and are not concentrated at the border in the stages of advance: this effect is regarded as subordinate.

The chemical migration of an assemblage of any particular substance advances through the rock in a manner resembling a "cloud" gradually expanding. The name *chemical front* is given to the limit of this "cloud" with the space not yet affected by the migration of these substances. We will see in the next chapter how we may visualize the development of a granite as a succession of chemical fronts which replace and succeed each other from the mass outwards. This process is revealed in the aureole but also provides an opportunity to interpret the border facies of the nearby granite.

C. E. Tilley and his collaborators have described several cases where granite in contact with limestone or dolomite forms a narrow zone of alkaline facies. They have shown that this resulted from an impoverishment of the granite in silica, alumina, iron and possibly soda, with the absorption of these substances into the aureole (C. E. Tilley, 1949; I. D. Muir, 1953). This granite is characterized by the development of a pyroxene, possibly alkaline, instead of biotite or normal hornblende, and now and then by the disappearance of quartz and by alkali ratios different from those in the interior of the mass.

In other more common cases, the marginal granites at basic contacts, such as with limestones, dolomites or greenstones, are enriched in lime and magnesia, their plagioclases being more calcic than in the interior of the massif and the content of ferromagnesian minerals increasing. The basic elements (Ca, Fe, Mg), corresponding to the composition of the surrounding rocks, are left in place or are moved outwards less quickly than the alkaline front, paving the way for the advance of the granite.

The reason for this difference in the pace of the various chemical migrations is not known. As has just been indicated, this duality is by no means characteristic only of limestone and basic contacts. Against schists granite margins are lighter coloured and often finer grained than in the interior of the mass, and sometimes enriched in muscovite; or else, on the other hand, a granite with an excess of biotite, or a granite with biotite and cordierite, or possibly with sillimanite, with andalusite, or with garnet may develop. The granite of the border can be charged with quartz; perhaps thanks to an excess of water, a mineralizer taken from the country rock, which augments its corrosivity and permits it to dissolve siliceous material. Nevertheless, the fronts of centrifugal migration seem to be the more effective at the margins of granites.

Other chemical regroupings may be effected in the interior of massifs. We will return to them below in connection with endomorphism in general. Here it suffices to note that heterogeneities such as dioritic endomorphic accumulations preserved for a long time and far enough within some massifs must finally be effaced by homogenization and chemical diffusion of their basic excess. This excess, when all is said and done, comes from the surrounding rocks and being ultimately diffused throughout the whole mass in the process of growth, the phenomenon amounts in large part to a chemical migration of the corresponding substances from the outside to the inside of the mass.

Finally cases where endomorphic variations within the granite or at its borders cannot be observed may result from freer chemical diffusion or from rheomorphism.

Gradual or Sharp Contacts

The gradational granitic contacts consist of rocks of the facies of migmatites. Some alterations of granitic gneisses (embrechites), with more or less granular and oriented textures, precede true granite over a thickness either small, of some decimeters, or large, of several thousand meters in great anatectic massifs. The tectonic structures of the country rocks are discovered, more or less deformed in the migmatites or the granite, in the form of septa or schlieren. Some aplite, pegmatite or even granite veins here and there cut the assemblage or inject it concordantly. Some rheomorphism is evident, at least locally.

Several types of sharp boundaries, where the contact can be specified, sometimes within a centimeter, occur. Sometimes they are found with "normal" granite, that is to say with granite resembling the material of the interior of the massif, sometimes with an irregular and heterogeneous granite. Such heterogeneities indicate that equilibrium was not attained. This may arise from the composite nature of the outer environment with some little-assimilable layers or from successive irregular phases in the process of granitization, or some "sluggishness" in the granite due to some physical or chemical deficiency of the fronts. It can hardly be specified. One important factor is rheomorphism, which could explain the sharpness of the contact, particularly if the granite at the immediate contact is homogeneous. But rheomorphism is excluded in many cases where the granite can be seen to be organized in place, because it preserves ghosts of the tectonic structures continuous with the structures in the enclosing rock.

Except in the case involving rheomorphism, the sharp boundary imposes the idea of a "front of the granular facies" marked by the appearance of plutonic texture and probably corresponding to a change of the physical state of the mobilized milieu in the course of granitization. This front constitutes the border of the granite. We will find that it can be discordant to the chemical fronts (p. 109).

Can an idea be obtained of the physical state of the environment in the aureole in front of the granular facies, before the arrest of the granite and before the completion of its crystallization? It can be conceded that, in this environment, many minerals existed already which can be observed today definitely fixed in the aureole. Moreover, the granite can be seen acting upon the biotites of the aureole and of the inclusions during its crystallization, scattering them, dispersing them, and destroying their schistosity. These biotites thus existed before this crystallization. On the other hand, the large feldspars of some aureoles are often identical in nature and facies to the large feldspars of the neighbouring granite. It is logical to suppose that the granite has incorporated them during its advance. These feldspars were in effect the forerunners of the granite, for they are the evidence of the alkalinization of the aureole, and it is highly reasonable that this alkalinization precedes the granite in the manner of an intermediate stage.

Thus the environment in front of the active front of the granular facies was an environment of high temperature, where the porphyro-blasts and the fine-grained minerals of metamorphism were continually developing. It can be added that although solid—the stratigraphic struc-tures were preserved—it was highly plastic and impregnated in pneumatolysts: the study of the aureole in chapter 6 will demonstrate its extreme facility to deform and the pneumatolytic character of its mineral make-up. The front of the granular facies is revealed by a special crystallization, completing the minerals of metamorphism already existing and making widespread a greater and more constant grain size in these minerals, which brings about a complete rearrange-ment of the texture. But the physical state of the environment behind this front, at the time when the front was active, namely moving slowly outwards or upwards, is not known. The proportion of a possibly amorphous material, either glassy, liquid or gaseous, has not been elucidated.

The Porphyritic Marginal Facies

A particular case is that in which the border granite adopts the texture of a microgranite resembling some volcanic porphyries.

For instance, the Ment granite in Central Morocco forms a massif 15 km in diameter with a sharp border cutting Palaeozoic shales and sandstones folded during the Hercynian orogeny. It shows a typically microgranitic marginal zone with a width of many tens or hundreds of meters at the southern margin of the massif. The feldspars, centimeters in size, drowned in the fine grained groundmass of this microgranite, consist of perthitic orthoclases resembling the large feldspars in the granite which is porphyritic in the normal manner in a goodly part of the massif. There is a gradual transition from the microgranite to the normal granite.

A Demay (1952) cites some similar cases in the French Massif Central. The Pelvoux granite, in the Alpes du Dauphiné, studied by Pierre Termier (1899), also grades into finely granular aplites and micro-granites. These rocks are of essentially the same chemical composition as the normal granite. The development of these border forms has a singular amplitude in the Combeynot massif which dominates the Lautaret Pass.

Very seldom does one see in the Combeynot massif true granites in direct contact with schists or gneisses. It is nearly always separated from them by a more or less great thickness of very fine grained aplite or of microgranite. There are also, in the schists and the gneisses, innumerable apophyses, some aplitic, and others, more numerous, microgranitic. These apophyses have outcrops of complicated form and with varying direction. Sometimes they are intercalated between the metamorphic layers. Many of them show, when traced out, variations in texture and grade alternately from aplite to microgranite. At the immediate contact of the aplite or the microgranite, the mica schists are often riddled with small feldspathic nuclei. The feldspars are identical with those of the granitic rock, that is, they are of albite or cryptoperthite. (P. Termier, 1899).

In the Basin and Range region, between the Rockies and the Coastal Cordilleras of the western United States, numerous stocks of porphyritic rocks outcrop, in general some kilometers in diameter. They have a granitic or monzonitic composition, notably in Arizona, New Mexico and Utah. These intrusions, which date from the end of the Cretaceous to the beginning of the Tertiary, have brought about strong mineralizations of copper, zinc, lead and precious metals in the region. The contact metamorphism produced by these porphyries is intense. These occurrences of eruptive rock appear to represent cupolas of very vast batholiths which almost reached the earth's surface at the time of their emplacement, and not laccoliths nor even isolated stocks. Actually the frequency of these occurrences, the similarity of their constituent rocks, their style of depressed subsurface domes, and their intense contact metamorphism, are indications of this aspect. Here we have on a very grand scale an example of the porphyritic facies in the roof of batholiths (Raguin, 1934).

Is it necessary to interpret such porphyritic borders as a magmatic facies consolidated under similar conditions to those of volcanism? I believe that *there are porphyries and porphyries.*

In effect reviving an old observation of A. Michel-Lévy about a microgranite from Mont Blanc, P. Collomb (1951) has noticed, in a microgranite dyke in the southwestern part of the French Massif Central, the late growth of the great orthoclase phenocrysts enclosing smaller phenocrysts of quartz, plagioclase and biotite, with a poecilitic texture as in the metamorphic crystallizations. A Demay (1952) has made similar observations in microgranites exhibiting two or three periods of crystallization. A metasomatic growth in place of large crystals in an already more or less consolidated rock, is thus not improbable for some granite porphyries. Let us also remember the very common observation of basic enallogenic inclusions, which, even though of sedimentary origin, adopt within the centres of granites the microdioritic facies (pseudo-microdiorite?) in passing to an endopolygenic state. This metasomatic theory has been supported by Perrin and Roubault (1939).

Under the microscope, the Ment microgranite shows diverse aspects. Sometimes it is a granophyre where a star-shaped micropegmatite attacks the large orthoclase crystals; sometimes a microgranite without special texture apart from the double size of the crystals; sometimes it shows quartz porphyroids poecilitically enclosing other crystals, or bipyramidal quartz of medium grain. Sometimes even a tendency to rapakivi structure (orthoclase encircled by oligoclase) is outlined. These variations denote disequilibria or irregularities related to local conditions. They show as well that the large crystals, feldspars and quartz, have followed a prolonged evolution and do not strictly represent an "early period" of crystallization as in the magmatic rocks. Finally it must be emphasized that whereas the large crystals of igneous porphyries, crystallized at depth and transported by the magma, came from elsewhere, the large feldspars of the granitic porphyries of the border seem formed in place like the same feldspars of the normal granite of the massif and like the same feldspars developed occasionally in the aureole[1].

The alternative is thus the following. It is a matter of an apparent convergence between the irregular granite types of the border and the microgranite facies of the rhyolitic lavas? Or else, must one admit that a partial fusion at the granite border was produced locally? The bipyramidal quartz, rare outside of the volcanic rocks, would be an argument in favour of this idea, as Demay (1952) points out. However, the phenomenon of the microgranitic border of granitic massifs is far from being general, and it occurs only occasionally and locally in the massifs where it is developed. It quite often happens that the geological environment of granites shows no other phenomena of volcanic appearance. The first hypothesis of the alternatives seems therefore preferable. However, in chapter 13 we will study the incontestable relationships, of much vaster dimensions, that exist between some granites and volcanism.

The Orbicular Facies

Orbicular granite encountered in some localities, and particularly in

---

[1] Not at Ment, however, where the aureole is not feldspathic to an extent visible to the naked eye.

Finland, is an exceptional facies of the margins of some granites or diorites. Its extent can be of some meters. It is sometimes connected with granites of heterogeneous structure, migmatitic or with inclusions (J. J. Sederholm, 1928; P. Eskola, 1938; A. Simonen, 1940 and 1950).

The rock is formed of spheroidal nodules of complex structure, of some decimeters in diameter, drowned in a granitic groundmass. The nucleus of the nodules may be a gross aggregate of crystals of plagioclase, in general oligoclase, possibly associated with a small proportion of other granitic minerals; it may be a small mass of the same granite as the groundmass; it may also consist of an enallogenic inclusion. Sometimes the nodules show a fringe rich in microcline. All around the kernel the material of the nodules is formed of a certain number of concentric shells, alternatively light and dark in colour and of thicknesses ranging from centimeters to millimeters. The light coloured envelopes are of oligoclase, finer and finer grained towards the outer layers and more fine grained than the groundmass; the dark envelopes are zones rich in biotite and occasionally amphibole.

Most often the crystallization of the kernels and their envelopes shows a disposition to be both more or less perfectly radial and concentric. The feldspars tend to have a radial elongation (elongation at right angles to the 100 face); the biotites are tangentially arranged after their basal planes; the hornblendes are arranged tangentially to their 100 face. In some cases a tendency is shown at the same time for a radial elongation of the biotites in prisms perpendicular to the base and an analogous elongation of the hornblendes by means of a prismatic development perpendicular to the 100 face as for the feldspars. The microscope may show a development of myrmekite in the feldspar of the nucleus and of the envelopes.

P. Eskola has explained the orbicular facies as a metasomatic process, with a crystallization directed outwards from the centre of the orbicules. It thus would be a matter of a centrifugal migration of more basic material of the kernels or enclaves, into the surrounding granite during the formation of this granite type. At the same time the kernels of the orbicules would also become granitized, sometimes with the crystallization of microcline. The delicate chemical transportations in two directions must have operated through the peripheral envelopes of the orbicule.

Observers have been struck by the deformations of orbicules, either along mutual contacts, or by the corrosive and mechanical activity of the surrounding granite on the envelopes. For instance P. Hupé (1948) notes that the orbicules at the border of the Néouvielle granite, of the Hautes-Pyrénées, near Pic d'Estaragne, penetrate each other at points of contact "in the same fashion as soft boiled eggs which are pressed against each other". The orbicules must have been plastic and deformable during the evolution, and the surrounding milieu must have had some fluidity. Sederholm concluded that everything must have been of a gelatinous consistency, which suggested to him an analogy with the rings of Liesegang. On the other hand, the centrifugal character of the crystallization of the ovoids is manifest by the fact that the inner layers have in some cases been deformed and partly resorbed before the crystallization of the outer layers.

This centrifugal character is also striking in the arrangement of the crystals, according to Eskola. The dark envelopes of layered biotite should be due to the dilatation pressure of the feldspathic mass of the nucleus during the crystallization. At the same time "during the growth of the orbicule, the biotite and hornblende crystals, tangentially arranged, may continue their development and attain the prismatic form unusual for hornblende perpendicular to 100, and for biotite parallel to the c axis".

The phenomenon of orbicular granites is encountered in granites and diorites of various compositions, and notably in the vicinity of or within migmatites. It serves as an example of a "basic front" pushed out on a small scale by the progress of the granitization through rocks alien to granite, and of a more basic composition than the resulting granite. The rhythmic appearance of this evolution remains enigmatic. The orbicules have actually in general several similar concentric shells, sometimes a dozen, of great regularity and of thicknesses of millimeters. This rhythm is attributed to the effects of diffusion. On the other hand the myrmekites in the feldspars of the ovoids are in accord with the hypothesis of a metasomatism in the crystals formed.

The Rapakivi Facies

The rapakivi granite facies, well known in Finland, Sweden and southern Russia, is another exceptional case. It develops at the border of some granite masses, or forms outcrops of an extent of kilometers or much more, such as the vast massif of Viborg, which has an area of more than 16,000 sq. km. These occurrences probably represent varieties of flat massifs of little thickness. That of Viborg shows several small "windows", from one of which the underlying limestone has been exploited. In an important publication, from which I do not however accept all the conclusions, H. G. Backlund (1938 b) described the principal characteristics of these granites. The layered structure of these massifs is very pronounced. But the Cloosian tectonics (chapter 7) of ordinary batholiths are not present at all. The rapakivis alter very easily and some layers literally collapse into dust, even far from any external influence, as proved by drilling. This strange instability is inexplicable.

The rapakivi texture is characterized by ovoids of some centimeters, composed of potash feldspar, enveloped in a thin skin of oligoclase and distinctively set in a surrounding normal granite. This skin is lacking in some types. The ovoids contain small inclusions of the minerals of the granite arranged concentrically and often recurring in successive zones. The quartz of these inclusions or of the border of the ovoids often has a micropegmatitic structure with the feldspar. Some rapakivis have miarolitic quartz. They also have bipyramidal quartz in the groundmass; according to Wegmann, Sederholm considered this feature as very important, almost as much so as the ovoids. Nearly always the content of fluorine expressed in the form of fluorite is high. However, these granites do not produce a contact metamorphism of greisen type. Associated pegmatites are rare.

Some ovoids in contact mutually mold each other, as if they had been plastic after their formation and before their final crystallization. In some cases the ovoids are occupied, in the centre of the feldspathic kernel, by a granitic aggregate resembling the groundmass. They are thus similar to some orbicular granites. The ovoids of the rapakivi are sometimes found in the rocks of the aureole a short distance from the granite contact.

Finally the Fennoscandian rapakivi massifs are often associated with rhyolitic effusive rocks containing the same ovoids and obviously related to the granite, a phenomenon which can be attributed to rheomorphism.

C. E. Wegmann (1938) has studied interesting granite massifs on the south coast of Greenland, which have a border zone of a thickness of some meters to decameters with a rapakivi texture. Moreover in the Swedish rapakivis the well formed ovoidal facies-types sometimes have a restricted extent in the massif as a whole. It may equally be marginal. In this marginal facies of the granites of Greenland Wegmann points out the abundance of "homoeogenic"[1] inclusions which give the rock the character of an agmatite. "Rapakivi do not seem to occur in the

---

[1]"Homoeogenic" is a term of A. Lacroix (*homoeogène*).

absence of such inclusions." Farther from the border the granite is penetrated by pegmatitie dykes. "The pegmatitic solutions rose to the rapakivi zone, but were transformed completely into the rapakivi" and disappeared there.

The formation of the ovoids resembles a metamorphic phenomenon, developed either at the expense of evolving granitic material or at the expense of the exogenic rocks of the inclusions or in the aureole. The idea of a metamorphic character has been supported by other authors (P. Eskola, F. K. Drescher-Kaden). L. J. D. Fernando, quoted by H. H. Read (1944) relates the formation of ovoids to the terminal sodic phase observed in many a granite (p. 32).

> The rapakivi texture is intimately connected with replacement associated with the general process of feldspathization. It is evident that the rim of plagioclase is clearly a replacement rim, and the corrosion of the potash feldspar is just as evident... these rapakivi rocks represent arrested stages in the replacement of potash by soda.

The opinion of H. H. Thomas and W. Campbell-Smith (1932), about the ovoids of rapakivi occurring along the contact of the Trégastel granite of Brittany, is similar to this particular case, if not for the cause, at least for the mechanism. A basification of this granite in the course of its formation, a basification produced by a subtraction of potassium (removal of biotite in the older included basic rocks) prevented the further crystallization of the potash feldspar, has absorbed spherically the borders of microcline already formed, and has fringed them with a crust of oligoclase.

There is, however, a contrasting hypothesis, which could also be maintained: enrichment in potassium of the environment, and a concentration of this potassium at special points. It would be supported by the generating role attributable to the arrival and the diffusion of pegmatites. Such a selective development of small local concentrations of potash feldspar in ovoid form (porphyroblasts) would consequently produce a local enrichment of soda and lime in their immediate peripheries. The same growth of the ovoids, with recrystallization, should thus work chemically through the environment and would provoke the formation of the oligoclase crust.

The two hypotheses have in common a chemical disequilibrium persisting between the centres of potash crystallization and the groundmass, either the groundmass being impoverished in potassium by external causes, or the potash centres being more and more enriched in potassium by diffusion of pegmatitic material and by a reorganization by recrystallization.

The remarkable property of rapakivi is the sphericity of the ovoids, unusual for phenocrysts in plutonites and volcanites and for pheno-blasts of metamorphism, as well as the sharpness of change between kernel and crust. With regard to the intermediate rings of inclusions in the kernels, they may indicate interruptions and repetitions in the growth of the kernel, as seen in many a porphyroblast in various rocks. This unique texture implies a tranquil environment, but a relatively deformable one: impressed ovoids; occasional rheomorphism produc-ing varieties of effusive character. Wegmann's opinion of a diffusion of pegmatitic material seems to bear much weight, from observations in the field and from the abundance in the rapakivi granites of dispersed pneumatolytic material, particularly fluorine and the radioactive elements (H. G. Backlund). But there have never been abundant addi-tions from the underlying granite, which would have homogenized and destroyed these delicate mineral assemblages. The small miarolitic concentrations give evidence of a slight excess of residual solutions.

However, such conditions are still exceptional in the formation of granites. Furthermore the rapakivi granites have a varied chemical composition. The granitization of agmatites is likely to produce them. "These granites," writes C. E. Wegmann, "have been formed at the expense of original rocks of very different kinds and ages." He has observed "thin sections of rapakivi where one can see both quartz and olivine. Also, anti-rapakivis are known, with plagioclase in the centre of the ovoids and potash feldspars around it[1]".

THE INCLUSIONS OR ENCLAVES[2]

In many granites, particularly near their borders, float *inclusions* or *xenoliths*, angular or rounded blocks of various size, derived from the surrounding rock invaded by the granite. Among these inclusions, A. Lacroix (1933) distinguishes between the *enallogenic* and *endopoly-genic*. Neither should be mistaken for *homoeogenic* enclaves, which are not derived directly from the surrounding rocks and which are not xeno-liths but represent small masses of differentiated granite which do not

[1] Verbal communication.

[2] Translators' note: the term used almost entirely throughout the text is *enclave* which can be translated *inclusion* in most instances bu not all, as the word inclusion in English geological literature has taken on a strong semantic flavour implying a xenolithic origin. Therefore the French word *enclave* is rendered *inclusion* or *enclave* as the case may be.

have the same composition as the surrounding granite. These are generally rare in normal granites and result from a lack of homogeneity. In chapter 8 the question of homoeogenic enclaves will be reviewed; in this section only the material provided by the surrounding rock will be studied.

An interesting category, remarked upon by Wegmann but still little studied, is that of the mineral inclusions such as of zircon, quartz or tourmaline, etc., which may be directly derived from the pre-existing rocks and which have resisted granitization. To distinguish them from minerals crystallized during the granitization is, in general, not easy.

Let us confine ourselves to inclusions of blocks of rock. The enallogenic inclusions are those which have preserved the aspect of the country rock but have been more or less recrystallized. In them are found condensed on a small scale all the types produced by contact metamorphism in the walls of the massif around the granite, depending on the nature of the rocks (chapter 6). The sedimentary schists or phyllites give rise to micaceous schists more or less crystallized, and often rich in andalusite, or to leptynolites characterized by a fine feldspathic impregnation. Marls give rise to hornfelses, variously composed of amphibole, biotite, epidote, garnets and feldspars.

The endopolygenic inclusions are those which occupy the place of enallogenic inclusions completely digested or metasomatized by the

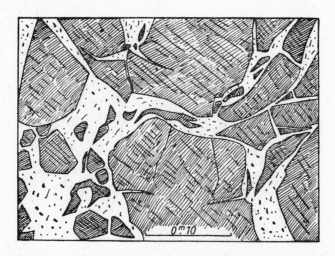

Fig. 8. Enallogenic inclusions (after M. Lelubre). Angular blocks of diorite in the granite of the Primel Massif, Finistère.

granite. They may resemble segregations formed by the differentiation in granite, for example, some homoeogenic enclaves, but they can be identified because of their gradation to enallogenic inclusions through intermediate types. Often, moreover, some feature of their original stratification has been preserved. They consist, for example, of small masses of schistose granite enriched with biotite and with an abundance of accessory minerals, or of ovoids of various types of diorite if the inclusion were calcic or of some basic rock.

An examination of the inclusions derived from the enclosing rocks thus provides a picture of the progressive absorption of these rocks by the granite, in other words, of the assimilation following upon contact metamorphism. The phenomenon is found arrested by cooling and fixed at a moment of its evolution, which permits the study of the intermediate stages.

Mechanism of Formation; Mobility of Inclusions

As will be seen in the next chapter, shearing and stretching in the aureole determine particularly pneumatolysed surfaces, along which the material evolves, either as metamorphic minerals, or as diffuse granite or aplite. The less deformed intervening sections, in the fashion of kernels, prove to be true rebels to the advance of the granitization front. If the phenomenon is arrested, the granite crystallizes around

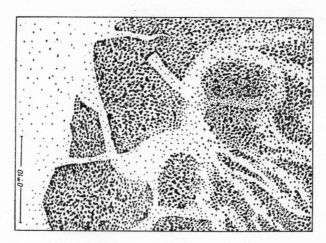

Fig. 9. Injection breccia in the course of assimilation (after M. Lelubre). The blocks are of an old diorite invaded by the granite of the Primel Massif, Finistère.

these and the kernels form enallogenic inclusions of metamorphic facies. If the phenomenon proceeds, the enclave itself becomes granite, but less readily than its surroundings (because of its compactness?) and remains long in an endopolygenic state. Thus have the inclusions of limestone or marl changed to the microdioritic facies in the Quérigut granite in the Pyrenees. It is a common observation that the xenoliths are more or less perfectly delimited by oriented surfaces following the older dominating joints (A. Cailleux, 1946).

It would seem *a priori* easy to determine by observation if the inclusions have stayed in place in the course of the granitization, or if they have been transported by the movement of an environment analogous to a fluid or viscous magma. This is, however, not the case, because many observations are contradictory or can be interpreted in different ways. It can be summed up in the question of the degree of *rheomorphism*.

In favour of the immobility of inclusions, one can recall the classic observations of the alignments of inclusions prolonging in the granite certain layers of the surrounding rock. Such alignments may coincide with differentiation bands in the granite of a hybrid facies, which mark the place of particular layers within the framework of the granite mass, layers which can be continuously followed throughout it. As H. H. Read (1953) says: "phantom stratigraphies within the interior of granite masses are the only proof of a granitization in place."

Some suggestive observations bear witness to a movement of the inclusions in a fluid milieu.

J. Cogné (1950) has described the arrangement of inclusions of embrechites in the Guérande granite (fig. 10) near Saint-Nazaire in Brittany. These are enallogenic inclusions, the gneiss being much

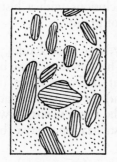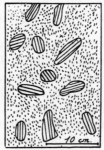

Fig. 10. Inclusions displaced in a granite, after J. Cogné.

D

older than the granite. In two places he observed that these closely packed inclusions create the impression of a breccia.

The elements are formed of fragments with rounded outlines, clearly elongated along their partings, and not more than 10 cm in length. Taken as a whole they are grossly parallel to each other and also to the orientation of the granite. But one often encounters oblique elements, or even sections perpendicular to the general orientation. The orientation of the granite is sometimes so pronounced that one can see the biotite trains contouring these last elements. Because of the look of these inclusions it seems difficult not to accept a state corresponding to a semi-fluidity of the granite at the time of its emplacement. The fragments oblique or transverse are too close together and the directions too variable for one to think of a crystallization in the solid state in a rock deformed earlier, apart from the fact that according to such a hypothesis it would be unreasonable not to find some embrechitic elements showing traces of these deformations. On the contrary, everything points to a perfect alignment of the constituents. Let us add that, by the orientation of the biotite, the granite acquires a semblance of fluidity flowing around the inclusions.

However, R. Perrin and M. Roubault (1955) have observed in the neighbourhood of J. Cogné's locality, migmatites "locally contorted in a very capricious way", and they have contested the validity of the displacement of inclusions by the granite. This puts the finger on *how difficult it is to obtain decisive arguments from isolated or local observations.* A structural analysis, as complete and exact as possible, over a sufficiently large area, is required of necessity.

N. R. Martin (1952) points out in the celebrated granite of Flamanville, Manche, the presence of inclusions with a history of different crystallizations in the same block of granite.

The one xenolith is crowded by large hornblendes, and the other by porphyroblasts of feldspar. This difference may be due to their incorporation in the granite at different times (by magmatic stoping, or granitization *in situ*) or to a difference in original composition and provenance. The fact remains, however, that the two, both undergoing recrystallization, have been brought together without disintegration.

This fact, as well as various structural characteristics of the massif, induces the author to believe that the material was partly a viscous fluid at the time of its diapiric emplacement.

According to R. A. Daly, the granites, which he regards as essentially magmatic, should be emplaced by "overhead stoping", a mining term signifying stoping from below upwards by loosening blocks and letting them fall. According to this hypothesis, one should often see xenoliths displaced from above downwards. Writes C. E. Wegmann in a personal communication:

> The observations are rather rare for a phenomenon which is supposed to take place almost everywhere. In contrast inclusions that have been carried upwards are not rare. I know a case in South Greenland where the fragments have been transported upwards more than 1000 m. In this case the mass which carried them could not have been a liquid in the ordinary sense. Ice also carries fragments much denser than itself, as do the salt rocks which raise even basalts.

In the granite of Pic Long of the Néouvielle Massif in the Pyrenees, P. Hupé (1948) notes:

> In some places where the eruptive contact cuts the stratification of the sediments at right angles, the enallogenic inclusions, instead of being along the prolongation of the strata, are arranged parallel to the contact; on the other hand, where the contact is parallel to the beds, the inclusions are often oblique to it. They have thus been subjected to displacement possible only in a plastic milieu.

Of comparable importance are various observations of alignment of fluidal aspect of granitic biotite parallel to sharp granite contacts and discordant with the enclosing stratified beds. For these micas are equivalent to microinclusions, according to what we have seen (p. 25) concerning the mode of development from the biotites of the aureole. I have observed this phenomenon during excursions with J. P. Destombes, for example in the western part of the granite massif of Caillaouas, Haute-Garonne, at the Pouchergues hydroelectric station.

However, returning later on to his observations on the orientation of inclusions in the Néouvielle granite, P. Hupé (1951) has suggested another interpretation, presented as a working hypothesis based on the fracturing connected with granitization, i.e., fracturing preceding and accompanying in time the granitization. He defines *phasmatoclastic* enclaves as chloritized and tourmalinized traces of small joints in the granite, fractures healed by the termination of granitization and enclosed in it. He writes:

> In the sector studied the statistic orientation of endopolygenic inclusions coincides "*grosso modo*" with that of the phasmato-clastic inclusions. From this observation and others in process (about 3,000 measurements of the orientation of inclusions to date) seems to emerge the idea that granitization was carried out from the beginning in a rigid material. The statistical orientation of the enallogenic and endopolygenic inclusions would not result from displacement of the residues of the enclosing rocks in a plastic environment, according to the classic concept of H. Cloos, and more recently of N. R. Martin, *a propos* the Flamanville granite. On the contrary, it is a case of original orientation. These inclusions should be of older tectonites, in the sense of A. Born (1936) and their orientation that of the principal joints which have given rise to them. The phasmatoclastic enclaves would be the remains of these same joints. The frequently observed parallelism, partly veri-fied in Néouvielle, between the boundaries of the granite mass and the inclusions at its border, would simply signify that a particularly closely spaced fracture system prefigured the limits and location of the future massif.

These observations made by P. Hupé cross-check similar remarks by B. C. King and A. M. J. de Swardt (1949).

In short I think that there are cases of granite contacts without rheomorphism and others with a definite rheomorphism. However, it is not certain that the rheomorphism of granite is often able to attain great amplitude and to provoke very important displacements *en masse* of granitic material in a magmatic state. This touches on the problem of granitic diapirism (chapters 3 and 7), When the border granites are accompanied by rocks of effusive facies (chapter 13), somewhat earlier or contemporaneous, it is possible that rheomorphism takes on a greater magnitude.

The Chemical Evolution of Inclusions

Inclusions show on a small scale effects similar to those which develop in the aureole, and which we will examine in the next chapter. It will be seen that they can be made clear by the assumption of the superimposition of a basic chemical front (Ca, Fe, Mg), and then an alkaline front (alkalis and silica) propagated in the rock by migration from the granite, the second in some way chasing the first before it. In a similar way, one often observes a thin basic fringe, some millimeters or decimeters thick, enriched in mafic minerals (barylites) and above all in biotite, around inclusions. Sometimes a leucocratic zone of similar thickness, enriched in feldspar, surrounds the first. However, the confined character of the small domain of each inclusion gives rise to an overlapping of the effects, which succeed each other in the same place. The phenomenon is thereby obscured. It would be necessary to draw up a balance sheet of exchanges in both directions between the granite and the inclusion; but how does one take into account successive moments?

When a fringe of light coloured feldspar encloses the dark border, and when this is frankly richer in magnesium and iron than the inclusion, the aspect correctly evokes the basic and alkaline fronts of Doris Reynolds, fixed in the course of their centripetal transportation from the granite to the inclusion. But as the inclusions must eventually be transformed into granite, there must also be a countereffect of centrifugal migration. I would freely agree that the two effects are real, but develop successively with some fractionation of the chemical elements.

The biotite fringes do not necessarily imply an important migration of material. In studying basic inclusions with hornblende in the granites of Connecticut and in the Adirondack region of New York, M. S. Walton (1952) remarked on their fringe of biotite derived from a transformation of hornblende by potash diffusion from the surrounding granite. The latter, impoverished in potash in the immediate vicinity, was found to be enriched in albite around the inclusions.

In general, arenaceous inclusions will rapidly take on a granitoid aspect after the biotite stage of contact metamorphism, and grade into granite, before fading away altogether in its bosom. The basic inclusions, like those originally calcareous, persist for a long time, feldspathized and similar to microdiorites.

This difference in behaviour is explained by N. L. Bowen (1928) in the hypothesis of a dissolution of the inclusion by a granitic magma. During the fractional crystallization of the magma, those inclusions would easily be dissolved whose compositions were equivalent to the fractions which still had to be precipitated (for instance, arenaceous inclusions), but basic inclusions whose composition was similar to fractions of the melt already crystallized would not dissolve directly. The magma would react with these basic inclusions with a tendency to transform them to a later member of the series of crystallizations until they eventually became assimilable. It does not, however, seem to be necessary to invoke the action of a magma in order to explain these facts. If one instead assumes a metasomatic process, the work accomplished by the metasomatism is greater in the second case than in the first. The substances in excess which must be eliminated are more abundant in the basic inclusions and they accumulate transitorily as a dark peripheral fringe. In the silica-alkaline inclusions, the excess biotite is better tolerated, now and then remaining for some time in the form of large spots of more micaceous granite than the normal definitive granite.

ENDOMORPHISM

It happens that the endomorphic facies, which we have described near the borders, are preserved well within the interior of massifs, instead of forming an ephemeral fringe rapidly diffused. Certain granitic masses enclose extensive zones very rich in inclusions, or even smaller or larger area of a petrographic type recalling the anatexites because of certain heterogeneities resembling phantoms of the pre-existing beds before granitization. It thus appears as if the whole of the granitic mass were influenced by endomorphism.

Sometimes the aspect is similar to that of some migmatite massifs. For example, in the Quérigut granite massif of the Ariègeois Pyrenees, the whole western and southern part is occupied by a migmatic facies for 50 km parallel to the alignment of the massif and for several kilometers across it (E. Raguin, 1949, 1950). This part is composed of heterogeneous granites with schlieren and often with agmatitic structure, whose blocks are sometimes delimited, sometimes frayed, diffuse or nebulitic. Further north in the massif, the facies grades into true granite, although zones of great dimensions, in the order of kilometers, and vaguely limited, can be found where the rock is enriched with biotite or else contains amphibole, absent elsewhere, and plagioclase more calcic than those in the normal granite; finally it changes to a real diorite. The modification recalls the material of the endopolygenic inclusions. One may suspect that there is a contamination by endomorphism on a large scale. In this massif, as in others, such an opinion can be based upon a geometric argument: the contaminated facies align themselves with old foldings of the domain invaded by the granite and represent certain major layers of the stratigraphic series digested in place by the granitization.

In those contaminated zones of the Quérigut granite, one also finds ultrabasic masses some tens of meters long, composed of melanocratic diorites, norites, hornblendites and even peridotites. These masses, formed in the heart of the heterogeneous granite with calcareous inclusions, were interpreted by A. Lacroix (1899) like the completion of granitic endomorphism upon dolomitic inclusions. We think otherwise; metamorphism of basic inclusions from volcanic formations were recently recognized in the setting of the massif (Guitard and Raguin, 1961).

To be sure, these basic occurrences in the granites or near their borders are to be distinguished from the early differentiated facies, which will be the subject of chapter 8. It is, moreover, mainly the geological context which facilitates this distinction, rather than local petrography.

Other examples similar to Quérigut are not uncommon. The granite of Jebel Tichka in the Moroccan Atlas has been studied by H. and G. Termier (1945), who compare it directly with the Quérigut granite.

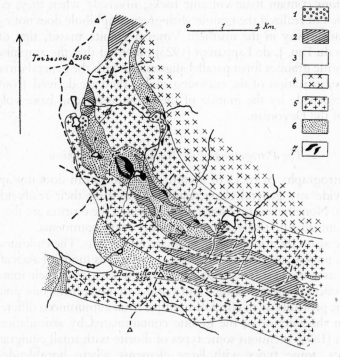

Fig. 11. The western part of the granite massif of Quérigut. 1. Recent alluvium. 2. Palaeozoic limestone. 3. Silurian and Palaeozoic non-differentiated shales. 4. normal granite. 5. schistose granite, or granite rich in inclusions (in the south, migmatites). 6. amphibole granite. 7. diorites, gabbros, peridotites.

One of the most characteristic traits of the massif is the existence of calcareous bands included in the granite. One such can be followed for 5 km. The position of these bands and the series of rock types which they present are comparable to those in the calcareous horizon which marks the Quérigut massif. At Tichka, as in the Pyrenees, endomorphism is strongly developed and it is particularly manifest in the vicinity of the calcareous horizons: the biotite granite acquires amphibole and grades obviously into granodiorite, to quartz diorite or to ordinary diorite; now this latter species is related on the one hand to hornblendite and on the other to gabbro. Every time that one meets a calcareous mass enclosed in the granite, one finds diorite nearby.

According to J. Jung (1928): "In the Vosges, the relatively calcic granites with green amphibole are encountered when the enclosing formations contain basic volcanic rocks; inversely when these conditions are not realized the granite with green amphibole does not exist." In a similar way in the northern Vosgian granite massif, that of the Champ du Feu, J. de Lapparent (1923) observed that the amphibolitic and dioritic granites form parallel alignments with the general direction of the stratification of the enclosing rocks; they are derived from the digestion made by the granite of the sedimentary and basic volcanic rocks of the Devonian.

The Petrography of the Rocks of Endomorphism

The petrography of rocks of granitic endomorphism does not appear to provide any general characteristics permitting their ready identification. Nonetheless, the basic facies, of which the diorites are the most important quantitatively, suggest the following comments.

Once again the rocks of Quérigut are referred to. The endomorphic diorites present an extreme diversity, a capricious mode of associations as well as some curious complications in the texture of their minerals. They reflect labile conditions and rapid variations from one point to another, probably as an effect of multiple local autonomous differentiations in the interior of the granite contaminated by assimilation. A. Lacroix (1899) mentions some types of diorite with small equigranular elements, some types with large elements where hornblende and biotite are of greater size than the plagioclases and tend towards an ophitic texture (even with the biotite), some types "speckled" (tigrés), where the plagioclases are grouped and isolated between them. Distributed haphazardly with regard to each other, these varieties may now and then be observed together over some meters or at other times over some hundreds of meters. In any case in the same rocks, of the same massif, the zoned plagioclases are remarkable because of the complexity of their zoning. Recurrences of basicity in successive envelopes, or corrosions of the kernel of the crystal by the feldspar of a more external envelope may be observed. These witness the singular instabilities during crystallization.

These facts have perhaps some universality for this type of diorite. For instance, near Thillot in the southern Vosges, the border of the Ballons granite came in contact with volcanic rocks and basic intrusions of the Tournaisian[1], and underwent endomorphism, which produced polymorphic diorites of considerable extent. A petrographic study of these rocks shows similar features.

Some aplitic and pegmatitic veinlets are likely to undergo a very pronounced endomorphism. A. Lacroix (1923) has named *dissogenites*, in other words, rocks of double origin, these veins of aplite radiating from granite and showing, along with quartz and normal alkali feldspar, small proportions of unusual minerals due to chemical elements borrowed from the surrounding rock: pyroxene, sphene, epidote, wollastonite, etc. in a calcic environment; andalusite, cordierite, sillimanite in shales. These phenomena prove the facility of endomorphic contaminations even in thin veins undoubtedly quickly formed.

The Roles of Mineralizers and of Contact Metamorphism

Contact metamorphism precedes assimilation. This is true of the margins of the granite but it is still more striking in the inclusions. One follows, in fact easily, the evolution of enallogenic inclusions, at first metamorphosed, then transformed into endopolygenic inclusions. These fade and disappear in the normal granite with or without an intermediate stage of contaminated granite. A. Lacroix has shown that the two phenomena, metamorphism and endomorphism, are bound together, and that the more the first is important, the more the second is developed. The essential factor in contact metamorphism will be seen to be the abundance of "mineralizers", that is to say, of emanations rich in water vapour and compounds of alkalis, halogens, boron, phosphorus, etc., compounds particularly fluid over a wide range of physico-chemical conditions.

[1] A division of the Dinantian or Lower Carboniferous.

D*

The mineralizers seem to be equally indispensable in facilitating assimilation. Writes Lacroix:

> Not only the intensity of the endomorphic phenomena, but also the abundance of the products of emanations localized in veins develop in our massif (Quérigut) in the same degree as the exomorphic transformations of the sediments. When the latter become very weak, the granite does not show endomorphic modifications. (A. Lacroix, 1900).

Endomorphism is not restricted especially to granites. The gabbros, for example, are affected by it. But the phenomenon seems to be less pronounced in gabbros than in granite, undoubtedly because the mineralizers are less abundant in plutonic basic rocks.

CONCLUSION

A definition of assimilation, independent of all theory of the granite genesis, was given at the beginning of this chapter.

In some cases, the introduction into enclosing rocks of an abundance of mobile fluids or pneumatolytes is revealed by a multiplicity of veinlets or microveinlets of aplites, pegmatites or quartz visible in the skein of the rocks. In other cases, the chemical migration occurs on a much finer scale and may be proportionally less important. Nature furnishes examples of both modes. In the first, assimilation may be envisioned from the magmatist's concept of progressive dissolution by an independent solvent, the heterogeneous portions being remnants which have only undergone an imperfect dissolution. In the second mode, a metasomatic interpretation may be preferred: the whole granite mass represents the product of assimilation, and the heterogeneous portions, inclusions and the variation facies are only portions of a particular chemical composition which have longer resisted the metasomatic homogenization.

Assimilation plays an incontestable role in the formation of granite, which will be dealt with further in chapter 17. Assimilation explains in some measure the surprising diversity of granites, a diversity which reflects some features of the stratigraphic layering of the original rocks. Assimilation is, however, intimately connected with other phenomena; I have indicated its bond with metamorphism and with the emission of emanations from granite and consequently with the suites of veins where the emanations are now and then localized. Assimilation facilitates certain differentiations because the mobilized environment of granitization is particularly propitious to chemical reactions of different kinds when it is contaminated by endomorphism. It is only for practical reasons of exposition that these diverse phenomena are presented separately; in reality they work together towards the evolution of the granite.

Chapter 6

THE GRANITE AUREOLE

When a granite in a circumscribed massif is approached across a sedimentary series, the normal rocks at a certain distance from the granite begin to undergo a recrystallization which becomes more and more accentuated towards the granite contact. This is the phenomenon of *contact metamorphism*. The transformed zone is called the *aureole* of the massif. Its thickness may be of the order of some hundreds or of thousands of meters. It can give the illusion of being larger, due to its width in outcrop, where the granite massif slopes very gradually downwards from the surface granite contact under the surrounding formations. Older eruptive rocks invaded by the granite can be equally recrystallized in the aureole, but the phenomenon is generally less distinct than in the sedimentary rocks.

The anatectic granites may also have an aureole of metamorphism ahead of the migmatite front, which is, however, less accentuated than that around the circumscribed massifs.

The essence of the transformation undergone by the rocks of the aureole has a *metasomatic*[1] character. As will be seen, an important rôle must be attributed to the diffuse chemical substances released from the granite. They are made up of aqueous alkaline solutions or vapours associated with compounds of the halogens (fluorides, chlorides), sulphur, phosphorus and of boron. These substances have strong chemical affinities, and their compounds have a high solubility and vapour pressure, so that they can persist for a long time in a liquid or gaseous state before crystallizing. The action of these emanations from the granite, or more generally from the plutonic and volcanic rocks, is called *pneumatolysis*. Following A. E. Fersman, the emanations themselves are called *pneumatolytes*. Because the efficacy of pneumatolysis is sometimes disputed, I will stress along the way the facts which justify this concept.

[1] See p. 6 for definition of the term.

Contact metamorphism without any appreciable chemical addition may, however, also be very important. The Barr-Andlau auerole in Alsace, described in H. Rosenbusch's classical study, is an excellent example. The contact metamorphism of the plutonic rocks in the neighbourhood of Oslo is of this type, and here it was first possible to group the constituents according to the phase rule and to show a tendency towards certain physico-chemical equilibria (V. M. Goldschmidt, 1911).

THE PRODUCTS OF METAMORPHISM

This is not the place to describe all the types of metamorphic rocks, for far too many varieties exist; only main lines will be treated: broadly the phenomenon includes three grades, which can be categorized by the most representative rocks of each: that of the phyllites, of the mica schists, and of the gneisses.

Consider indeed a series of argillaceous shales, which are among the most common of the sedimentary rocks. They are first transformed into *phyllites*, that is to say they become hard, and take on a lustrous, brilliant aspect through the microscopic crystallization of cryptocrystalline or amorphous elements of the shale, such as the clay minerals or sericite, with a cleavage surface often wrinkled or finely folded. Nearer the granite, but over very short distances, biotite develops at the outset finely dispersed in the microscopic fabric of the rock resulting in *micaceous schists*. These often assume the facies of *spotted* or *lozenged schists*[1]: they are strewn with spots some millimeters to centimeters in size, which are lighter or darker than the surrounding fabric of the rock. The microscope reveals that these spots are either "islets" which have escaped crystallization or are "islets" in which the metamorphism is more advanced. In the latter case particular minerals, such as andalusite or cordierite, may appear. Often they alone form the spots in the schist. Staurolite occurs under similar conditions, preferably in carbon-rich layers (Ch. Barrois, 1934).

In the next stage the grain size of the micaceous schists becomes larger and clearly macroscopic. The rock becomes a *mica schist*, a metamorphic rock with quartz and biotite as essential minerals. Biotite is without doubt the most important mineral of the new-formed minerals of contact metamorphism, as far as frequency in different stages is concerned. Microscopic tourmaline is very common in micaceous schists and the mica schists. It is, however, quantitatively much less important than biotite.

[1] *Schistes macliféres* = chiastolite schists.

Feldspar appears finally, either as very small crystals dispersed in the substance of the micaceous schist or the mica schist, and the rock becomes what is called a *leptynolite*: or, if the grains are larger and more abundant, a true *gneiss* develops, that is, a rock made up essentially of quartz, mica and feldspar. Among the other neogenic minerals in mica schists and gneisses, there are: andalusite, sillimanite, cordierite, garnet, sphene and scapolite. The interior zone of the aureole does not, however, always consist of gneiss; leptynolites or micaceous schists may be found in direct contact with the granite. I will return to the caprices of contact metamorphism later. On the whole, the increasing intensity of contact metamorphism is expressed by an increase in the grain size of the neogenic minerals and by a larger variety among these.

When the shale is marly, rocks are formed at its expense which are extremely fine grained or homogeneous to the naked eye, composed exclusively of newly crystallized minerals, very hard, compact and with a hornlike fracturing. They are called *hornfelses*. Their composition varies. Garnet, wollastonite, epidote, zoisite, pyroxene, amphibole, feldspar and quartz are among their more usual constituents. *Tactites* are calcic hornfelses of coarse grain. Some hornfelses, formed for instance at the expense of volcanic tuffs, are not calcic. The term hornfels designates rather the very fine texture in aggregates of new-formed silicates produced by contact metamorphism. Purer limestones transform to crystalline marbles, that is to rocks in which the calcite is mainly crystallized. These marbles are often sprinkled with minerals such as garnet, amphibole, mica, and are called *cipolins*. They alternate with beds of banded hornfelses. In the case of dolomitic sediments, a paragenesis of magnesian minerals appears: talc, tremolite, forsterite, diopside, phlogopite, etc., with humites if there is an important pneumatolysis.

Sandstones change to *metamorphic quartzites*. If the sandstone is impure, the fabric of the quartzite is charged with various neogenic minerals, most often microscopic in size: biotite quartzites, diopsidic quartzites, garnetiferous quartzites, etc.

Older eruptive rocks long since consolidated can also be subjected to contact metamorphism if a young granite is emplaced nearby. There results either pseudomorphosis of the minerals of the original rock, or new minerals may crystallize at their expense. These effects varying with the nature of the original rock are often difficult to detect, as for example in the metamorphism of an old granite by a new one. At the intermediate stage of contact metamorphism, i.e., the stage of micaceous schists or leptynolites, the development of fine grained biotite in great abundance and dispersed throughout the rock is a characteristic of the metamorphism.

If it is possible to define the aureole broadly by the succession of the three zones of phyllites, mica schists, and gneisses, a more detailed study will show that the phenomenon actually is one of a very delicate balance. The fine layers of interbedded sediments of different compositions or textures become metamorphosed in different facies and their

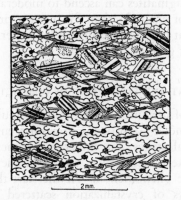

2 mm.

Fig. 12. Microphotograph of a leptynolite from Quérigut (drawn after A. Lacroix). Matrix of fine grained quarts, feldspar, biotite. Observe the cross structure of the biotite.

crystallization often accentuates their mutual differences. One can demonstrate that metamorphism is *selective*, that is, it takes place much more intensely in some beds or in certain more favourable layers. The monomineralic rocks, such as the siliceous sandstones, marbles, gypsum, or particularly compact rocks are less sensitive to metamorphism than are rocks rich in various chemical elements, such as the pelites, marls and graywackes, or more porous rocks. Arkoses of a chemical composition approaching that of a granite metamorphose in a particularly active fashion, and at a greater distance in the granite aureole. A. Jamotte (1944) has observed this fact in the Roan beds in the Musoshi mine, Katanga.

The Case of Migmatites

Ahead of the migmatite front an aureole is sometimes observed, of course more so where the front is pronounced, which is the case when the migmatites rise to a sedimentary series little metamorphosed in itself. This aureole, called the *transition zone* by Jung and Roques (1952), has already been mentioned on page 51. It is of relatively little intensity.

A. Michel-Lévy held to a different concept and saw in the migmatites themselves varieties of gigantic aureoles around the deep granites (our granites of anatexis). The enormous difference in scale in comparison with the gneissic zone in the aureoles of circumscribed massifs was attributed by him to the great depth that he assigned to the "injection gneisses" (which we call migmatites). But this interpretation is not correct, since the migmatites can ascend to moderate depth, less in the Hercynian chain, for example, than for many a circumscribed granite elsewhere. The great migmatite domains are rather unfinished granites than the aureoles of granites.

THE DEVELOPMENT AND STRUCTURES OF CONTACT METAMORPHISM

The development of metamorphism entails a simultaneous crystalliza-tion of various mineral constituents in a solid environment. Never-theless in the initial stages, the minerals commence successively to crystallize in a determined order, and continue according to the development of the phenomenon.[1] At the start there is a local ger-mination in centres of crystallization scattered through the rock resulting in the *spotted* or *nodular* schists. However, some "spots", previously mentioned above, may be in contrast retarded islets which have avoided the incipient recrystallization of the surroundings. Some of the new-formed minerals scattered through the rock develop much more rapidly than those of the surrounding fabric. They are therefore of much greater size than the others and bring to mind the porphyritic crystals or phenocrysts of the eruptive rocks. They are called *porphyro-blasts* or *phenoblasts*. The suffix "blast" (from the Greek: to sprout, germinate) is used for the metamorphic textures called *crystalloblastic*, and signifies that the development of the crystals took place in a solid environment by means of a kind of germination.

Sometimes the porphyroblasts have formless outlines, and growing along all the interstices between the grains enclose inclusions of small minerals from the original rock (poecilitic texture, fig. 33). Sometimes they have very sharp outlines, and are made up of purer material, having dissolved or chased at their edges the small particles of the surrounding fabric. Certain porphyroblasts such as of andalusite (variety chiastolite) and sometimes of cordierite or garnet, have even been able to group these particles along well-defined geometric zones in their interiors. Carbonaceous particles or small grains of ore minerals are generally so

[1] This is also true in general metamorphism. See p. 190.

arranged. The same can be observed in neogenic feldspars, but mainly in general metamorphism.

These phenomena can be partly explained by the distinction between *strong* and *weak minerals* of F. Becke. A crystal in the course of its growth is able to produce a mechanical force to push aside obstacles to its growth. Common examples are the rupturing of rocks by frost and the distension of schists through the alteration of pyrite crystals. According to A. Harker (1952): " geological observation and experiment alike go to prove that growing crystals are capable of exerting forces of the same order of magnitude as their own crushing strength". If crystals of two minerals of unequal force develop side by side the stronger will impose its form on the weaker. It has been possible to classify the common minerals according to their relative forces of crystallization by means of this kind of observation. Nevertheless, physico-chemical conditions in the environment may modify the force of crystallization. In general, tourmaline and garnet are strong; cordierite and andalusite are weak. Porphyroblasts of the weak minerals are often poecilitic or have ameboid outlines; porphyroblasts of the strong minerals can push aside impurities at their outer surfaces.

Nevertheless, weak minerals can be idiomorphic, as for example chiastolite, and the phenomenon seems to take place peacefully and almost imperceptibly in many cases. Ch. Barrois (1884) speaks of "the formation of chiastolite crystals 5–6 cm long in schists where the layering and fossils are not even disturbed". They "seem to have taken the place of an equal volume of the minerals of the original rock". He mentions similar observations for the crystallization of neogenic quartz.

The simultaneous crystallization of different minerals is a collective crystallization by a gathering together of material: a nourishment of the growing grains takes place at the expense of their neighbours of the same mineral species, such that the grain size slowly increases. This can be verified by observations on poecilitic textures, where the growth of the grains included at the beginning of the crystallization of the porphyroblasts has often been brought to a standstill and thus the grains have preserved a smaller size than their free growing counterparts in the surrounding material.

A. Harker has stressed the influence of the force of crystallization relative to the form of crystals and the texture of the rock of contact metamorphism. The force of crystallization is a vectorial property. Brought into play by the resistance of the environment, it is manifest by the form adopted by the crystals produced. This form is simple

Fig. 13. Micrograph of decussate texture (simplified drawing after A. Harker). Phenoblasts of andalusite in a groundmass of biotite.

Fig. 14. Micrograph of a diablastic texture (simplified drawing after A. Harker). Garnet, axinite (uncoloured) and hornblende.

compared to the form of the same minerals in plutonic and volcanic rocks, or in hydrothermal veins: in general only the principal faces and particularly those parallel to a good cleavage appear. From this he says "we can infer that the force of crystallization is greater along than across the cleavage". This results in an abundance of lamellar and acicular formes. The mica lamellae have irregular outlines, and amphibole prisms lack end faces. Twins are rarer than in plutonic and volcanic rocks.

If all the crystals were oriented parallel to each other from an originally isotropic aggregate, the consequence would be an elongation of the rock, whence an increase in the internal stresses. The adoption of a *decussate texture* consisting of a felt of very elongated or tabular minerals is common in the hornfelses, and is a manifestation of a tendency to minimize internal stresses. The same tendency explains several other types of textures. In initially well-stratified rocks, the crystallization will be, on the contrary, parallel for the same reason. These are *lepidoblastic textures*, i.e., those in which the flaky minerals are parallel to the cleavage of the rock, and *nematoblastic*, where elongated minerals are arranged in the cleavage and parallel to one direction. Such textures, according to Harker, most often reflect the original stratification along which the minerals adapt themselves with least effort. *Diablastic* textures (systematic compenetration of two or more minerals) and *poeciloblastic* (poecilitic inclusions or particles of the fabric in large crystals) can in the same way be explained as a rearrangement in order to minimize internal stresses. Nevertheless it is not necessarily so in compenetration textures of two or more minerals; other effects may interfere, as for instance reactions that contemporaneously produce two minerals. As for *granoblastic* texture, i.e., a mosaic type of arrangement, it is the result of each crystal having the same force of crystallization in any direction and the crystals being oriented at random.

This theory on the role of the force of crystallization with regard to texture is not accepted by some authors, who doubt the efficacy of this force and tend, here and in general metamorphism (p. 179), to see in the directions of the easiest chemical diffusion, such as the original stratification, etc., the reason for the platiness of crystals following these directions. E. Friedel writes to me that the force of crystallization seems to him a metaphysical notion which is used here in an arbitrary way. He adds:

> There is quite probably the possible development of a force of crystallization during the growth of crystals; but when it is manifested, for example, by the widening of the lips of a fissure in which fibrous rock salt crystallized, it is a totally different thing from isolated crystals substituting themselves for pre-existing material.

I recognize that crystallization by the substitution so common in metamorphism complicates and obscures the possible role of the force of crystallization. However, the microscope shows that in many cases the crystals have developed by expanding in the interstices of pre-existing crystals and by gradually pushing them apart.

THE CHEMICAL FRONTS IN THE AUREOLE

Some aureoles are formed exclusively of phyllites and micaceous schists, having the same total chemical composition as the sedimentary rocks; their metamorphic crystallization does not seem to have been accompanied by chemical changes. In other, leptynolites and gneisses figure with an important development of feldspar. If the original rock did not contain a sufficient quantity of alkalis, there must of necessity have been an *addition of alkaline material* which emanated from the granite. Even if it is not always certain that the crystallization of the aureoles expresses a chemical evolution, very often layers of the metamorphic series with a very high proportion of certain minerals, such as feldspar, tourmaline, mica, etc., indicate that it is so.

If the feldspars can indicate the influx of alkalis, the enrichment in magnesium and iron of layers originally low in both is expressed by the development of biotite and cordierite. The same observation has been made for titanium of sphene and for the chlorine of scapolite. Influxes of iron or of sulphur in great quantities are known near granite contacts within sediments which were devoid of them. Such are the various deposits of magnetite of the Urals. W. Lindgren has drawn attention to remarkable examples of this phenomenon: at Clifton, Arizona, a pure calcic limestone has been transformed into a garnet-pyroxene rock over a thickness of 600 m by the addition of silica and iron; at Bingham, Utah, a limestone has been enriched in silica, sulphur, iron, magnesium, aluminum and sodium, additions amounting locally to 29% of the volume of the rock. These transformations are essentially *metasomatic*, because they largely preserve the structure of the rocks.

The concept of a zone of chemical influence radiating from around a granite by the propagation of "mineralizers", vapours and solutions, and preceding the granite is an old intuitive idea. It has been refined by the works of C. E. Wegmann, D. Reynolds and others, and has become the theory of *chemical fronts* of granitization. Each front is the limit of propagation of a certain group of chemical elements. The fronts succeed each other, sometimes at intervals, sometimes overlapping each other. Their propagation is not necessarily connected with the transport of fluids, but may be by diffusion of ions in the microsolutions along crystal boundaries, or even, according to the opinion of certain authors, by diffusion across the crystal lattices themselves.

C. E. Wegmann first recognized clearly an alkaline front and a magnesian front in migmatite domains in the process of granitization. In 1931 he wrote:

Around the *filtering columns*, to use an expression of Pierre Termier, an envelope forms with several varieties of enrichments. In the

interior the rocks have a tendency to become potassium feldspar-
and quartz-bearing; they thus effectively immobilize potassium
with silica. In the outer parts they stabilize above all magnesium.
The formation of andalusite, cordierite, sillimanite, garnet, etc.
is connected with the granitization.

And writing about the rocks of Torra-Hästen between Helsinki and
Onas he noted how they have been deformed a long time after their
emplacement, then basified to the point where volcanic breccias, tuffs,
and pillow lavas have acquired a truly abnormal ultrabasic character
through the development of hornblende and biotite during the granitization, in the vicinity.

Wegmann writes (1935):

He who is familiar with the migmatite domains will recall the
common case where enrichments of feldspar are widespread in the
form of spots or stains in the rocks. This is Termier's simile, and it
describes the case perfectly . . . The enrichment in feldspar is
generally the most obvious expression of the influx of material . . .
Most often it is imagined as a rush of material issuing from a
hearth. For the migration of alkalis it is principally so. For some
other substances the conditions of migration are not so simple.
For example, with magnesium many ways are probable; they must
be studied for each particular case. Hornblendes and garnets are
often biotitized, the biotite loses its colour and is used in the formation of feldspar; the result is a light coloured quartzo-feldspathic rock
with a dust of ore minerals. In these cases, one is inclined to
acknowledge a migration of magnesium; when cordierite occurs
in abundance in the migmatite front of these massifs, one is led to
conclude that magnesium migrates ahead of the migmatite front.
With the advance of this front, these cordierites are altered and
reformed towards the outside of the front as new cordierites.
One could almost speak of a cordierite front moving outwards
with the migmatite front . . . The magnesium was not, however,
provided by the magma, but by the rock masses already overwhelmed by the migmatization. A great part of the mobilizable
magnesium from a volume of rocks would be accumulated in a
fraction of this volume. Such zones can also be overwhelmed by
migmatization. Traces of them can survive for a long time in the
migmatitic granite, even if at first glance the granite appears
uniform. Some analogous phenomena appear on a small scale in the
dark biotite fringes along light-coloured veins in migmatites.

Doris Reynolds (1946) clearly distinguishes the two successive fronts: When *pelitic* and *semi-pelitic* rocks are metasomatically altered in contact with granite "magma" they undergo changes in two distinct stages. During the first stage of alteration they become molecularly *desilicated* relatively to the bases present, sometimes to such an extent as to become chemically under-saturated. The products of this desilication changes, which may attain the composition of syenite or of basic or ultrabasic igneous rocks, are characterized by a higher percentage of alkalis and/or cafemic constituents than either the parent sediment or the adjoining granite. For such an increase of any constituent beyond the amounts present in the parent rock and the neighbouring granite the term *geochemical culmination* is proposed. When the disilication change is wholly or largely one of basification (introduction of Fe, Mg, Ca) it is characterized by increase, commonly attaining geochemical culmination, of one or more of the minor constituents TiO_2, P_2O_5 and MnO; when it is essentially one of feldspathization, however, TiO_2, P_2O_5 and MnO may all decrease. During the second stage of alteration the desilicated rock is *granitized*, i.e., its composition approaches that of the associated granite. Silica and one of the alkalis are added, whilst alumina, cafemic constituents, and the minor constituents TiO_2, P_2O_5 and MnO decrease. (p. 390).

When the first phase reaches an alkali culmination, this alkali is not necessarily the dominant one in the nearby granite.

The concept of a *geochemical culmination* gives distinct firmness to the chemical fronts resembling successive waves. Let us also note, along with Wegmann, that fronts represent a regrouping of material not necessarily implying an origin distant for this material, which is without doubt often selected in the neighbourhood.

Within the aureole, it seems to me that one can *define diagrammatically three fronts*, the existence of one precluding the existence of another: a basic front, a silico-alkaline front, and possibly a late pneumatolytic front. This last develops in an environment already stabilized, and this explains why it is not largely diffused like the preceding ones, but is expressed by vein-fissure fillings or metasomatism of local extent at more or less numerous places in the vicinity of the granite.

One could perhaps also speak about a *metalliferous front*, because pyrometasomatic and hydrothermal metalliferous deposits often seem to radiate broadly from the periphery of granite stocks and. batholiths.

Nonetheless, such a front has not the universality of the preceding ones and we will postpone until chapter 14 the study of granitic metallo-genesis.

As a rule the basic front and the alkaline front successively pass a given point in the aureole exposed to the increasing influence of the granite in the course of advance. The second normally remains behind the first. The amplitudes of the fronts can vary from meters to hecto-meters. However, the phenomena are not so simple: there are recur-rences in these successions and above all migrations in two directions, all very delicate phenomena. We will see, moreover, that *some pneu-matolysis is probably never absent*, and is often expressed in the para-genesis[1] of these two fronts. I will only present the outlines of the three fronts as an approximation valuable along broad lines. We will examine below the characteristics of each of these fronts, after having studied pneumatolysis.

The complexity and the sensitivity of the reactions appear clearly at contacts between limestone and granite, where the aureoles are of restricted dimensions and show characteristic and varied mineral assemblages, two circumstances permitting more exact and even quantitative observations. The remarkable study by C. E. Tilley (1951) of the contacts of dolomitic limestones with Tertiary granite on the Isle of Skye can be cited. At the margin of the limestone, itself mineral-ized by sparse crystals of forsterite and tremolite, there are successions or alternations of thin, diverse hornfels zones over some centimeters or sometimes some decimeters at the boundary of the granite. A first group all along the granite is characterized principally by a monoclinic pyroxene, garnet, wollastonite and possibly plagioclase; it indicates an influx of silica and alumina from the granite and an elimination of magnesia, while the granite at the contact has been alkalinized by the loss of alumina, or endomorphosed with an increase of plagioclase. A second group, contiguous with the first moving away from the granite, is enriched in magnesia and characterized principally by forsterite and numerous magnesium minerals with fluorine and boron, clinohumite, ludwigite, etc. This group is here and there invaded by a later-developed monticellite, and finally by solutions producing magnetite skarns. The zoning of this aureole in the immediate vicinity of the granite results from the diffusion of chemical compounds, because it is not pre-determined by chemical heterogeneities due to a sedimentary strati-fication. Moreover, certain chert nodules in the dolomitic layers where

---

[1] The term *paragenesis* signifies the mineral association present in a particular rock.

they form siliceous "accidents" have reacted in a similar fashion where they are found within the zone of influence of the granite: they have produced small concentric aureoles, similar to the preceding zones by means of a migration of their constituents in two directions. The nodules have given up silica and absorbed calcium and fluorine. They show a central zone consisting of wollastonite surrounded by a zone of diopside, cuspidine, and finally alternating zones with associations of pneumatolytic magnesium minerals such as forsterite, clinohumite, etc.

The Role of Pneumatolysis

Pneumatolysis plays an important role in the whole evolution of the environment during granitization. This is not surprising because the pneumatolytes are essentially water-based, and water is everywhere present, in more than negligible proportions, in all rocks and particularly in sedimentary rocks with argillaceous constituents. The pneumatolytes are diffused in the aureole in front of the granite, as if they were provided by the granite and represented an *emanation* from it; but they seem rather to be chased ahead of the granite and to be squeezed from the environment[1].

Granite in this regard differs from volcanic rocks. The latter often reveal an abundance of volatile materials, manifested by the vesicules in the lavas and the formation of crystals in small cavities in these rocks. But these volatile materials do not impregnate the neighbouring rocks in a permanent fashion. At the contacts of argillaceous rocks with basalts, thin zones of "porcelanite" are formed, a substance resembling china and indicating a simple thermal action at much higher temperatures than that of granite, but of shorter duration and much less efficient as far as the extension of pronounced chemical modifications is concerned. The effect of these basalts calls to mind what can be observed in "burnt-out coal mines", where spontaneous combustion of shales has crystallized cordierite, anorthite, augite, magnetite and spinel in extremely fine-grained aggregates, but no alkaline or hydrous minerals[2].

The reality of granitic pneumatolysis appears in the composition of the neogenic minerals developed in the aureoles or crystallized ultimately in the fissures of the neighbourhood. One finds there minerals such as feldspar (alkali), tourmaline (boron) and numerous hydrated minerals, or minerals with oxyhydroxides in their chemical formulae:

[1] Concerning pneumatolysis, see also chapter 9, p. 139.
[2] A. Lacroix (1893–1913). See the minerals indicated.

micas, amphiboles, epidote and zoisite, chlorite, etc. These minerals can be regarded as pneumatolytic minerals, although some of them can form under other conditions. Other less common but very significant minerals may occur in some aureoles or among the products of what I have referred to as the late pneumatolytic front: axinite, scapolite, lepidolite, topaz, apatite and even pyrite.

A Lacroix has pointed out the capriciousness of the distribution of the pneumatolytes and the unequalness of their action around a granite massif. Sometimes abundant, sometimes almost absent, varying from one massif to another, they are also in most cases very irregularly distributed in the periphery of one and the same massif. This irregularity undoubtedly reflects their extreme mobility. In this regard, the Bordères granite, south of Arrau in the Pyrenees can be cited (A. Lacroix, 1900). It has reacted strongly on the limestones and shales along its southern contact, but not along its northern border. A study of microscopic gaseous and liquid inclusions in the quartz of the granite, could provide more exact information. But this type of study has to date been little developed (G. Deicha, 1955). It seems as if carbon dioxide and water play an important role there.

Do pneumatolytes operate in the aureole as solutions of liquids or vapours? Pneumatolysis in the original strict sense designated gaseous action. It must be noted that the distinction between the gaseous and the liquid states of these fluids is without doubt not as clear cut, as we tend to consider it in everyday experience. The conditions of pneumatolytes may be close to the critical state. Now, near this state the characteristics of liquid and gaseous phases converge progressively towards common limits. Perhaps the pneumatolytes in the aureole were in a supercritical state. There is little documentation concerning the critical points of complex aqueous solutions and the question remains obscure.

C. N. Fenner (1933) assumes that the hypothesis of action in the gaseous state is completely valid for tourmaline which forms particularly far from contacts and seems to represent a maximum in volatility. Some observations suggest instead the intervention of liquid solutions. The pneumatolytes concentrate here and there in veinlets of aplites and of pegmatites which degenerate at the end of the process into simple fracture fillings of a drusy character of the same type as hydrothermal fillings. A. Lacroix (1899) has shown that the dissogenites of the Quérigut granite grade into veins incompletely filled with quartz, adularia, albite and epidote, and neighbour similar veins of tourmaline and quartz. He regards them as the last stage of pneumatolytic action at the end of the *mise en place* of the granite.

There is no essential difference between the formation of these total or partial fillings of fractures and contact phenomena, both are manifestations of the same thing; it only must be noted that as the fillings of a fracture require the pre-existence of a rock which can be healed, these mineral products have necessarily followed upon the formation of metamorphic rocks in the proper sense; they constitute the last act of the phenomenon. When sedimentary rocks have been saturated with hydrothermal mineralized elements, these elements, being unable to act upon them further, have been able to settle in the fractures.

Thin coatings of biotite or muscovite, and fine veneers of tourmaline, along the walls of the joints in the rocks of the aureole, are not rare. These effects are late and local. But there must have been produced beforehand, in the same mass of metamorphic beds, a sort of general impregnation caused by the same pneumatolytes. The channels made use of by them remain indiscernable, consisting probably of ultramicroscopic interstices. They seem to have been similar to those which make possible the metasomatism of minerals of metallic veins. In those the microscope sometimes reveals networks of capillary channels, but sometimes these networks fade out becoming invisible because of their fineness.

The works of A. Lacroix have also brought to light what he calls the *fugitive constituents* of magmas. These "magmas" designate the materials of plutonic and volcanic rocks in general, and not only of granites, all rocks which he conceived as magmatic, granites included, in keeping with the ideas of his time. This theory is based on the following considerations. There is a certain inertness of metamorphosing rock to the production of an aureole of a particular mineralization: the pneumatolytes are the important factors and they are similar for all metamorphosing rocks. The pneumatolytes are thus independent of the generating rocks at this stage. It even happens that they do not figure at all in the final chemical composition of the rock. From this comes the idea that they can be completely removed and that they can be regarded as fugitive constituents. Thus the Pyrenean granite, which has the famous axinite contact of Arbizon, near Pic du Midi, does not contain any boron. The contacts of the lherzolites and ophites[1] of the Pyrenees show a considerable development of various minerals, particularly scapolite (dipyre), albite, tourmaline and sodic minerals with chlorine and boron. The adinoles, or albite hornfelses, are standard developments

[1] Ophite is a local name in the Pyrenees for triassic diabase.

along the dolerite contacts. These facts are paradoxical, particularly for lherzolite which contains no alkalis and for ophite, which is poor in them. The magma of Vesuvius often produces fumaroles with boron, arsenic, lead, copper and sulphur, which are not contained in the lavas themselves; one actually finds crystallization of realgar, galena, sassolite, etc., in the fissures of this volcano.

One could assume that, if there are fugitive constituents completely driven from the generating rock, and fixed in the aureole, there are also some fugitive constituents which have passed across certain zones in the aureole without leaving any apparent trace, or without being fixed in the development of specific minerals. This depends on the texture and the composition of the surrounding rocks. For instance, some sandstones may remain unchanged because they are like filters of too great a mesh. We must realize that in certain cases these vagabond substances exert a catalytic effect, permitting a stabilization of other substances, accentuating the seeming capriciousness of contact metamorphism.

The Basic Front

The appearance of biotite, at first sparse and microscopic, at the debut of the aureole some distance from the granite, then its growth into bigger flakes and then clusters nearer to the granite, is the most characteristic aspect of aureoles. With the development of cordierite, sometimes in great abundance, one can see in these two minerals the mark of the basic front. An enrichment of hornblende may also take place, as around the Osi granite in Nigeria, where the basic front of the porphyroid granite is marked by the development of biotite and hornblende, driven ahead and concentrated particularly along shear zones which control the granitization (B. C. King and A. M. J. de Swardt, 1949). The ferruginous black tourmaline (schorl), widespread in the schists of aureoles, has in part the same significance. J. Thiébaut (1951) described the expulsion of iron giving rise to black fringes, both of biotite and of tourmaline, in the margin of the borders of the metamorphism or granitization. Tourmaline testifies to the role of pneumatolysis in the basic front. D. Reynolds has shown that the geochemical culmination of the basic front is generally accompanied by a culmination of titanium, phosphorus and manganese. For instance, around the Osi granite, King and de Swardt note an enrichment of apatite, sphene and allanite connected with an enrichment of ferromagnesian minerals.

The perigranitic aplites and pegmatites are often bounded by a dense rim of biotite, which represents on a small scale a very common type of basic front. On a very large scale the border of migmatites shows the same phenomenon, already noted by C. E. Wegmann (1935). As J. Haller (1955) writes on the subject of the Caledonian metamorphic complex of Greenland:

> In the peripheral shells of the migmatite bodies, fringes of melano-cratic rocks, often 5 to 10 meters thick, are present. They represent a paragenesis rich in Fe, Mg, Ca (hornblendites and hornblende gneisses often rich in garnet and sphene). They have a direct genetic relationship to the granitization and represent products of basic exudation from the central granite body.

In the marginal granite of batholiths or very close to their borders masses of basic rocks, diorites, and even gabbros or peridotites, which may possibly represent culminations of the basic front in the coarse-grained plutonic facies, sometimes appear, where the question of a simple local endomorphic effect is not involved.

In their classic work, F. J. Turner and J. Verhoogen (1951) made the following objection:

> If the basic front really represents a zone of concentration of material expulsed during the granitization in place of the rocks, the great extent of a number of granitic masses, compared with the restricted number of rocks associated with a basic front, con-stitutes a very striking anomaly.

The basic masses certainly have little extent vis à vis the granites upon which they depend. But it has been seen with regard to endomorphism that such basic rocks can to a certain degree be dispersed and homogen-ized within the main granite before it has completely crystallized. Furthermore the diffusion of material in the form of biotite, cordierite, etc. in the aureole is extremely widespread and difficult to appreciate. It is even possible that part of the basic elements escape in the form of hydrothermal solutions beyond the outer limit of the aureole. More-over, the importance of the inventory of cafemic mobilizable elements depends on the quantity of pre-existing rocks rich in calcium, mag-nesium and iron.

On the other hand, the basic front can be reduced to almost nothing, if a granite produces no contact metamorphism. It may also have been formed as a transitional stage and have been obliterated by the influence of other fronts, save for some resistant vestiges.

The Silico-Alkaline Front

The silico-alkaline front is above all evident because of the conspicuous development of feldspar, often in eyes, sometimes identical to the feldspar of the granite. This feldspar habitually shows a more pronounced concentration along certain beds of the rock of the aureole. However, I have observed at the contact of the granite of Oulmès, Central Morocco, an outcrop where a feldspathic zone some decimeters thick parallels the border of the granite, lying oblique to the stratification of the invaded rock: this makes the chemical front clearly visible and makes it obvious.

To be sure, in cases where one can see that the rock of the aureole contained an amount of alkalis before the arrival of the granite of the same order as after the feldspathization, an alkaline front would not be in question; only a recrystallization in conformity with a new stage of equilibrium would be involved. It also happens that there is not an appreciable development of feldspar in the aureole and that the edge of the granite is in direct contact with the mica schists of the basic front. In this case, the alkaline front can be regarded as represented by the granite itself.

We have seen that, according to D. Reynolds (1946), the alkaline culmination in front of the granite may not be of the same alkali as the one that dominates in the adjacent granite. With regard to one particular case (the Bort-les-Orgues gneiss, Corrèze, formed by alkali metasomatism of mica schists wholly independent of all the neighbouring granites), J. Jung (1949) has shown that the potassium and sodium have been emplaced separately according to temperature and pressure conditions. Supported by the experiments of A. Michel-Lévy and J. Wyart (1947) and of J. Wyart (1947), he envisions the transport of potassium by supercritical water and that of sodium by liquid water. The variation of conditions in time and space might explain the contrast of alkaline fronts, either sodic or potassic, successive or superimposed.

The Late Pneumatolytic Front

Assemblages of pneumatolytic quartz veins, sometimes radiating in very great number around some granite massifs, belong to this front. Some late pegmatites rich in pneumatolytic minerals are also related, although the development of pegmatites would in general often seem to embrace the whole time of granitization. Pegmatites will be especially studied in chapter 9.

The new chemical conditions connected with the late pneumatolytic front entail a metasomatism of a special genre, which produces *greisen* characterized above all by colourless mica which is sometimes lithium-bearing. The feldspars become unstable and are destroyed; quartz and muscovite form. Greisen is a rock essentially composed of quartz and white mica, sometimes with occasional pneumatolytic minerals, such as tourmaline, topaz, cassiterite, etc. It results from a metasomatism of granite or hornfels, of little thickness, along pneumatolytic fissures. Greisen also sometimes forms independent veins of intrusive appearance in which case it has been referred to as *esmeraldite*. When it borders pegmatite veins and forms its marginal facies (observed at Manono, Katanga, for example), it can be disputed whether a greisen or esmeraldite is involved. But even in the latter case, it may have been metasomatic, because metasomatism certainly participates in the formation of pegmatites themselves.

The pneumatolytic quartz veins comprise particularly quartz with cassiterite and wolframite, occasionally with scheelite, or simply with muscovite and tourmaline. Veins of *tourmalinite*, formed almost exclusively of black tourmaline, are extreme cases.

The phase of formation of the pneumatolytic veins is subsequent to that of contact metamorphism in the strict sense, which refers to the preceding fronts. The metamorphic minerals, such as andalusite, staurolite and cordierite, to say nothing of feldspars, are sericitized by these veins. For instance, in Cornwall "one sees clearly that the formation of the tin-bearing veins was later than the metamorphism caused by the granite and that their alterations have been superposed on the latter" (Lacroix, 1934). In the same way, in the Kalima region (Maniema, Belgian Congo), N. Varlamoff (1948) writes:

> The aplite, pegmatite and quartz veins, the fluids which have given rise to the greisens of lithic mica, the tourmalinization and deposition of cassiterite, wolframite and topaz, and later fluorite, do not derive directly from the muscovite and biotite granites which they intersect, in which they are enclosed, or which they have transformed into greisen, for they come from deeper down. The pneumatolysis is superposed on contact metamorphism, particularly in the apical portions of massifs or of small apophyses.

Nevertheless, many times one sees that such veins follow immediately upon the granite. Thus in the El Karit tin deposits at the border of the Oulmès granite massif of Central Morocco, it has been observed that stretching connected with the *mise en place* of the massif gave rise to boudinage of the vein beds of quartz with cassiterite and beryl in the schist of the aureole.

The quartzose pneumatolytic emanations constitute a complex

ensemble divided into several phases over a certain period, each with a composition, a temperature and consequently varying properties depending on the moment of their formation: they are not only the result of the pegmatitic phase. As N. Varlamoff (1946) reveals, A. Fersman has shown that the pneumatolytic "distillates" may be emitted in the course of different phases of the formation of granite massifs, earlier than some pegmatites, during the successive periods of the evolution of some pegmatites and at the end of the process.

J. B. Scrivenor (1928) cites some cases where aplites with topaz in the Malayan granites cut quartz-topaz veins lacking feldspar. At the border of the Montmins granite, Allier, France, G. Carette (1946) has shown that the aplites cut and rework wolframite-bearing quartz veins. Similar observations have been made by N. Varlamoff (1948) in the tin-bearing granites of Maniema, where some quartz is earlier than some aplites and pegmatites of the same granite. In Central Morocco, I have observed at the border of the Oulmès granite quartz veins intersected by aplite veins with pegmatite(fig. 15). In the neighbouring

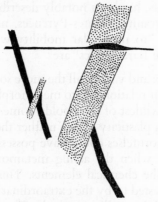

Fig. 15. Veins at the margin of the Oulmès granite massif, Morocco. In black: quartz. Dotted: aplite. The vertical dimension of the figure is 1.5 metres.

granite massif, the Ment granite, tourmalinite veins alternate with veins of quartz; at Zrari, at the border of the same massif, quartz with wolframite has been broken up by tourmaline veins, themselves intersected by more recent quartz.

Thus the emission of pneumatolytic quartz in the aureole does not necessarily represent a final episode in the evolution of granite massifs. Similarly there are *avant-garde* pegmatites of granitization and late pegmatites; there are also, and independently, early quartz and late quartz. However, quartz, in which most of the pneumatolytic minerals concentrate and crystallize (with the possible exception of a part of the tourmaline) corresponds to relatively late phases, which are only exceptionally followed by terminal aplitic and pegmatitic veins.

Perhaps it is necessary to add to the late pneumatolytic front a *fluorite front*, pointed out particularly by Sederholm around the Precambrian granites of Group III in Finland and the rapakivis. It has also been observed by Wegmann in southern Greenland.

MECHANICAL DEFORMATIONS IN THE AUREOLE

At the border of the circumscribed massifs, the rocks of the aureole reveal a strange mobility, conspicuous in every way in the outcrops. This mobility is not apparent in the neighbouring granite of a homogeneous aspect and where the final crystallizations have effaced transitional phases. This mobility of the rocks is contemporaneous with metamorphism. The phenomenon, which is well known at the border of various granite massifs, has been notably described by P. Hupé (1948) for the Néouvielle granite, Hautes-Pyrénées, near Refuge Pake. He relates this plasticity "to molecular mobility which characterizes the metamorphism". The Barégiennes[1] are

> even more complex and varied, all the more so as one comes closer
> to the contacts; their relationship to metamorphism is thus evident.
> Now, among the wildest of these folds, some are not fractured at
> all, which implies a plasticity which neither the original sediments
> nor the resulting hornfelses could have possessed. They date then
> from the moment when the acting metamorphism permitted a
> high mobility of the chemical elements. This mobility is more-
> over splendidly attested to by the extraordinary actions of calcium
> carbonate, which injects siliceous beds. The compact hornfelses
> show some boudinage[2] and some preferential orientations of rod-
> shaped minerals, both contemporaneous with the metamorphism
> and reflecting, in the same way as the Barégiennes, the action of
> oriented forces. The age of these phenomena is shown by their
> relationships to aplites. The oriented minerals (amphibole) are
> parallel to very closely spaced schistosity ·planes, oblique to the

[1] The term applied in the Pyrenees to folds in sediments consisting of alternating calcareous layers and siliceous or silicate-rich layers.
[2] Boudinage is the stretching of a rigid bed between more plastic beds with periodic tearing apart of the bed.

stratification and emphasized by the presence of aplitic veins . . .
The schistosity results from compressions contemporaneous with
the aplites. Concerning the boudinage, the zones of constriction
between the boudins are often striped with fissures *en echelon*,
sealed by an aplitic filling; the style of the zoning of the boudings
indicates a plastic stretching; the lacerations, a stretching in solid
contemporaneously with aplites. In both cases it is a matter of
extensions.

As C. E. Wegmann says (1931), "mobility increases with the
chemical introductions". J. Goguel (1952) points out that the conditions making the recrystallization of minerals of some rocks possible
at the same time reduces the resistance of these rocks to deformation.

This mobility, prominent in the aureole, is in conformity with the
geometric structure of granite massifs (chapter 7) and with the general
tectonics of the region if the granite is synkinematic (chapter 10). But
on a local scale the framework of these deformations plays a role in the
development and propagation of the granite itself.

B. C. King and A. M. J. de Swardt (1949) have analyzed this aspect of
the phenomenon. They have studied in detail, in the neighbourhood of
Osi, Nigeria, two successive granitizations which have developed, in
the ancient basement of the region, a granite gneiss of syntectonic
character and post-tectonic porphyroid granite with many discordant
contacts. This granitization shows itself at first and preferentially along
small shear zones in the enclosing rocks, on the scale of an outcrop.
It is indicated at this stage by aplitic bands with indistinct borders,
oblique or parallel to the banding of the surrounding gneiss. At a more
advanced stage, this banding of the gneiss is more and more erased,
after substituting for a long time in the form of a phantom structure.

Semiplastic shearing appears as the principal mechanism responsible
for the location of subsequent but closely related granitization.

In the ruptures of shearing of the enclosing gneisses the biotite assembles
or develops under the influence of the basic front of the aureole. After
the granitization such basic bands may subsist in the form of schlieren
in the granite.

The control exercised by deformation structures on the emplacement of the main granite mass has been emphasized, and it is also
to be observed that the frequent occurrence of small partially
healed shears in the granite itself testifies to the continuance of
stress throughout the porphyritic granite phase.

E

P. Hupé (1951) has observed such more or less obliterated shearings in the Néouvielle granite; he has stressed the important role of deformation as a condition for granitization (p. 77).

SURFACES OF DISCONTINUITY OF THE AUREOLE;
SCREENS; THE GRANITIZATION FRONT

We have so far restricted ourselves to continuous phenomena in connection with chemical diffusions in the aureole. But some marked limits involving texture and chemical composition are also present either as "screens" having more or less escaped metamorphism, and enclosed by rocks of the aureole, or at the contact of granular plutonic rock, granite and its variation facies.

Screens.—The chemical and mechanical evolution of the rocks of the aureole is slowed down or arrested in formations which have constituted screens and which have subsisted in a less evolved form in the middle of much more metamorphosed rocks. Their alteration is restricted to a partial recrystallization localized on a microscopic scale often for example with the development of a little biotite or quartz.

They are very fine-grained rocks, compact and rigid, which have resisted the deformations which played such an important role in the development and accentuation of metamorphism. Or again, they are rocks resistant to metasomatism because of their chemical composition: monomineralic rocks such as quartzites or pure limestone. Finally, they may be rocks in which the earlier paragenesis remained in equilibrium with the new physico-chemical conditions of metamorphism. Some dolerites, which are otherwise little deformable, seem to correspond to this case.

These screens can survive until the conclusion of granitization, throughout the passage of diverse chemical fronts. This explains the platy form of stratiform granite bodies for which they form the boundaries. The vast septa enclosed in the migmatites or in the granites themselves, as well as the "antecedent" veins[1] included in the granite (p. 155) are related to the same phenomena.

In his classic study of migmatites, C. E. Wegmann (1935) points out that "various rocks of the ancient basements are transformed at different

---

[1] Old veins existing in the environment before the granitization and having resisted it, the environment itself having become granite. One can speak of antecedent veins for all other transformations of the environment, for instance, hydrothermal metasomatism in metalliferous deposits.

rates. The pure amphibolites resist the longest." B. C. King and A. M. J. de Swardt (1949) write:

Regardless of whether they are products of an initial basification or whether they represent a portion of the original rock complex, the gneisses and schists richest in biotite and hornblende are relatively resistant to granitization.

G. Guitard (1953) shows that the migmatite front at Canigou, eastern Pyrenees, has been arrested by basic bodies and layers of cipolin. B. C. King (1952) describes the transformation of a thin layer of Torridonian sandstone in a Tertiary granite on the Isle of Skye; the floor is of untransformed Cambrian limestone, the roof of Tertiary basalt transformed into gabbros.

Granitization front. Following a generally well-marked surface, one passes from the aureole into the granite, the rocks becoming suddenly granular. This occurrence has no direct relationship to chemical composition: the "normal" granite (the granite of the central parts of the massif) is not always found at the contact, but usually a mixed facies, of heterogeneous type and particularly often a basic type resembling gabbros.

H. H. Read (1948) following D. Reynolds, admits that such basic concentrations of "igneous" aspect are ferromagnesian culminations. These culminations could explain "certain basic or ultrabasic bodies found at the borders of granitic massifs, or the multitude of small masses in the interior of migmatite complexes".

To be sure, the presence of basic, melanocratic types towards the peripheries of some plutonic massifs has often been interpreted as due to a magmatic differentiation: starting from a gabbro the differentiation would produce successively more acidic facies which would be emplaced towards the centre of the massifs, reshaping and partly dislocating the basic border zones, possibly with the formation of igneous breccias enclosing large fragments of melanocratic material (it will be seen in chapter 8 that my opinion of differentiation is not necessarily "magmatic"). One could evoke this mechanism, for instance, with regard to the Adamello granite in the Alps (A. Bianchi and G. B. Dal Piaz, 1937).

It is probable that both can occur. The choice of an interpretation will above all depend on the geological context, for instance the presence of basic vein-satellites from a possible initially gabbroic body.

Thus the basic front of D. Reynolds implies two distinct geological entities. On the one hand, and outside the limits of the granite massifs, an enrichment of cordierite, biotite, amphibole, producing metamorphic schists or hornfelses, which are connected to the basic front and grade progressively outwards into unaltered material. On the other hand, on the inner side, within the granitization front, one may find more basic and more melanocratic granite than the definitive or more alkaline granite, a facies analogous to gabbros or syenites (deficient in silica). These rocks already represent a portion of the granite massif, even though they belong chemically to the basic front. They can be regarded as "souvenirs" of the external basic front, which has not yet disappeared at the conclusion of the process. We shall classify these rocks in the "variation facies" of the granite (chapter 8).

The granitization front evidently represents a change in the conditions of mineralogical equilibrium. Some minerals of the aureole disappear. The changes probably correspond to a change in the physical conditions of the environment during the granitization, but we are unaware of its nature, and we are under no particular obligation to admit it as a gradation to a magmatic stage.

THE RELATIONSHIP BETWEEN CONTACT METAMORPHISM AND ASSIMILATION

There is a connection between a granite massif and its enclosing rocks. In the aureole indeed the rocks undergo a long evolution in order to approach progressively the state of a granite. This fact is conspicuous in the septa of migmatites and in inclusions. Their transformation often attains a degree such that there is scarcely any difference between them and the granite itself, and they seem to disappear within it. It is possible to establish a continuous series in some deposits from the enallogenic inclusions of micaceous schists and the endopolygenic inclusions of contaminated granite, a little darker than the normal granite. From schist to granite there is thus a gradation visible in a series of hand specimens. The same holds true for septa in migmatites: at first they are similar to leptynolites, finally they become identical with the injection gneiss which surrounds them, and all finally ends in anatectic granite. In short there is continuity between the effects of contact metamorphism and those of assimilation. Metamorphism which has reached this point and granitic endomorphism become equivalent.

This fact can be observed not only in inclusions but also at the border of the aureoles near the granite. Along some contacts, the transition from granite to the enclosing rock is gradational. There is no doubt that this is an important phenomenon to consider in the theories of the emplacement and formation of granite. It was put forward by A. Lacroix (1899): "The elements transported through the schists combined with the schists themselves can produce rocks of a mineralogical composition very close to granite itself". Assimilation in the proper sense of the word, that is, the passage of the granitization front, is certainly facilitated by it.

However, even where the transition to granite in circumscribed massifs is gradational (which is not always the case), it is very rapid. The contact between granite and the enclosing rock can be traced to within a few decimeters or a few meters at most. For the anatectic granites, the discontinuity is found in front of the migmatites and not between the anatectic granite and its envelope of migmatites.

Having passed the front of granitization, the rocks evolve according to the laws of assimilation. The physical discontinuity related to this front does not prevent the evolution from proceeding along the same lines as the metamorphism of the aureole: growing crystallization with increasing size of the grains, a tendency towards isotropism and homogenization, resorption of nongranitic crystals and structures (following the norms of normal granite, that is to say, granite of the interior part of the massif). Both stages, separated by passage of the granitization front, are analogous to what could be referred to for a particular inclusion: the enallogenic stage and the endopolygenic stage. But between the two types of inclusions the discontinuity is not striking, because in general each one belongs completely to either one of the two stages, while the border of the granite is marked geometrically. Now regarding the neighbouring inclusions of different degrees of evolution, one has the feeling of a succession of the same phenomenon, the feeling that contact metamorphism and assimilation correspond to two different stages of a unique evolution. This makes the interpretation of the passage from one moment to another proportionally more enigmatic.

Chapter 7

THE GEOMETRIC STRUCTURE OF GRANITE MASSIFS

Some characteristics of the texture and of the structure as a whole of granite, attributable to the mobility of the still-plastic environment and to the deformation of the rock after its consolidation, represent mechanical phenomena having affected granitic massifs at the time of their emplacement. They consist of "oriented elements" revealed within the very heart of the granite, and related to what can be called the plastic phases and the rigid phases of the emplacement. These phenomena were discovered and especially studied by H. Cloos, who has grouped them collectively under the name "granite tectonics" (*Granittektonik*).

B. Sander's study of petrofabrics[1] (*Gefügekunde*) extends this type of investigation to the microscopic scale, through the statistical study of the preferred crystallographic orientations of crystals in the rock. These orientations are also related to the field of forces at the time of crystallization, without prejudice to other factors such as the physical state, anisotropy, grain size, and the texture of the pre-existing material. Petrofabric analysis is, moreover, not restricted to the microscopic field, but is also concerned with tectonic structures on the scale of outcrops. When petrofabric analysis is applied macroscopically to granite, it overlaps "granite tectonics". However, the two disciplines are generally used in different ways: petrofabric analysis utilizes frequency diagrams which show statistically the average directions of lines and planes; granite tectonics presents its results on maps on which such directions are marked at the points where they were observed. It goes without saying that if the number of observations is increased, accidental fluctuations will be corrected and the geometric structure will be revealed satisfactorily. On the other hand, the construction of

[1] *Structurologie* in the French text.

petrofabric diagrams on the spherical Schmidt net[1] has the advantage of making apparent the symmetries that the system of orientated elements can show, as well as the importance of these different elements compared with each other from the point of view of their statistical dispersion.

We will first examine the various categories of observations which can be made. It must be noted at the outset that the term "fluidal" is descriptive in the passages below and does not necessarily signify that the physical state of the material was that of a fluid, either amorphous or mixed with a suspension of crystals.

ORIENTED ELEMENTS OF THE PLASTIC STAGE

They are parallel to a planar or a linear direction, in every part of the massif, and are classified in the following way (S. von Bubnoff, 1922; R. Balk, 1937).

Schistosity of the granite. Most granites have a gneissic structure, similar to a schistosity, scarcely visible although present, or in other cases more or less strongly accentuated. The platy minerals, and above all the micas, have a tendency to be oriented parallel to a plane whose direction may vary from one place to another within the massif. This arrangement is sometimes less accentuated, and is noticeable only upon close examination. At times, according to R. Balk, it is marked only by the parallel orientation of a certain proportion of the grain boundaries of quartz and feldspar.

Planar fluidal structure. Consists of an alternation of layers of granite with slightly different aspect, for instance, porphyritic granite and ordinary granite. The phenocrysts of the porphyritic granite may show a preferred orientation parallel to each other. There is a continuous gradation between fluidal structure and schistosity whose orientations coincide.

Differentiation banding. Results from the alignment of small elliptic zones or lenticular bands of some decimeters or meters in length, which are distinguished from the general background of granite because of their more aplitic or more basic composition.

Swarms of platy inclusions. Their disposition is similar, but involves trains of enallogenic inclusions. The swarms and trains of inclusions are arranged along the plane of fluidity.

Direction of linear stretching of granite or linear fluidity. This is a direction of parallelism of the elongated minerals: hornblende if there is any present or feldspar in which the greatest dimension clearly surpasses the

[1] Bibliography: Sander, B., 1930, 1950; Schmidt, W., 1932.

others. The direction of stretching is often in the plane of fluidity. Certain authors, following Cloos, interpret this as a linear flow of the material or a tendency towards such a flow.

* * *

One must admit that the characteristics of the plastic phase are the result of pressures reigning before consolidation and are the consequence of plasticity of the environment in the course of granitization. They do not seem to be the result of a schistosity produced in the solid state, as in the slates; because some of them, such as the alignments of inclusions, and differentiation banding, would imply a degree of schistosity extremely high which is not expressed by the partial and often tentative orientation of the mineral constituents. On the other hand, one could assume that they simply reflect the stratification of sedimentary beds, occupying locations where granite has been formed, that they have a palingenetic character, to use the language of Sederholm. Support for this idea is provided by the alignment in the granite of the elongated inclusions of sediments from the wall rock, an alignment which does not seem to be at all displaced, or only slightly. However, such cases may depend on a conformity, which occurs frequently but not necessarily, between the actual fluidity of the forming granite and the stratification of the surrounding rocks. The fluidal structure is often, however, clearly different from the stratification and the schistosity developed in the solid state of the surrounding rocks, if they have any: it outlines, for instance, large low cupolas, even though the enclosing beds are tightly folded vertically with a vertical schistosity. It is at times oriented parallel to the border of the massif, and at the same time obliquely cuts the stratification of country rock. This is the basis for the idea that the oriented elements depend on pressures affecting a mobilized environment during the process of granitization.

ORIENTED ELEMENTS IN THE RIGID PHASE

Partings[1]. The partings of granite (rift, grain, etc.) are the directions along which the rock may split into planar surfaces when struck by a sharp blow, and which can be demonstrated by means of a wedge. The distinction between the schistosity of granites related to the plastic phase and the parting of the rigid state is a delicate one. It is based on the observation that the parting is generally oriented in conformity with the joints of the rigid phase. The relationship between parting

[1] Clivages in the French text.

and schistosity is at times close, however. The parting may in some cases be due to microscopic cracks in the crystals or to the alignment of bubbles in quartz (R. Balk, 1937).

The direction of the preferred parting shown by some granites, but not by all, is often called the *rift*. In granites with an accentuated fluidity the rift is identical to this fluidity. In other cases it exists, but without obvious cause: undoubtedly an effect of tension of the same kind as that which has produced the joints, but more diffusely. Another less easy parting at approximately right angles to the first is often encountered. It is called the *grain*, a term not related to that used for the dimensions of the crystals. These partings are sometimes constant, sometimes variable from one point to another in an extensive granite massif. They may follow one or another system of joints, but at times they proceed diagonally to the joints. Often one parting is almost vertical and the other more or less horizontal, intersecting along the direction of elongation of the granite.

Joints. The joints, or fissures, of a granite are approximately either vertical or horizontal. The vertical or very steep joints regularly extend to a great depth in the massif. Their direction is almost constant for great distances in a given massif. There are generally two almost vertical joint sets at about right angles to each other. The horizontal or slightly inclined joints, moreover, give the surface of the massif a bench-like aspect. Near the topographic surface they may be combined with other joints, roughly parallel to them, which are produced by variations in temperature. With the exception of cases where conditions are more irregular, the spacing of the joints, fairly constant in a mass, may vary between 1–2 decimeters or 1–2 decameters, depending on the massif.

The direction of the joints thus forms a trihedral, more or less tri-rectangular. According to H. Cloos, two of the directions of this trihedral intersect along the direction of stretching. They are commonly closed fissures. The third direction is perpendicular to the stretching and often consists of open fissures, which may contain vein fillings: aplites, pegmatites, quartz, lamprophyres or porphyries. Apart from the directions of this trihedral there are diagonal fissures following two directions, bisected by the normal joint of the stretching and making an angle of less than 45° with this joint. Finally striated mylonitic surfaces are found where the horizontal projection of the striae is systematically parallel to the stretching.

It must be stressed that the oriented elements of the rigid phase extend into the enclosing rock, which is fissured on a similar plane but with a different modality, for instance, with different spacing.

E*

GRANITE TECTONICS

As previously mentioned, H. Cloos has grouped the preceding phenomena under the name "granite tectonics". Actually they are by no means random phenomena resulting from accidental causes, but are related to the regime of mechanical forces of the time of the emplacement of the granite. Together they define a structure reflecting something of this regime and appearing on a map of the oriented elements.

The general jointing of the granite takes place immediately after the crystallization of the granite. Some fissures are actually filled with differentiation products of the granite such as pegmatites, lamprophyres, etc. On the other hand there is very often accord between the oriented arrangements of the rigid phase and those of the plastic state: coincidence of the direction of the linear stretching in the granite with the line of intersection of two families of joints; a frequent coincidence between fluidal structure and one direction of joints. The forces acting in the still-plastic granite may thus be extended beyond crystallization. The different elements produced during this evolution thus complement each other.

To be sure, these apply to granite massifs which have not been later caught up in orogenic zones of intense deformation. The Hercynian granites of the Alps, for instance, have been too deformed during the Tertiary for the reconstruction of their granite tectonics. But such a reconstruction is on the other hand possible in most of the granitic massifs which have remained rigid after their formation. It has been claimed that there ought to exist fissures formed by the shrinkage of the granite upon cooling, fissures which should be controlled by local irregularities, particularly at the border. It can be shown that if this effect exists it is subordinate. According to H. Cloos, the fissures due to the shrinkage of the granite must be oriented tectonically and do not form a special category.

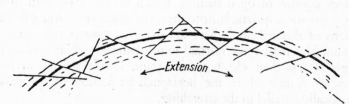

Fig. 16. Vault-shaped massif cut by conjugate fissures of stretching (after H. Cloos). The differentiation banding has been emphasized along a pseudo-stratification in order to show the schistosity of the granite.

Granite tectonics vary according to the general forms and dimensions of massifs, probably also according to the conditions at their emplacement within an immobile setting or in the course of folding. The general direction of stretching follows, when it exists, with a remarkable fidelity throughout a whole massif. Various structures are outlined: domes and vaults of lines of stretching. The planes of flow often outline vast cupolas or flattened vaults, from the centre to the border of large granite massifs. On these vaults a system of joints parallel to the axis of the vault is arranged in a fan; at times subvertical joints at the centre become progressively inclined towards the border. H. Cloos interprets this fan as an effect of extension along the tangents to the profile of the vault. The fan may also be turned downwards; the interpretation is the same, because the system is conjugated with the foregoing, with which it may moreover co-exist (fig. 16). In other massifs the elements may outline depressed structures, bowl-shaped, synclinal-shaped or barrel-shaped, etc.

For instance, the Flamanville granite of Manche (N. R. Martin, 1952) possesses a certain fluidity revealed by crystals and xenoliths, arranged as a cone opening upwards with radial joints.

It happens that these structural assemblages reveal in large composite massifs several elementary massifs, whose individuality is not revealed in the simple petrographic aspect of the rock. This is the case in the double cupola of the Sierra Nevada batholith near Yosemite, California (E. Cloos, 1933). Finally, H. Cloos establishes the absence of structure, that is to say an ordering of elements, for some massifs which could be laccolithic granites and which seem to have been immobilized before crystallization (H. Cloos, 1933).

In the case of certain subvolcanic granite massifs, few if any traces of "granite tectonics" can be observed in their interior. This fact is a paradox, considering the important movements visible along the borders of such massifs. H. Cloos and K. Chudoba (1931) have noted this fact at Brandberg and Erongo in South-West Africa. In the Caledonian granite of Rosses, Donegal, Ireland, which is a granite of the annular system of the same type as the granites of the "Cauldron Subsidences" of Scotland (p. 42), W. S. Pitcher (1953) finds that the elements of the plastic phase are very vaguely developed and that for the rigid phase the joint system is the same as in the enclosing rocks, without relationship to the structure of the ring complex. It seems as if the subvolcanic massifs had reacted as one unit in their setting. This fact does not seem to be attributable to the shallow depth of formation of such granites; some diapiric granites, with conspicuous *Granittektonik*, have probably been emplaced at shallow depth. I think that it may more likely be attributable to an evolution of the "volcanic" style, that is to say, rapid, and not to the rhythm of the "tectonic" style, that is to say, slow, for most of the granite massifs.

MECHANICAL EFFECTS AT THE BORDERS

Mechanical effects are above all visible at the border of the intrusive facies, particularly in the diapiric granites and the subvolcanic granites (p. 35 and 39). H. Cloos (1929) has compared them to the fissures observed at the border of glaciers. There, bordering crevasses oblique to the border delimit blocks which rotate slightly relative to each other, because the flow of the ice is less rapid at the border than at the centre of the glacier. The crevasses consequently turn little by little going in the downstream direction, the pivot of each one being close to the border. This gives rise to a series of step-like dislocations between the blocks, passing from an upstream block to a downstream one. These dislocations are rendered visible in outcrops of stratified ice (fig. 18). When the crevasses have turned through a large enough angle, they close and heal up, while others are formed with the original orientation.

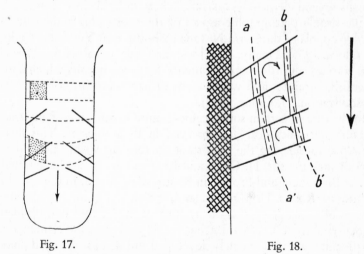

Fig. 17.   Fig. 18.

Fig. 17. Sketch showing formation of bordering crevasses in a glacier. An imaginary square, traced on the surface of the glacier, is drawn out into a rhombus by the more rapid flow in the centre. The crevasses form normal to the stretching.

Fig. 18. Rotation of the bordering crevasses of a glacier. aa', bb': exposures of beds of stratified ice, broken up by the movement.

A similar arrangement has been observed at the border of certain granites, notably that of Strehlen in Silesia (fig. 19a). The flowage operated upwards in the opposite sense of a glacier. The fissures are inclined from the walls towards the base of the granite mass. They are at times striated or mylonitic, or may contain laminated aplite. Now and then, however, the dislocations are in an opposite sense (fig. 19b), which could arise, according to H. Cloos, from the fact that the pressure of the intrusions against the walls was more pronounced and that the rotational movement of the blocks was less developed than the movement upwards.

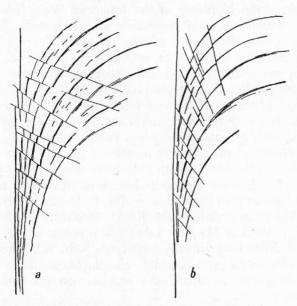

Fig. 19. Scheme of the border of a plutonic rock massif with dome structure (after H. Cloos). a: downward faulting in the dome near the border. b: upward faulting.

The marginal fissures are normally related to one of the defined joint systems in the granite mass, a system which becomes particularly important at the border. Besides, mylonitic joints with considerable displacements are more common in the border zones because of an exaggeration of the mechanical effects.

This holds true not only for the elements of the rigid phase but also for the plastic. One actually finds at times, in a thin border zone, a vein network of granite, pegmatite, aplite or quartz which has been completely deformed by a system of packed ptygmatic folds. Such is the case at the border of the Lys granite, Haute-Garonne (E. Raguin, 1934). Moreover, in a general way, at the border of the circumscribed massifs in the Pyrenees, the Palaeozoic lime schists are crumpled into singular zig-zags, due to the local deformation at the contacts. Their bizarre appearance was sufficiently striking that the early geologists gave the rock a special name: "barègieennes" (from Barèges, Hautes-Pyrénées).

In some cases a veritable driving back of pre-existing sedimentary layers at the borders of the circumscribed granite massifs can be observed on a large scale. The intrusion of granitic and monzonitic domes, in the desert highlands of the American West, has created favourable conditions for the formation of rich metallic deposits. Around one of these domes, that of Hanover, near Silver City, New Mexico, the southern periphery of the massif is enclosed for several kilometers by an anticlinal fold in beds of Palaeozoic formations, a fold flanked on the granite side by a squeezed syncline. Farther north, the western border of the massif shows a vertical driving back of the enclosing beds. The ascending mechanical action of granite capable of producing the folding is manifest (Sydney Paige, 1933).

The Flamanville granite, already mentioned (p. 117), is a diapiric massif, approximately circular with a diameter of 5–6 km. Along its western border, Palaeozoic formations have been affected by repeated peripheral folds measured in hectometers (N. R. Martin, 1952).

The Elk Mountain granite in the Rocky Mountains of Colorado, described by E. Suess in *The Face of the Earth*, may also be mentioned. It bulges and drives back laterally Cretaceous beds. Why should we consider "folding as the primary and dominating phenomenon and the pressure of the granite as an accessory phenomenon, controlled only by this folding?"

The greatest phenomenon of this kind is found in South Africa in the Vredefort mountains, straddling the frontier between the Orange Free State and the Transvaal. The granite presents an outcrop of surprisingly regular circular shape, 40 km in diameter, visible along three-quarters of the circumference, the rest being covered by younger strata. Along the whole visible part of the periphery the layers of the old formations enclosing the granite are driven back and overturned towards the exterior of the circle by a centrifugal pressure (fig. 20). As the granite does not seem to penetrate the enclosing formations from which it is separated by this circular dislocation, and because the metamorphic aureole in these formations is not regularly constant around the

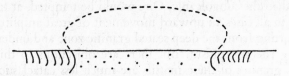

Fig. 20. Schematic section through the Vredefort massif.

granite, Hall and Molengraaf (1925) thought that the granite may have been emplaced passively, after its consolidation, without any relationship to its intrusion, by a vertical pressure, or else that it remained stable while the whole of the surrounding terrain moved downwards, these singular movements being caused by the action of another granitic magma hidden under this granite. It seems to me that the phenomenon would be better explained by considering the visible granite itself entirely responsible for the whole phenomenon, and by admitting that the anomalies of the contacts arise rightly by peripheric dislocations which have obliterated the actual contact zone.

The movements of the whole of granitic massifs are particularly remarkable in the subvolcanic massifs. The "cauldron subsidences" show the descent of the granite during or at the end of its emplacement (p. 42). We have, however, also seen that there existed movements in the opposite sense. This is the case at Brandberg, South-West Africa, studied by H. Cloos (1933). Circular, and some twenty kilometers in diameter, it outcrops in an environment of ancient formations of undetermined age, which are covered here and there by slivers of the Karoo formations spared from erosion. It is fringed along the greater part of its periphery by a rim of Karoo formations which dips toward the granite. The massif has thus been the subject of a descending movement relative to its setting; but this descent has been preceded or followed by an ascent which has lifted up the shreds of Karoo which cap the massif.

On the other hand, H. Cloos envisions the possibility of movements of the whole granite ensemble, upwards or downwards, during tectonic movements much later than the consolidation of the granite and belonging to another orogenic cycle. The granite massif would behave passively as a "dead body". The case should be strictly distinguished from the phenomena related to the emplacement of granites.

It has been shown that it is sometimes possible to calculate the amplitude of the vertical displacement of a subvolcanic massif relative to its frame, by means of the moved fragments of sediments which may show faulting of some hundreds of meters. But this is not the case for the diapiric massifs, which in more or less typical form are much more common than the subvolcanic. One would be tempted, at first glance, to suggest in all cases an upward movement of great amplitude for the granite, starting from the deep seated granitic zone and under the effect of a strong rheomorphism. But there are objections to this point of view. The granites of these massifs are much less cataclastic or proto-clastic than the synkinematic stratiform granites. In them exotic blocks transported from depth are not observed, as is often the case in salt diapirs and in kimberlite pipes. One could maintain that crystallization of the granite takes place during the ascent, that its material must form simultaneously and proportionately by using that of pre-existing rocks, and that the possible blocks from far away have had time to be assi-milated.

In opposition to the hypothesis of a great amplitude of displacement, one could ask if the assembly of the Cloosian scheme in such massifs, including their borders, does not actually represent a *mimicry (mimétisme) of rheomorphism* rather than a genuine rheomorphism: a mimicry depending on the existence of a stress field at the end of the evolution, with a marginal brushing upwards of the strata, and corresponding to only a slight movement relative to the final crystallization. Because of the importance of both hypotheses, we will not favour one to the exclusion of the other. Each particular case should be studied from both angles.

Of a much more modest order of magnitude in every respect, although related to the final rigid terminal phase, the movements con-nected with the final emplacement of the batholith are reflected extern-ally by repeated dislocations of hydrothermal, peribatholithic veins, during their filling with metallic materials over a long period (E. Raguin, 1949 b). H. Cloos in the past has pointed out the direct relationship between the border dislocations of the Sierra Nevada batholith of California with the gold veins to the west (H. Cloos, 1947).

PETROFABRIC ANALYSIS (STRUCTUROLOGIE)

A great number of directions of the lines and planes of the constituent crystals of the rock (crystallographic axes, crystalline faces) are meas-ured in thin sections with the aid of the Fedorov stage. The thin sections are previously oriented relative to the terrain.

The macroscopic elements, such as those of the tectonics of Cloos, observed in outcrops, are oriented in space with the aid of a compass.

For each category of object observed, microscopically or macro-scopically, usually 100 to 500 observations are plotted on the Schmidt spherical diagram. Each observation is represented by a point on the sphere, which defines its direction in space. On the diagram it is possible to show the frequency of these points in different domains of the sphere, that is to say in various directions of space: lines of equal frequency are drawn to delimit these domains. The method makes evident intuitively the relative importance of various statistical distributions of the elements studied, as well as the symmetries which exist between these distributions. Through comparison of several diagrams derived for different elements, the symmetry between one element and another can be perceived. These techniques, much elaborated, are described in the works referred to at the beginning of this chapter.

In the application of petrofabrics to granite massifs, I will mention two types: (1) For the batholiths, to aid in defining the elements of the plastic phase, by uniting the criteria of Cloos with the microstructural criteria based on the crystallographic orientation of certain minerals. To bring out better a linear direction of the massif. However, if quartz is used, its ease of recrystallization must be taken into account along with the fact that it shows only the very latest phase of the evolution. (2) For the migmatites, to analyze the phases of migmatization and to correlate them with the tectonics of the geological setting, that is to say, the external formations. Taking into account the complexity of the migmatites, the use of statistical data has no doubt an acute interest. The study will bear above all on macroscopic criteria. These are notably: the ghost structures reflecting the previous tectonics, the pegmatites or aplites or diverse petrographic types; the surfaces of stretching granitized in diverse degrees; axial lines (hinges) of folds in different material, etc. Such a study may elucidate the chronology of events of the migmatization.

CONCLUSION

The study of the geometric structure of granites based on the principles mentioned above makes it possible to define the individuality of massifs. These are actually complex, formed by coalescence of several adjoining massifs. A granite tectonic study of large distinct cupolas, which one must take care not to confuse with topographic cupolas formed by surface erosion, will be revealed in these cases. One will see, for instance, if the alignments of the large inclusions at the surface of a batholith correspond to deep septa isolating different granite upwellings (*venues*), or if they only represent superficial remnants of sedimentary layers which have better resisted assimilation.

Another reason for interest in such geometrical reconstructions lies in the possibility of correlating the tectonics of granites or of migmatites with the general tectonics of the neighbouring terrain, and the possible recognition of the principal phases of evolution.

The analysis of the distribution of the movements and of the stresses during the course of granitization is more hazardous because the phenomenon has lasted a long time in many phases. Moreover the field of forces is probably never unequivocally determined by an array of oriented elements in the rock. The reconstruction of the successive movements and deformations is more conceivable for the migmatites and the domains of anatexis, which have many macrostructures, than for the batholiths, which have few.

In the batholiths, many of the oriented elements seem to bear on the ultimate stage of the crystallization, responsible for the structure and texture of the resulting rock. It would be very interesting to go back to the stages before the granitization. Certain of the oriented elements of the plastic phase are better in this regard, because they represent ghosts of the original state before the granitization: some schlieren, certain systems of inclusions. For the reconstruction of the movements, the effects conspicuous at the borders of the massifs are better than the patterns of linear fluidity of the interiors. It is actually possible to correlate them with the deformation of the settings where interpretation is not in doubt. But the amplitude of displacements is scarcely revealed by these methods.

It is futile to compare the *Granittektonik* and petrofabrics from the point of view of their respective merits in the elucidation of granite massifs. There is a place for the combination of these methods depending on the problem at hand: the microscopic and macroscopic criteria, the statistical diagrams and structural maps can complement each other. The aim to pursue in these investigations is the "structural analysis" of C. E. Wegmann on different scales and of different times.

Chapter 8

DIFFERENTIATION OF GRANITES

Differentiation, according to J. P. Iddings, is the separation of an eruptive magma into several portions of different chemical composition. One might imagine a differentiation of structure and texture without any chemical variation, giving for instance the zones, masses or veins of different grain size. This would not be in keeping with the above definition. In fact, chemical variations generally accompany structural variations.

What is the general basis for the concept of differentiation? Writes N. L. Bowen (1933):

> Observation commonly shows that, although a wide range of chemical and mineralogical constitution may be exhibited by the rocks of a given area that have been intruded during a single period of igneous activity, nevertheless they exhibit certain mineralogical or chemical peculiarities common to the group. This fact is believed to indicate a common origin from a single parent magma and the processes whereby different rocks have arisen from the parental magma are referred to as magmatic differentiation. (p. 107).

This point of view is manifestly applicable to the successive emissions of volcanoes, which suggest an evolution in deep-seated reservoirs. In what measure can it be extended to the plutonic rocks and in particular to the granites? If it is admitted that granite forms in a "mobilized milieu", physically mixed and including a liquid part, there can *a priori* be no objection to the extension of the concept of differentiation to this liquid portion. There seems moreover to have been in some cases a connection between "magmatic constituents" postulated for the mobilized environment and ordinary volcanic magmas. We will return to this in chapter 13. If on the contrary one believes that the liquid or gaseous constituent is restricted to small proportions of pneumato-lytes, and that the formation of the plutonic rocks is essentially a non-magmatic process, differentiation is more difficult to con-ceive.

One fact must be emphasized: the possibility of constructing *differentiation diagrams*. These are curves showing the proportions of amounts of the main oxides as a function of the amount of silica, as based upon chemical analyses of the different rocks emitted in a complete eruptive assemblage, at different times and in different facies. Such diagrams often encompass several types of granular rocks, associated lamprophyric veins, neighbouring porphyritic dykes, and possibly related lava flows. That they have real significance and that they do not represent arbitrary groupings is shown by the fact that petrographically similar assem-blages from regions far apart sometimes give very similar diagrams. These diagrams also can serve as a means of placing a new rock in a given rock association, whose geological occurrence on the other hand makes the union probable.

For instance, L. U. and C. M. de Sitter (1949) show the Permo-Carboniferous age of the Val Biandino granodiorite and the "gneiss chiaro" of the Alpes Bergamasques, because of the similarity of their diagrams to the diagrams of the Aar granite and the Permian porphyries. They also assign a Tertiary age to the porphyritic dykes of this region because their chemical composition conforms with the diagram of the Adamello granite, a fact made credible because these dykes are geo-graphically situated as a bridge between the granitic massifs of Adamello and Bregaglia, both of which are of Tertiary age.

The possibility of constructing such diagrams, provided that there is a real significance which can be confirmed by the local geological relationships, is an important fact, independent of any theory. This fact evokes a *simili-magmatic* evolution for the group of phenomena con-nected with the emplacement of a granite massif, with its local varia-tions, its dyke satellites contemporaneous or later, and possibly por-phyritic dykes or volcanic rocks farther from the massif. Nevertheless all in this evolution is not necessarily magmatic. The chemical compo-sition of the metamorphic rocks of the aureole, or of inclusions, may converge in a remarkable way with that of the neighbouring granite. A. Lacroix (1900) has remarked upon this in days gone by for the Quérigut massif. He gives for instance the analysis of an inclusion which lies chemically between the normal granite and an endomorphic dioritic facies. M. Roques (1941) shows in his study of the crystalline schists of the French Massif Central that the chemical composition of migmatites can be placed very well on the curves of the plutonic rocks of the same region.

So the differentiation of the granular rocks and associated rocks does not seem to be a criterion of certain magmatism.

Causes of differentiation

Formerly it was envisioned that the differentiation of magmas took place by a fractionation of the initial magma while still in the liquid state. It is generally admitted today that fractionation takes place above all during the crystallization. This is a phenomenon of long duration, giving rise successively to the formation of different crystals, which are solid solutions and which are generally not in equilibrium with the remaining magma after their formation, due to the continual evolution of chemical composition. The crystals thus formed may be modified. Various rocks may be formed either by an incomplete mixing of one portion of the magma in another, or by successive partial phases of emission of the magma during the course of a phenomenon of a greater magnitude.

The separation could in certain cases be accomplished simply by gravity, the first formed, heavier, ferromagnesian crystals (barylites) accumulating to form a basic rock, and the lighter residues crystallizing as more siliceous or more alkaline varieties. Generally an effect of "filter-pressing" is also invoked: the orogenic forces would squeeze out the still fluid portion of the magma from the spongy and vesicular mass formed by the first crystallizations.

These simplified explanations are more adapted to volcanism. For the differentiation of plutonic rocks, and particularly granite, the "filter-pressing" effect probably plays a role, although one cannot prove whether it plays a major one, nor even if it plays any role at all. The chemical migrations of the fronts of metamorphism (chapter 6) hint at other possibilities of explanation. For differentiations on small scales ("variation facies" below), a part of the phenomena can be confused with the effects of assimilation (chapter 5).

Observed facts

Differentiation is displayed on several scales: in the facies of variation, in composite massifs, in lithological series.

The *facies of variation* are the small scale, local differentiations dispersed in a mass of eruptive rock. Writes A. Lacroix (1933):

Sometimes there appears in a lithological type mineralogical associations in the form of spots with either diffuse or sharp contacts, corresponding to rock types which may belong to a different family than that of the enclosing rock. They are generally differentiations richer in coloured minerals, produced *in situ*. For instance: the dioritic or gabbroic spots in calcalkaline granites, mesocratic spots in the riebekite granites of Corsica and in the aegirine granites of Rockall.

When the facies of variation are sharply circumscribed, they form inclusions of a peculiar nature. These are the *homoeogenic* inclusions (*enclaves*), residues of an earlier state of the environment before the conclusion of the major differentiation which produced the mass of enclosing rocks, or else agglomerations of crystals formed earlier during the normal fractional crystallization: anomalous local crystallizations formed early and not reabsorbed because of fortuitous circumstances. On the contrary, some homoeogenic inclusions resemble the lamprophyres of the same granite, in other words are of types considered to be formed late. The *pneumatogenic* inclusions (*enclaves*) or miarolitic spots are of small late crystallizations from concentrations of residual pneumatolytes.

The facies of variation represent imperfections in the crystallization of granite massifs.

The *composite massifs* show the association of several plutonic types, granitic or otherwise, systematically arranged, for instance, concentrically or vertically, within the body of the massif.

The *lithological series* are, according to Lacroix's terminology (1933), assemblages of rocks due to a large-scale differentiation, and successively emplaced in a manner which gives rise to distinct geological entities: batholiths, stocks, dykes, effusions. The differentiation of lithological series proceeds in a definite direction, as is evident for those which have been the object of exact studies revealing a chronological succession in the eruptions of this series. Starting with more basic material (lime, magnesia and iron oxides), the series proceeds towards a higher content of silica or towards an enrichment in alkalis. It thus reflects the normal order of N. L. Bowen for the crystallization of silicate melts. This rule applies to plutonic rocks. In volcanism, various circumstances no doubt interfere, modifying this direction of differentiation. In particular, the volatile constituents seem to have a particularly strong effect.

In the following we will restrict ourselves to differentiation in the granites.

THE FACIES OF VARIATION OF GRANITES

These local anomalies of granite, whose dimensions vary from some millimeters to several tens of meters, are of various character. In one case, they are more siliceous or more alkaline, that is to say, richer in quartz or feldspar, and may grade into true pegmatites. Their shape is that of streaks (schlieren) or of more or less diffuse veins. A local concentration of pneumatolytes, in the "generating mobilized environment of the granite" seems to give rise to these effects. If it is very accentuated, it may result in pneumatogenic crystallizations in miarolitic pockets. One example has been described by G. Lucas (1942) in the Beni-Snouss granite at the Algerian-Moroccan border. Spherolites of radiating tourmaline and quartz, 30 cm in diameter, are enclosed in the alkaline granite, itself slightly tourmalinized. The "suns" of arfvedsonite of the marginal granite of Brandberg, South-West Africa, are likewise undoubtedly pneumatogenic (Cloos and Chudoba, 1931).

In other cases homoeogenic enclaves richer in biotite or hornblende than the surrounding granite are evident, sometimes with the addition of pyroxene and olivine. They occur as irregular rounded kernels,r darker and finer grained than the granite. Formed in part of the same minerals as the granite, they are always richer in minerals from the beginning of the normal order of crystallization. These dark enclaves may be difficult to distinguish from endopolygenic inclusions due to the assimilation of materials of the enclosing rocks. Moreover this distinction should have no justification in a granite formed entirely by metasomatic crystallization without an appreciable amount of an amorphous phase. It is defensible if the mobilized environment has contained an important proportion of liquid during a period of its evolution. Observations in the field may facilitate the distinction: transitions to enallogenic inclusions or, on the other hand, petrographic similarity to lamprophyric dykes.

The relatively basic homoeogenic enclaves of the circumscribed granites of the French Massif Central have recently been interpreted by Didier and Roques (1960) as representing the residues to magmatic intrusions of a microgranular facies, preceding the development of the granite. At Sidobre for instance a quartz-doleritic microdiorite is involved, which then was granitized. The process, which they call "indirect granitization", would be quite common in the circumscribed massifs of various regions. These massifs would thus approach the subvolcanic massifs so far as their evolution is concerned. However, there are no manifestations of volcanism in the strict sense, as in the classic ring complexes.

Even when it is possible to distinguish between assimilation (endomorphism) and differentiation, to interpret the phenomena, one finds cases where these two processes are associated. Some very active differentiations take place, in fact, in mobilized granitic environments strongly contaminated by endomorphism. The diversity of the endomorphic diorites of the Quérigut massif illustrate this fact (A. Lacroix, 1899 and 1900).

There is reason to separate the case of anatexites from differentiation in the true sense. In *migmas*, local disordered differentiations are related to a partial assimilation expressed by the associations of schlieren, septa and enclaves of various facies. The phenomenon is no longer in a definite direction either towards acidic or basic. It is a tangle of phenomena. When the mass has attained homogeneity, it can no doubt behave in its differentiation like any granite.

On the whole, apart from the case of anatexites, the internal differentiation of granite massifs consists of facies of variation and of local and relatively less abundant anomalies. It rarely precludes the homogeneity of granite bodies over the extent, for instance, of a batholith.

STATISTICAL STUDY OF THE VARIATIONS IN A GRANITE MASSIF

With the refinement of petrographic and chemical methods, however, a more precise and quantitative evaluation of the imperfections of this homogeneity may be envisioned. For some time now various geologists have tackled the problem of the study of heterogeneties in granite by statistical methods.

According to Mehnert and Willgallis (1961), the comparison of modal analyses, i.e., the proportions of the different mineral constituents, with chemical analyses gives interesting results. The first variety of analysis avoids involving accidental variations due to local secondary reactions in the rock, or to incipient alterations likely to modify notably the chemical composition of the minerals. It is therefore necessary for equal precision in chemical analyses to have a greater number of samples, or else a precise petrographic study, which takes into account secondary reactions and evaluates their influences.

The results of these statistical studies are expressed as isomodal or isochemical lines on the geological map of the particular granite massif. The accuracy obtained is determined by the usual statistical methods based on a sufficiently large number of samples. This number can be

from 0.5 to 2.5 samples per square kilometer, as in the studies of Mehnert and his co-workers, and in those of E. H. T. Whitten and others.

G. Rein (1961) has studied the Malsburg pluton of the southern
Black Forest both with regard to the size of the grains of zircon, apatite,
biotite, plagioclase, potash feldspar and quartz, and for the quantitative
proportions (modal analysis) of the same minerals and for orthite and
hornblende. In the same time Mehnert and Willgallis studied the
chemical distribution of soda and potash in this granite. Although on
the whole these criteria show a similar internal structure for the massif,
interesting nonconformities also appear which demand explanation.
These studies have in particular revealed a late potassic phase, which is
shown by the chemical as well as the modal distributions: it agrees
with petrographic observations, which indicate a late potassic blastesis
eccentrically located in the Malsburg massif as a whole.

From this we can conclude, as the above authors have emphasized,
that results may not be interpreted simply from the chemical or mineralogical standpoint, but must be supported by all geological and petrographic data. The succession of more or less independent petrogenic
phases may obscure the overall result through the superposition of
heterogeneous statistical populations.

By using a different statistical technique, Whitten (1960) took as a
point of departure modal analyses of one portion of the old Donegal
granite of Ireland. He determined, as is usually done for geophysical
calculations, an average variation surface representing the regularized
values of each number (modal proportion of a determined mineral)
at every point in the area studied. This surface is calculated according to
the method of least squares. It reveals the variations of the mineral
assemblage of the massif. Whitten finally showed, by curves of equal
divergence, the difference of the result relative to this surface of average
compensation. These differences, which are analogous to the "local
anomalies" of geophysical studies, reflect in particular the stratigraphic
ghosts in the interior of the pluton as is shown by the concordance with
the fragmentary data given by the study of the enallogenic inclusions.

THE COMPOSITE MASSIFS

"Very commonly", writes Daly (1914), "diorite, quartz diorite,
granodiorite and syenite grade imperceptibly into granite, in a way
suggesting that the granitic magma is a late product of differentiation of
these magmas". Apart from the idea of a magma, which is disputable,
the observation is entirely justified.

Some dykes or laccoliths show, moreover, a grand differentiation from gabbro to granite in limited masses, on a scale more restricted than in batholiths. The Brefven dyke in Sweden, for instance (fig. 21), is considered by T. Krokström (1932) to be a result of successive intrusions from the same differentiating magma[1]. The example of the Sudbury gabbro, on the other hand (chapter 16), concerns an enormous plutonic body.

Fig. 21. Map of the Brefven dyke, Sweden (after T. Krokström). Black: dolerite. Dotted: microgranite.

In the great composite batholiths (p. 35), a differentiation towards an acidic composition is observed: the successive generations grade for example from diorite to granite. The rocks first formed are represented by a more basic phase at the roof, or at the borders of the batholith, possibly as a "congealed" phase of finer grain. The rocks which follow constitute a more acidic phase; they may dislocate and partially modify the portions first crystallized. This can be observed particularly well at the borders of granites. Nevertheless it is possible that the effect of assimilation is superposed on this process at some points along the border.

As examples of basic rocks at the border of a batholith, rocks dislocated and cemented by granodiorites and more recent granites, the observations of G. B. Dal Piaz (1937) at the southern end of the Adamello are worthy of mention. The Adamello is a post-Alpine, Tertiary batholith. The granite encloses inclusions of all dimensions, composed of gabbro and diorite (Fig. 22). The sequence seems to be gabbro and diorite, quartz diorite (tonalite) and granite.

In the structural assemblages which composite batholiths represent, one might suspect a vestige of older pregranitic structures, partially preserved by an incomplete assimilation. Structural analysis will clear up this doubt. This has been done with regard to the Sierra Nevada

[1] His opinion was, however, not too well substantiated and he also envisioned for this microgranite a fusion of the old granite by basaltic magma and a later differentiation of this endomorphosed magma (conversations with C. E. Wegmann).

batholith in California by E. Cloos (1933). In the region of Yosemite, west of Mount Lyell, the batholith divides, as we have seen in chapter 7, into twin massifs, defined by criteria of *Granittektonik*, in other words into autonomous structures due to the emplacement of the granite itself. The massifs are separated by a septum of metamorphic rocks and extend respectively about fifteen and thirty kilometers in east-west

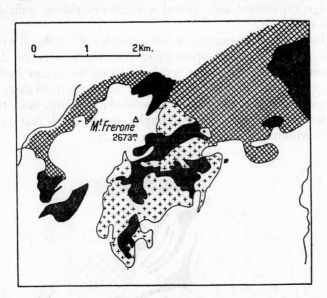

Fig. 22. Map of the southern end of the Adamello (after G. B. Dal Piaz, simplified.) Black: Greenstones (gabbros and diorites). Crosshatched: tonalite. Crosses: granite. Blank: Triassic sediments.

transversal direction. The western massif is composed of successive enclosed masses from the periphery inwards of diorite, then of granodiorite, three at least in number, such that each one dislocates and encloses fragments of the preceding one. The eastern massif is composed of a mantle of granodiorite rich in basic inclusions and a younger kernel of porphyritic granite with a still younger mass of microgranite at its centre.

The granite massifs of Malaya and Indonesia, which are related to the tin deposits, show hornblende-bearing monzonitic varieties which are cut by normal more differentiated and more acidic granite. These basic varieties represent a facies which was first formed at the roof or border of the batholiths (J. Westerveld, 1936).

THE LITHOLOGIC SERIES

The lithologic series, as has been indicated, are plutonic or volcanic rocks which show a chemical and mineralogical kinship and which occur in the same region in the form of distinct geological entities. The differentiation diagrams which are made up on the basis of their chemical compositions may reveal a regular variation indicating a chemical evolution.

It will suffice here to examine a few examples of lithologic series.

As R. Daly indicates, approximate contemporaneity of dioritic and granitic intrusions is often evident. Some important bodies of granite are surrounded by dioritic satellites: an arrangement that may be interpreted as a differentiation more advanced in the large body than in smaller satellites. He gives many examples, but a notable one is that of the Castle Mountain stocks of Montana (fig. 23).

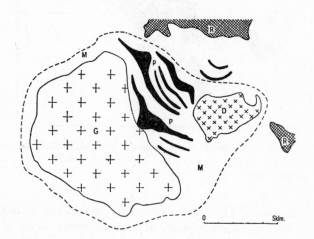

Fig. 23. Map of the Castle Mountain intrusions (after R. A. Daly). G. Neogenic granite. D. Diorite. P. Neogenic rhyolitic porphyry. R. flows of Neogenic rhyolite. Blank. Mesozoic sedimentary rocks. M. Metamorphic aureole.

The "banatites" constitute a very complex assemblage of granular or porphyritic rocks along the border of the southern Carpathians. They result from the differentiation of the same assemblage, but the succession is not too clear. Their age is upper Cretaceous. They form a series of outcrops aligned along the border west of the Bihar Mountains and to the south in Yugoslavia. They are rocks varying in composition from granite to gabbro, holocrystalline, and whose texture is either granular as in deepseated rocks, or microlithic and porphyritic. There are quartz diorites with their suite of dyke rocks, and some gabbros arising in small massif. But the dominant rock is a granodiorite with gradations to all the preceding types. Composition and texture vary capriciously in the same massif: the conditions of formation were unstable. These intrusions play the same role on the inside of the arc of the Southern Carpathians as do the post-Alpine granites on the southern slopes of the Alps, as for example the Adamello granite.

Of particular interest are the succession of basic rocks, then granitic or syenitic varieties in the orogenic zones. Such successions seem to represent a differentiation which is long overdue in relation to the orogenic evolution.

Along the Caledonian chain in Scandinavia, for example, there is a series of intrusions, at first basic, and more or less metamorphosed (saussuritized gabbros, amphibolites), then granitic: opdalites (granodiorites) and finally trondhjemites (akeritic granites). Both have been accompanied by important pyrite deposits.

Apart from the Urals, we have a similar case in the Alps, where the greenstones (*Roches vertes*) are older than the main tectonic overthrusts, and where the Tertiary granites cut across the orogenic edifice, already formed as a whole.

In the Western Cordilleras of the United States, W. Lindgren (1933) has studied differentiation in the grand style of plutonic rocks progressively emplaced in the Pacific chains as far as the eastern border of the Rockies in the centre of the continent, from the beginning of the Cretaceous up to the Tertiary. The phenomenon begins with some peridotite stocks at the western margin of the Sierra Nevada in California. A little later diorites, gabbros and quartz diorites appeared. Then came the great batholithic mass of the granodiorites of the Sierra Nevada, containing certain differentiations towards granite or quartz monzonite. Farther to the east and later smaller massifs occurred, which are essentially monzonitic. In all of these regions, some alkaline rocks, mainly syenites, occur. It is, however, in eastern Montana and Colorado that there are real gradations to syenitic types. This evolution is reflected in the metallic deposits connected with the eruptive rocks. The metallic paragenesis becomes more complex: the gangues become enriched in carbonate, in barite and in fluorite. The last mineral is the most characteristic element, and seems to be related to the alkalinization which would have included a concentration of fluorine among the volatile constituents of the differentiation. A similar development towards a predominance of alkaline types to the east can be observed in the volcanism of this period, and there also the related metal deposits are enriched in fluorine.

CONCLUSION

The problems of differentiation are among the most fascinating of those involving the eruptive rocks, for they can be expected to increase profoundly our understanding of the Earth's crust. We will not detail ourselves here by a consideration of broad theories which are still little founded and which envision in differentiation of deep magma, or *sima*, supposedly existing under the crust, the source of activity of the generating mobilized environments of the plutonic rocks. However that may be, the results achieved in the matter of differentiation provide insights into the mutual relationships of bodies of eruptive rocks, into their formation and their evolution which are not independent, but for which these rocks condition each other.

Granite often appears as the concluding member of an originally more basic lithologic series at the end of orogenic development. This fact is sometimes attributed to assimilation on a grand scale of a geo-synclincal series. But granite appears to be more widespread than merely an episode of the downsinking of geosynclines; it extends beyond geosynclinal settings. More deepseated causes undoubtedly intervene. Aside from this differentiation in grand style, the mobilized granitic environment evolves in batholiths and their satellites, obliterating here its first-formed facies, concentrating elsewhere the surplus of alkalies, and balancing everywhere the chemical anomalies due to assimilation or to other causes. Finally differentiation brought to the final stage would be the principal suorce of the material of chemical fronts, which condition the extensions of granitization and of metamorphism. But we enter here the realm of hypothesis.

Chapter 9

THE DYKE AND VEIN SATELLITES
OF GRANITE

Numerous dykes and veins usually accompany granite massifs. They radiate from the massifs, sometimes in fissures in the granite itself near its periphery, and sometimes mainly outside in the enclosing bedrock. Every so often, instead of a radial arrangement they follow rectilinear alignments of fractures in parallel swarms, or they may be lined up around a protruberance, a boss of outcrop of the batholith. They may also grade into more or less shapeless bodies. The dykes and veins have lengths of meters to kilometers and widths from millimeters to tens of meters.

The satellites belong to four categories and comprise on the one hand aplites, pegmatites and pneumatolytic quartz; on the other microgranitic and microdioritic porphyries; the lamprophyres; and hydrothermal metalliferous veins. The last, related in a distant way to granite and generally independent of the other satellites, will be studied in connection with the subject of metallogenesis (chapter 14).

The aplite, pegmatite, quartz group is customarily separated from the porphyries and lamprophyres, between which there may on the contrary be transitions. The group either occur as forerunners of the granite, or as residual material developed at the end of granitization. One remarkable category of pegmatites of varied paragenesis and zonal arrangement, called "complex pegmatites" in contrast to "simple pegmatites", forms large masses, or small massifs beyond the granitic rocks belonging to the same cycle. In addition to those preceding or accompanying circumscribed massifs, aplites and simple pegmatites are found associated with truly granitic dykes in regions of heterogeneous migmatites, where they take the form or enormous pockets, lenses or a myriad of veinlets. In such a case they are not satellites of the granite at all, but elements of migma capable of forming anatectic granite (chapter 4).

The porphyries are generally considered as granitic residues of magmatic character. The granophyres, characterized by the micropegmatitic texture of their groundmass, represent a particular type more closely related to granite.

The lamprophyres, which are of aberrant chemical composition and rich in pneumatogenic minerals and hydrates represent, according to

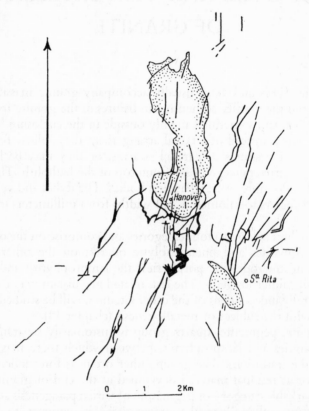

Fig. 24. Satellitic dykes of the Hanover granodiorite batholith, New Mexico (U.S.A.) (drawing after A. C. Spencer). Dotted: granodiorite. Black: porphyritic dykes.

P. Eskola (1954), a hydrothermal non-metalliferous facies of the residue of granitization.

The lamprophyres and porphyries only accompany the circumscribed massifs. The anatectic granites do not give rise to them, a lack undoubtedly due to their absence of tranquil differentiation. In contrast, aplites and pegmatites are more common.

APLITES AND PEGMATITES

Definitions

Aplites are rocks of fine sugary grain which are almost devoid of coloured minerals. The term designates above all a texture, and one can speak of granitic, syenitic or dioritic aplites, etc. The granitic aplites are formed of the same minerals as granite itself except for an extreme poverty of mica. They are thus composed essentially of quartz and feldspar. They are remarkable "because all the constituents have their own crystal forms and are in general equally developed in every direction". (A. Michel-Lévy, 1889).

Their aspect is in vivid contrast to that of the *pegmatites*, rocks of very coarse grain, analogous to a monstrous granite. There likewise exist granitic, syenitic and dioritic pegmatites, etc. The minerals of granitic pegmatites are essentially the same as those in a granite, with the addition in some cases of important rare minerals, which often have a pneumatolytic character, particularly in the *complex pegmatites*.

Veins of pneumatolytic quartz, with muscovite or tourmaline, often occur in the networks of pegmatite veins as a kind of degeneration of the latter with the disappearance of feldspar. Thus N. Varlamoff (1956) observed transitions between pegmatite and quartz veins with intermediary quartz veins with microcline. Such intermediary dyke-rocks have been called *alaskites* by J. E. Spurr (1923). The tourmalinites, also in vein form, sometimes occur in great abundance in the dyke systems of pneumatolytic quartz.

There is a common and intimate association of pegmatites and aplites which is the more striking because of the contrasting texture of the two rocks. Aplites for instance form the walls of veins with pegmatitic centres, or *vice versa*. Sometimes also the association is disordered with a turbulent and confused pattern. Quartz may also form massive segregations in pegmatites, either in the centre of masses of complex pegmatites, or as veinlets in pegmatite dykes. Independent pneumatolytic quartz veins extend generally farther from the granite than do those of pegmatites; either one may straddle part of the border of the granite.

The Specific Characteristics of Pegmatites. Pneumatolysis

The characteristics of pegmatites, according to J. H. Kemp (in W. T. Schaller, 1933, p. 145) are as follows:

F

Pegmatites (that is, granitic pegmatites) are coarse-grained granites in which some individual crystals or masses or one mineral may reach a relatively enormous size . . . (They) are usually characterized by one or more other macroscopic structures and features again not characteristic of typical igneous rocks, such as the regular intergrowth of two or more minerals as quartz and feldspar (graphic granite), banded structures, crystal-lined cavities, marked irregularity of grain, sudden changes of mineral composition of large mass, and the presence of minerals containing the less common elements such as columbium, bismuth, tin, lithium, beryllium, fluorine, boron, which are not present in the minerals of the normal igneous rocks to the extent that they are in pegmatites.

The particular texture of the pegmatites where their minerals interpenetrate, often in regular fashion and sometimes in skeletal form, is explained by either a simultaneous crystallization of adjacent minerals, or by partial metasomatism of earlier-formed minerals. A typical example is that of the association of quartz and feldspar in the *graphic pegmatites*, where the quartz drowned in the feldspars displays shapes calling to mind cuneiform characters in slabs of rock.

The less common substances mentioned above are found particularly and in some abundance in the complex pegmatites, which will be described under the sub-heading *Mode of Deposition*. They appear in special minerals, often of great size and well-defined shape, among which the most important are beryl, topaz, cassiterite, lepidolite, different kinds of tourmaline, garnet, spodumene, amblygonite, columbo-tantalite, lanthanide minerals, apatite and phosphates of manganese, uraninite and sometimes graphite, etc. Many of these minerals are pneumatolytic[1].

The simple pegmatites seem to be ordinary exudates of the mobilized environment during the course of granitization. The complex pegmatites seem to represent late residues, after a more complete differentiation: they do not always form, or are more localized and more rarely preserved. W. T. Schaller has emphasized in a very definite manner the distinction between the two types. For him the simple pegmatites are formed essentially of quartz and microcline. I can add that tourmaline is common in them in small quantities. According to Schaller the complex pegmatites are the result of a hydrothermal reworking of the simple variety, during which microcline and quartz

[1] Pneumatolysis was defined in chapter 6.

are partly resorbed and replaced by various minerals, particularly albite. An originally potassic chemical composition becomes sodic. The "geodic" (vuggy) structures result from this rearrangement. Sometimes microcline is re-established late in the second phase.

The pneumatolytic character of the pegmatitic minerals must be stressed. Many contain chemical elements such as hydroxyl, OH, which indicate activity of water vapour, the halogens F and Cl, various metalloids, S, P, B, C. These elements enter into the constituents of what are called *pneumatolytic emanations* or *pneumatolytes*. Water, in the form of vapour or liquid, appears to hold a dominant place in this group, along with the alkalis, which are present in most rocks but are particularly well-represented in the pegmatites in the form of feldspars and as accessory constituents in other minerals. The pneumatolytes were in the past called *mineralizers* by Elie de Beaumont because of their ability to facilitate the crystallization of various minerals. They in fact carry exceptional chemical elements, which allows for crystallizations of greater variety. They are apt to form particularly fluid mother liquids, giving rise to favourable conditions for the development of beautifully-formed crystals.

The concept of pneumatolysis applies above all to the phenomena produced by fumaroles which contain water vapour, various gaseous chlorides, sulphides and carbon dioxide, etc. They deposit in fissures and cavities of lavas various metallic compounds such as hematite, various sulphides, e.g., galena, sphalerite, pyrite, pyrrhotite and covellite, as well as a number of oxides, oxy-chlorides, and chlorides of metals (C. N. Fenner, 1933). Moreover A. Lacroix (1907) has shown through his investigations at Vesuvius the formation of feldspars, feldspathoids, biotite, augite, hornblende, fayalite, apatite, etc. under the same conditions.

In a like manner, certain authors admit that veins and veinlets of cassiterite with topaz, or scapolite and apatite, or tourmaline can be related to the same gaseous mode of formation. Others think that they arise from liquid or supercritical solutions. As these minerals are represented in the pegmatites, the same question will arise concerning the physical state of pneumatolytes which contribute to the formation of pegmatites.

The fundamental role of pneumatolytes has been defined in the early works of Fouqué and Auguste Michel-Lévy, subsequently by A. Lacroix, and more recently by Albert Michel-Lévy and J. Wyart. Their effectiveness stands out unmistakably in the synthesis of minerals in the laboratory. It is common knowledge that numerous silicate syntheses are easily obtained in a hydrous and alkaline environment. For instance, G. Friedel has obtained many natural silicates by heating various substances at around 500° in the presence of excess water and a little alkali carbonate. Michel-Lévy and Wyart (1947) have been able to obtain all the granitic minerals by operating in the presence of water vapour and other ingredients at pressures from 3,000–4,000 kg per cm² and temperatures from 500°–700°, i.e., under conditions similar to those that probably exist at a depth of 15 km in the Earth's crust. But the synthesis of such minerals has also been obtained at ten times less pressure, indicating the great range in stability with regard to pressure, where the temperature range is without doubt more restricted. The action of water vapour, and particularly of supercritical water vapour, has been emphasized by J. Wyart (1947), who showed its ability to dissolve potash. Van Nieuwenburg and van Zon (1935) have demonstrated its ability to dissolve silica.

Although some of these syntheses have been accomplished with the aid of vapours, it does not necessarily follow that the "mineralizers" always act in the gaseous state in nature. The critical constants of complex solutions are not well known and the high pressures existing at depth may keep the residual solutions in a liquid state, if they are on the right side of the corresponding critical temperature. Opinions are not unanimous in this regard. Whatever it may be, I maintain the term pneumatolysis not only for the reactions from gaseous products (volcanism) but even from solutions when these contain easily volatile components, or are apt to assume the gaseous state during some stage of their evolution.

Mode of Deposition

Simple pegmatites and aplites

The simple pegmatites and the aplites, together or alone, occur in extremely numerous veins and veinlets in the aureoles of circumscribed granite massifs and in the migmatites. These veins, of all sizes and shapes, often extremely small, seem to have had a surprising ability to move and infiltrate widespread areas. Perhaps they have also been able to form almost in place. They often cut each other in several cycles. Apart from veins, one may also find bodies of irregular shape.

As these aureoles and the migmatites represent stages in the course of granitization, the aplites and pegmatites form forerunners of the granite. Often they crosscut the granite itself, which affirms the late character of a certain part of them in the granitization.

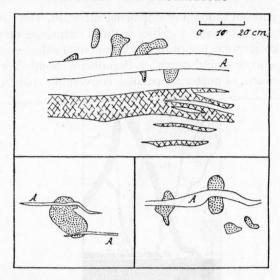

Fig. 25. Veins without dilatation (after B. C. King). Blank: Gneiss and granite. A. Aplite. Crosshatched: Pegmatite. Dotted: Inclusions.

In the migmatites, these dykes often occur in the unique type of *ptygmatic folds*, which have been explained as a development in a domain affected by intense deformation (figs. 34 and 35). Even where they do not show these singular contortions, the aplitic and pegmatitic dykes often display hazy banding localized in the rock mass, without any apparent derangement or dislocation of the rock itself. They do not represent a case of filling of open and injected fissures; they are formed by metasomatism of the rock, probably along capillary fissures. They have then been referred to as "*non-dilational*". This characteristic, observed by C. E. Wegmann in 1935, has been stressed by B. C. King (1948) and by Perrin and Roubault (1949). F. L. Hess (1933) had already distinguished between magmatic pegmatites and "metamorphic" pegmatites, the latter formed by replacement and possibly with dyke form. To be sure, it is not easy to conclude whether they are of non-dilational character, when the dykes have sharp contacts with the country rock, which does not seem to be displaced. A study in three dimensions is indispensable. J. Jaegar (1951) has stressed this difficulty.

As examples of non-dilational dykes, let us consider those described by King (1948), which are found in the Osi gneiss of Nigeria and in Scotland (figs. 25 and 26), The structure of the enclosing rock extends without a displacement across the emplacement of the dyke, if one eliminates it without thought of displacing the walls. The two walls of the dyke cannot be brought together without disturbing the structural and textural correspondence of the rocks on either side.

Another example found north of Brandberg, South-West Africa, consists of a swarm of numerous parallel, converging aplitic dykes and

Fig. 26. Network of aplite and pegmatite dykes in a syenite at Cnoc nan Cuilean, Scotland (after B. C. King). Black: aplite. Crosshatched: pegmatites.

with a thickness of 3 or 4 meters. According to J. G. Dennis (1952), they are formed by metasomatism, because the structure of the enclosing schists is never disturbed in spite of the considerable volume occupied by the aplites, as could be expected if they had been emplaced by intrusion.

On the other hand there are *dilational* aplitic and pegmatitic veins, that is fracture-fillings with displaced walls. A meticulous study taking into account the three dimensions must in this case make it possible to join together exactly the surrounding rocks, if we imagine the removal of the vein and the border walls brought together until they touch. H. Cloos has pointed out in the Silesian granites the dilational character of aplite veins which have been emplaced inside and outside the plutons during different epochs. He has shown that the vein walls can be rematched. More recently, E. Niggli (1953) has shown that veins of the Sept-Laux granite massif, in the French Alps, are dilational, and he has made beautiful reconstructions of the puzzle obtained by an imaginary suppression of the veins.

Such veins indicate a massive addition of fluids. Certain details can illustrate this movement of augmentation through the study of the behaviour of the wall rock. We have seen in an aplite in the Lys granite massif, Haute-Garonne, the same pattern as in figure 27, reproduced after E. Niggli (1952) of an aplite in Cornwall. A similar figure has been presented by N. R. Martin (1952) from the Flamanville granite. Near

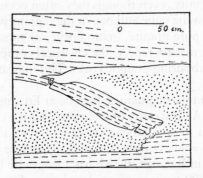

Fig. 27. Splinter torn and twisted from the wall of an aplite vein in the Godolphin granite, Cornwall (drawing after E. Niggli, 1952). Dotted: aplite. Blank: pegmatite. Dashes: schists. The dashes are oriented parallel to the schistosity.

the Oulmès granite, Morocco, the veins fill little faults of appreciable displacement and probable pushing apart of the walls (fig. 15).

I have observed above Baren, near Luchon, Haute-Garonne, aplite veins and granite injected in the graphitic Gothlandian. These veins, of perfect whiteness and with sharp walls, certainly do not form by metasomatism of the carbon-rich rock, but have been injected.

The foregoing different cases seem to be *limiting cases*, Nature more often combining both processes, fracture-filling and metasomatism. A filling of more or less open fissures with a strong metasomatism of the walls is probably the most common case.

Complex pegmatites

The complex pegmatites more often have the shape of masses than of veins. Their dimensions may vary from some decimeters to over a kilometer in length and from some centimeters to 200 meters in thickness. They are characterized by an arrangement of minerals in concentric zones, conforming to the boundaries of the body, and by the presence of the unusual minerals already mentioned. According to E. N. Cameron and his co-workers (1949), who have studied a great number in the U.S.A., the form of the deposits shows the following varieties:

tabular form, sometimes in thin branching lenses; pear-shaped or tear-shaped; arched chimneys; and eye-shaped. The shape depends on the structure of the enclosing rocks, not only when the borders are concordant, but also when they are discordant, for the walls of the bodies are controlled in such cases by the intersections of fractures.

The complex pegmatites are practically independent of the plutonic massifs in the vicinity, even though they often occur in swarms. However, according to the same authors, in the regions where there are such granitic rocks as pure granite, granodiorite, or monzonite, the plagioclase of these pegmatites reflects the chemical composition of the feldspars in the neighbouring granitic rocks. This indicates a certain genetic relationship.

Among the famous pegmatites, the one at Etta, near Keystone in the Black Hills, U.S.A., is worthy of mention. This is a circular stock, 70 m in diameter, rich in spodumene crystals of several meters in length. The most remarkable example, and perhaps unique in the world, is the Manono deposit in Katanga, which has a length of 14 km and a maximum width of 800 m in outcrop. Its zoning shows a flattened anticlinal vault, which cuts vertical mica schists. The pegmatite is rich in disseminated cassiterite in commercial amounts, and contains spodumene and columbo-tantalite.

The structural zoning of complex pegmatite bodies has been closely studied by the American authors mentioned above. They distinguish:

(a) border zones with a total amplitude of scarcely more than a decimeter;

(b) wall zones of a somewhat coarser grain, of a thickness often less than 3 m and constituting the whole body in some occurrences;

(c) one or more intermediate zones, often incomplete or absent, the average grain size of which is clearly coarser than in the foregoing.

(d) kernels or hearts, which are lenticular units, coalescent or disjointed, more or less central and reflecting on a smaller scale the general form of the body. These units are formed of massive quartz, or quartz, feldspar and mica.

A mineralogical and petrographical zoning overprints the above structural zoning, and comprises eleven associations from the outside to the interior according to these authors:

1. Plagioclase, quartz, muscovite;
2. Plagioclase, quartz;

3. Quartz, perthite, plagioclase with or without muscovite and biotite;
4. Perthite, quartz;
5. Perthite, quartz, plagioclase, amblygonite, spodumene;
6. Plagioclase, quartz, spodumene;
7. Quartz, spodumene;
8. Lepidolite, plagioclase, quartz;
9. Quartz, microcline;
10. Microcline, plagioclase, lithium micas, quartz;
11. Quartz.

But few pegmatites contain these eleven associations at the same time. The plagioclase of the outer zones varies from andesine to albite, depending upon the individual case and depending upon the plutonic rocks of the region. In the body, there is sometimes a systematic variation, the proportions of anorthite in the plagioclase decreasing from the walls towards the interior, whereas the opposite variation never takes place.

In association with this structural zoning, the bodies show important phenomena of replacement, indicated by what the authors quoted call "units of replacement". These are masses with discordant boundaries or where the minerals of the zones are pseudomorphosed under the influence of chemical migrations coming from more internal zones of the same pegmatite, or by foreign solutions. The replacements also occur in the form of veins or discontinuous veinlets, likewise emanated from the internal zones. Quartz, albite and muscovite are their most common constituents.

Some similar zoned pegmatites have been described at Zenaga in Southern Morocco (Ph. Morin, 1952) and in Madagascar (M. Roubault, A. Lenoble, A Gangloff, 1952). For example, in the Malakialina deposit, Madagascar, one finds, after a border zone of tourmalinite, a wall zone of quartz and muscovite, with a maximum width of 20 cm; then a zone of microcline with quartz, muscovite, tourmaline, apatite and garnet, of 1 meter maximum width; then a zone of plagioclase and quartz, with tourmaline, muscovite, beryl, garnet and columbite, reaching several meters in thickness; finally a kernel of perthite and quartz.

The pegmatites of north-eastern Brazil (W. D. Johnston Jr., 1945), show a disposition in four zones (fig. 28). The border zone, some centimeters to one meter thick, is characterized by an abundance of usually large muscovite crystals; it is sometimes rich in tourmaline. Occasionally cassiterite is present. Zone 2, which is the widest, consists

F*

of normal pegmatite. Zone 3 contains predominantly large feldspar crystals, which may attain dimensions measurable in meters. The greater part of the beryl, tantalite and spodumene occurs in this zone. Zone 4 is a central mass of quartz, milky or rosy, and sometimes slightly vuggy. It sometimes contains beryl and at times some sulphides.

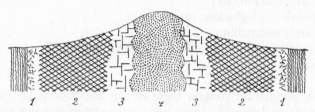

Fig. 28. Sketch of a complex pegmatite deposit in northern Brazil (drawing after W. D. Johnston). 1. muscovite zone. 2. zone of normal pegmatite. 3. zone of large feldspar crystals. 4. kernel of quartz.

The beautiful works of A Fersman (1931 a and b), summarized by N. Varlamoff (1946), have demonstrated the existence of a succession of phases, corresponding according to him to declining temperature during the genesis of pegmatites. He distinguished between 10 classes of pegmatites which can be emitted during successive periods of cooling. The transformation point of quartz near 600° gives him the first divisional boundary. Above it there is no distinctive difference between liquid and gaseous phases (super-critical state). Near 400° the critical point of the aqueous solutions provides him with a second boundary. He thus defines three phases: epimagmatic (800–600°), pneumatolytic (600–400°), and hydrothermal (400° and lower). The most typical minerals of the epimagmatic phase are: plagioclase, monazite, orthite, sphene, columbo-tantalite, uranium niobates and tantalates, and garnet. At about 600°, pegmatites with lanthanides and actinides occur. In the pneumatolytic phase, in order of decreasing temperature, are:

1. Pegmatites with boron and fluorine (tourmaline, mica);
2. Pegmatites with topaz, beryl, cassiterite;
3. Pegmatites with sodium-lithium: albite, lepidolite, amblygonite, spodumene, cassiterite, possible recurrence of columbo-tantalite; ilmenorutile;
4. Pegmatites with iron and manganese phosphates.

Near 400° cryolite appears. Below this, with the appearance of the liquid phase, pegmatitic residues with fluoro-carbonates, zeolites, with colourless apatite, fluorite, clay minerals, autunite and sulphides appear.

It must be noted that some authors do not believe that the fluids have evolved at the supercritical stage, and that many have a less magmatic notion and make metasomatism a dominant factor, as said below.

N. Varlamoff (1954 b) has verified, in the course of extensive studies in the tin districts of the Belgian Congo, that with increasing distance around some batholiths, the pegmatite bodies of the region present individual facies corresponding to successive phases of declining temperature in Fersman's classification. The correlation between zoning of individual deposits as described by E. N. Cameron and his co-workers, and the successive phases of Fersman, seem to be less precise, perhaps because of the effects of metasomatism remaking the zones of the deposit as early as their formation and up to the end of the evolution of the deposit.

The structural relations minutely described by Cameron and his co-workers indicate a centripetal formation of the deposits.

. . . the material of an inner zone may extend outward along fractures into an outer zone or even beyond it into the wall rock, whereas the reverse is not true. Also it seems significant that whereas a mineral of an inner zone may replace a mineral of an outer zone, the reverse has not been found . . . As the anorthite content shows a decrease from the outer to the inner zones in those pegmatites in which the plagioclase shows any change, it would appear that the spatial order of zones from the walls inward is likewise the chronological order of development (p. 101–2).

N. Varlamoff (1954 b) also says: "When the pegmatites show a pronounced zoning, the phases succeed each other from the wall towards the centre." In some deposits it is quite clear that a litho-sodic phase forms the centre and a borofluorine phase the border.

The *role of metasomatism* must be emphasized. Its spatial importance in the deposits has been demonstrated. In detail, the very pronounced albitization of the microcline is recognized by the authors. The graphic pegmatites arise through a corrosion of feldspar by the deposition of quartz (Drescher-Kaden, 1948). Many examples are known of muscovitization of tourmaline, and of feldspathization of beryl, as for instance at Malakialina. Although always obvious in the final stage of the formation of the deposits, little is known of the share taken by metasomatism during the initial formation of the zones. It is known that the graphic associations of quartz-feldspar which we admit are metasomatic are

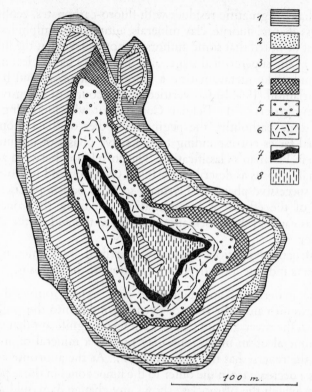

Fig. 29. Complex pegmatite, Mongolian Altaï (drawing after K. A. Vlassov, 1935). 1. Zone with graphic texture. 2. Complex of fine grained albite with beryl and tantalite. 3. Monomineralic microcline zone. 4. Zone of quartz and muscovite with beryl, tantalite, and residual microcline. 5. Quartz complex with spodumene and clevelandite with residual microcline. 6. Albite and tantalite. 7. Quartz zone. 8. Zone of lepidolite and albite.

The surrounding rock (Gabbro) is left blank. One should note the importance of the monomineralic zones.

considered by Fersman to be formed in the first phases of the formation. Finally the presence of pneumatolytes, introduced at various moments, increases the possibility of the evolution of the environment.

The evolution closing the formation of the deposits is certainly long and complex. It includes *rejuvenations*. Thus quartz veins formed in the interior of the deposits may contain hydroxyl minerals, oxides, wolframite, hematite, manganese oxide and sulphides, which belong to the hydrothermal stage. A. Safiannikoff (1954) has often found in such veins in the Belgian Congo deposits of minerals identical to the constituent minerals of the first phases of the pegmatite: microcline, albite, tourmaline, muscovite, lepidolite, beryl, apatite, cassiterite and niobite.

Mode of Formation

Aplites and pegmatites are often associated, and one can subscribe to the opinion of N. Varlamoff (1954 a) that "depending on the conditions of cooling and the rapidity of the release of the volatile components, either aplites or pegmatites may form, or rocks of intermediate texture". Among the volatile substances, water probably plays the most important role. It is evident that lack of mica in aplites associated with certain simple pegmatites is compensated by the frequent presence of garnet, absent in related pegmatite and indicating a lack of water. This can be observed particularly in migmatites: the section of Gorges d'Heric in Montagne-Noire, Southern France; the migmatites of Aston, Pyrénées-Ariègeoises.

Excluding the complex pegmatites, which are the result of a complicated sequence of processes mentioned above, pegmatites and aplites can be produced by granitic exudates and their intergranular fluids, according to Drescher-Kaden (1948), who noticed that such veins are often "blind" and generally do not have inclusions. Or again, they may be lateral secretions from the surrounding rocks, according to K. R. Mehnert (1953), for certain migmatites in the Black Forest. The idea of the eutectic character of pegmatites has been supported by A. Fersman, based on the fact that the proportion of quartz in the typical pegmatite assemblage would be fairly constant and of the order of 25 per cent by volume. Mehnert has the same point of view. On the other hand, Drescher-Kaden has observed in the graphic pegmatites a variability of this proportion, and above all an emplacement of quartz later than feldspar, in a way which points to quartz metasomatism.

Here we touch on the dualism of opinions: either the magmatic or the metasomatic formation of the pegmatites and aplites. N. L. Bowen, in support of the hypothesis of magmatic origin, regards the residual magma of granitization as enriched in "hyperfusibles", in other words, in pneumatolytes. The abundance of these would explain the remarkable textures of pegmatite. "Mineralizers" lower the viscosity of the silicate magma by lowering its fusion point. Their first effect is to retard and then to facilitate crystallization. The supersaturation being at every instant very slight and diffusion very easy, crystals of great size with even, well-developed faces, form readily (G. Friedel, 1926). Crystallization at a lower temperature and within a more restricted temperature interval, permits a simultaneous formation of several minerals which interpenetrate each other and produce textures of the "graphic" type. These, common for quartz-feldspar, occur also in other minerals, either between themselves or with feldspars. The skeletal forms indicate the same thing, for instance, for the beryls or for quartz with tourmaline. In these textures, many constituents of a given mineral, separated by the development of another, actually form part of one large crystal. Finally the irregular disposition of crystals, the disordered association of aplite with pegmatite, would be accounted for by the conditions of easy nourishment of crystals in a very fluid environment, and also by irregularities in the distribution of the mineralizers as a consequence of their mobility. A chemical variation of the environment would also explain the succession of depositions revealed in the zoning of the complex pegmatites.

Another explanation of the formation of pegmatites is based on metasomatism. Many details of their structure incontestably indicate a corrosion of some minerals by others. W. T. Schaller (1933) has elucidated this aspect. The residual magma of granitization should consolidate in the form of aplite. Microcline in large crystals should be developed at their expense by metasomatism. Then quartz of the graphic variety should be deposited, at the same time as a substitution of albite for potash feldspar took place. The albitization of microcline is a very widespread phenomenon in pegmatites. In the complex pegmatites the various minerals characteristic of Fersman's different classes seem to be emplaced in a final stage by corrosion and reworking of the preceding mineralization, at the same time that albitization is prolonged. These final crystallizations often have a vuggy structure.

For A. Zavaritsky (1947) the circulation of mineralizers, gas and solutions transforms the surrounding rock and makes it more coarse-grained "by a phenomenon analogous to that used in chemistry, on keeping the precipitate in contact with a saturated solution". During this phenomenon, the chemical composition of the fluids changes by diffusion or fractional distillation; the minerals formed successively are different: those of preceding stages are reorganized. The recrystallization produces a segregation of the minerals. The first stages are analogous to a metamorphism, the last to a hydrothermal ore formation.

However, two reservations must be made. The first, made by Zavaritsky himself, is that if the final solution is of metalliferous type "there nevertheless still exists some antagonism between the pegmatites and the metalliferous veins, which generally come from different magmas". The second is that pegmatitic textures do not resemble the crystalloblastic textures of metamorphism. Does a higher temperature and a higher proportion of fluids explain the difference? Drescher-Kaden (1948), however, admits that there are transitions between the two types of texture.

Let me say at once that metasomatic formation is not very probable for certain aplites. Actually N. Varlamoff (1954 a) has described aplites with an accentuated fluidal structure. Large crystals of microcline, of quartz and of books of mica are seen in the aplitic groundmass, in the manner of islands surrounded by river currents. I have already mentioned the case of split walls of aplite veins, torn off without being completely detached from the wall, and rotated through a more or less large angle due to the flow of the material (fig. 27). In the reverse sense, the aplites of the non-dilational veins are formed by metasomatism.

B. C. King and A. M. J. de Swardt (1949) think that pegmatites form during relaxation of pressure, and the aplites under stress. This suggestion is in accordance with the fluidity of the aplites, indicating a flow under stress, and with the fact that aplites form ptygmatic folds more often than other rocks in the migmatitic domains. Reciprocally the formation of pegmatites should be favoured by an influx of the mineralizing fluids in places of released pressure. The common case of the association of the two rocks should indicate alternating phases of pressure and release of pressure, or local irregularities in the distribution of the stresses.

LAMPROPHYRES

In contrast to the pegmatites, the lamprophyres appear to be of incontestably magmatic character. Their definition can be summarized from A. Lacroix's work. Lamprophyres are fine grained holocrystalline rocks, very melanocratic, that is, very rich in coloured constituents, and among them the pneumatogenic minerals hornblende and biotite are exceptionally abundant. This richness in pneumatogenic elements is striking, if one compares lamprophyres with ordinary eruptive rocks of an analogous chemical composition. They are devoid of feldspar phenocrysts and are more alkaline than their melanocratic facies at first would indicate. The abundance of calcite, chlorite, apatite, and possibly talc, is striking. Eskola believes these minerals to be primary. Finally their petrographic texture is diverse and even capriciously variable microgranular, microlithic and doleritic.

The lamprophyres, like the pegmatites, are not restricted to granite massifs. They constitute a facies determined by the evolution of plutonic rocks: a phase of concentration of residual ferromagnesian components in an alkaline environment, in contrast to a phase of concentration of mineralizers yielding pegmatites. In the case of granites, the lamprophyres and the pegmatites, with the aplites, have for a long time been considered as representing two poles, one ferromagnesian and the other siliceous, belonging to a differentiation pushed to the extreme in opposite directions. Such a radical differentiation is no longer accepted. P. Eskola (1954) relates lamprophyres to a final hydrothermal phase rich in carbon dioxide.

As A. Harker expresses it in his *Petrographie* (1902): "These rocks show various transitions from typical lamprophyres to quartz-mica porphyries. One finds that very different species of rock occur in a state of imperfect mixing in the same dyke". This is the case, for instance, in the Champ-du-Feu granite cited below.

Lamprophyre dykes seem in general to be dilational; they often contain inclusions. According to K. H. Scheumann (1952) the constituents of the assimilated xenoliths participate materially in the lamprophyric differentiation and control its nature and direction. S. S. Kaitaro (1952) also emphasizes the influence of contamination by the walls of the lamprophyric dykes of Åva, in the Åland Islands. The fluidity of the lamprophyres in the manner of a magma can sometimes be proved with the aid of the inclusions. P. Hupé (1949) cites some inclusions of the Gothlandian schists reworked by a lamprophyre of the granite at Néouvielle, Pyrenees, starting at the floor of this granite.

The dykes are often thin. These rocks are relatively rare; and even altogether absent in the associations of some granite massifs. On the other hand, other massifs are extremely rich in them, such as those in the Vosges. One knows of lamprophyres discharged as volcanic flows, but they are connected with alkaline magmas and lie outside the present subject.

Minette is one of the most common of the lamprophyres connected with granite; it has the chemical composition of a syenite. The rock was "named by the miners of Framont, Vosges, because of its resemblance to the iron ores exploited in this locality. It is composed almost exclusively of flaky mica in an unoriented, almost massive pulp of mica, with a little orthoclase" (E. Nivoit, 1887). *Kersantite* (oligoclase, biotite, hornblende) has the compsoition of a monzonite, and *spessartite* that of a diorite or a gabbro. *Camptonite*, a barkevikite-bearing rock, forms the transition to alkaline lamprophyres.

The granitic lamprophyres sometimes grade into andesite or microgranite dykes. A Lacroix has shown that the carboniferous granites of the Central Pyrenees and the neighbouring Precambrian terrains are traversed by numerous andesite dykes with lamprophyric affinities. These rocks, studied by A. de Romeu (1907), are labradoritic or andesinic andesites, often rich in hornblende and more rarely in glassy material. Their texture is doleritic or microlithic. Although they are later than the granite which they cut, they belong to the same eruptive cycle, because they contain in their fissures the same granitic emanation minerals present in the fissures of the formations of the granitic aureole. For instance, in the Lys granite, near Luchon, they are very compact, black or dark green rocks. In the Pyrenees of Ariège, the granites are much poorer in dykes of this kind.

The Champ-du-Feu granite, in the northern Vosges, described in the works of H. Rosenbusch (1877), and later by J. Jung (1928), is cut by numerous dykes consisting of various lamprophyres and porphyries. The porphyritic granite of the central Vosges, less rich in dykes, emits in the gneiss to the west microgranites, with pyroxene, of the same chemical composition as this granite.

Kersantites are associates with these microgranites and show close analogies to them. The kersantites contain the same diopside and a very large quantity of biotite. The colourless constituents are represented above all by plagioclase, but in smaller amounts also by quartz and orthoclase. Sometimes the kersantite shows the development of a kind of light-coloured, vague smoky material: these are the more acidic portions.

There is a gradation through these to porphyries (J. Jung).

A. San Miguel Arribas (1952) has studied the lamprophyres, camptonite and spessartite, of the Costa Brava granitic massif in the coastal chain of Catalonia. On the basis of the nature of their contacts with the granite and the microscopic texture of the transition between the two rocks, he ascribes these dykes to basaltic dykes formed before the granitization and preserved from it except for a certain amount of metamorphism. They are thus *antecedent* dykes, that is, pre-existing dykes which have preserved their i ndividuality and form during the transformation of the environment.

This case seems to be similar to that of the metabasites of Finland, subsisting in the domains of palingenesis and forming veins that are at the same time younger and older than the surrounding rocks (p. 54). But even if such an occurrence is well known for migmatites, since the work of J. J. Sederholm, it seems to be much less usual in granite massifs. As it scarcely seems doubtful that many lamprophyres must be interpreted as magmatic, one could have in the Costa Brava a phenomenon of convergence between antecedent basaltic dykes and lamprophyres.

In contrast to the classic theories summarized in the beginning of this section, R. W. van Bemmelen[1] has suggested an original hypothesis about certain lamprophyres:

Would it not be possible that they derive from the metamorphic zone which envelopes the granitized mass and they have been injected from the outside inwards? In Indonesia (Java), I have observed the presence of these lamprophyric rocks (malchites, vogesites, etc.) in the upper zone of neogenic granites formed by metasomatism. This border, mobilized during the granitization, has later been injected into fissures formed in the more rigid granite which was consolidated and pushed upwards. In the deeper portions of the granite, the lamprophyric dykes seem to be more rare or absent. Such phenomena perhaps can explain the relationship between the metamorphic roof of the monzonitic intrusions of Predazzo in the Dolomites, and the dykes of lamprophyres (camptonites) in the monzonites, dykes which outcrop all along the way and which, at certain points, become thinner from the top downwards. The solution of this problem of the origin of basic dykes can only be attained by studies, on small and large scales, of the spatial relationships of the rocks in the field. One can thus not claim *a priori* that the injections of basic rocks in more acidic granular masses always derive from the depths; the possibility of their origin from the roofs of these masses must also be reckoned with.

PORPHYRIES

The porphyritic dykes in the granitic suites are quite variable, but most often are of an ordinary character. They belong to some categories of microgranites and some microdiorites. Often they grade into a petrographic facies of typical rhyolites and andesites. This is particularly so in thin dykes or the walls of thicker dykes (p. 218).

L. de Launay (1901) observed this fact in the Carboniferous intrusions near the volcanic tuffs of the Culm, on the plateau of Guéret north of the French Massif Central (fig. 30). For instance, in the Sannat dyke, southwest of Evaux, a dyke 12 km in length and 1,500 m thick, there are all the gradations between holocrystalline microgranite and granophyres or types of a more or less cryptocrystalline association with quartz and orthoclase. The granite massif from which this type of dyke derives has not been identified (it is not at all certain that it is

[1] Observation noted by A. San Miguel Arribas (1955).

the Guéret granite), but the intimate liaison of the microgranites with the rhyolites must be emphasized. The analogous microgranitic facies south of Limoges has given rise to similar observations (E. Raguin, 1927).

Porphyritic dykes are most often dilational. However, this is not always the case with the granophyres, whose mode of occurrence often resembles that of granite. Microgranitic porphyries, particularly those with rhyolitic borders, probably had the fluidity of a magma. P. Collomb (1952) cites a microgranite from Villefranche-de-Rouergue, where an inclusion of granite and gneiss was brought up from a depth which he estimates at some hundreds of meters.

Among the numerous dykes that intersect the Champ-de-Feu granite in the Vosges, one finds a microgranite older then the lamprophyres; it often shows the fluidal and spherulitic texture of a rhyolite according to J. Jung. This gradation into a volcanic facies suggests conditions of rapid cooling and probably low pressure. Consequently these dykes must be much later than the end of the cooling of the portions which they occupy in the granite massif or in the adjoining terrain, and also later than the release of the compressed granitic emanations.

Apart from this fact, the character of late formation of the porphyritic veins stand out because of the fineness of the grain size apart from the phenocrysts, a fineness which can be explained by the absence of mineralizers. These latter were thus able to be already released.

At Azegour in the Moroccan Atlas, there is a deposit of scheelite, molybdenite and copper in the aureole of a small batholith of granite. The mineralization is due to contact metamorphism in limestones and to the degeneration of the granitic emanations into hydrothermal solutions. Porphyritic dykes cut this metalliferous mineralization and are thus clearly later than the release of the mineralizers. However, in certain peribatholithic deposits in Arizona, U.S.A., the porphyries alternate with repeated phases of metalliferous mineralization. But it is a question there of hydrothermal phases less warm than in Azegour and also later. Besides, these particular porphyries seem to represent less products of differentiation of the batholith than the material itself from the upper part of the cupola of the batholith (E. Raguin, 1934 b).

The suite of veins rich in pegmatites rarely contains porphyries and vice versa. There is an antipathy between the two categories, made explicable by what precedes. For instance, the group of granites with white mica of the western part of the French Massif Central, which contains pegmatite occurrences, rarely contains microgranite. On the other hand, the batholith of Azegour, which has few pegmatites, is accompanied by numerous large dykes of microgranite and andesite.

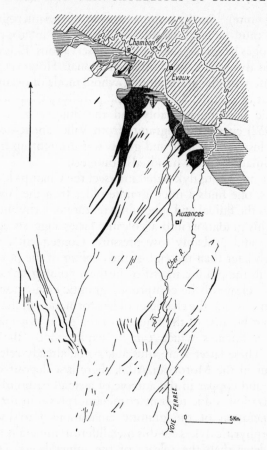

Fig. 30. Microgranitic dyke swarm in the Guéret plateau. Blank: granite. black: veins and bodies of microgranite. Inclined hatching: gneiss. Horizontal lines: Dinantian (sandstone, tuffs and volcanic flows).

In the dyke suites of the granites, the porphyritic dykes are the most independent, because of their extent over great distances reaching several kilometers. They may occur without any outcropping of granite. Has their magma reached the surface of the earth and flowed out as volcanic lava? This is a problem to which we will return in chapter 13.

CONCLUSION

Satellites confer a special character in every case to the whole of a granitic lithological province: by their presence or absence; by the possible existence of complex pegmatites or a special chemistry; and more generally by the rhythm of the chemical and mechanical episodes upon which they depend, preceding or accompanying the granitization, or succeeding it.

The simple pegmatites are either relatively earlier than the granites, i.e., forerunners in the aureole, or later and cutting the granite after it became rigid, as for example plane dykes. The earlier are affected by symmigmatic processes of the aureole (p. 106). The complex pegmatites independent of the granite massif are exceptional and seem to correspond to the latest products of differentiation. Their internal evolution is complicated.

The aplites range in time with the pegmatites.

The pneumatolytic quartz veins are generally late and are connected with the phase of final relaxation. We have seen, however, that there are numerous exceptions to this rule (p. 104). The example of the El Karit tin deposits, at the border of the Oulmès granite massif in Morocco, shows in the schists of the aureole veins of quartz boudined by the deformation connected with the emplacement of the granite: in the points of low pressure (*Streckungshöfe*) of the bevelled edges (*biseaux*) of the boudins, cassiterite, beryl and muscovite crystallize, sometimes abundantly. Here the pneumatolytic quartz is thus synkinematic with granitization.

The granophyres, in dykes or pockets, may be late as are the porphyries, but they may also be a facies of granite in creation, particularly in paravolcanic granitization; e.g., ring-dykes of Scotland; the granite associated with rhyolites in Sarrho, southern Morocco, p. 216.

The microgranitic or microdioritic porphyries are late when they occur as dykes. The case of a border microgranitic facies of the large granite massifs is different and has already been discussed. The lamprophyres are late in the same way. These categories of rocks are absent in the domains of migmatites, which are unfinished granites. Some cases of transportation of inclusions by microgranite and lamprophyres have been noted above, which proves the fluidity of these rocks. There has probably been a certain amount of rheomorphism of the microgranites and fluidity by release (afflux) of solutions for the lamprophyres.

One sees that it would be possible to obtain by analysis of the succession of the mechanisms of the emplacement of the satellites of the granite, in favourable cases, a chronology of the phases of evolution of granite massifs.

Chapter 10

WEATHERING AND CRUSHING
OF GRANITE

To be complete, the study of the evolution of granites must encompass the phenomena which preside over their destruction: weathering by infiltrating water and tectonic crushing and deformation. Weathering of granites has a geochemical role of great significance, because of their abundance and because of their chemical instability near the surface of the earth, which is more pronounced than in most other rocks.

On the other hand the granites are tectonically fragile and "react" to deformations with marked facility, giving rise to a whole gamut of deformed rocks. This phenomenon takes place in the domain of tectonic movements, but outside the zones "mobilized" by granitization or metamorphism, in other words, at a higher level in the crust, everything else being equal.

WEATHERING

Description
In areas of granite exposures, the outcrops in general have the singular aspect of great irregular knobs some meters in diameter. These knobs sometimes appear either isolated on the surface or crowded in picturesque chaos. Usually the upper surface of these knobs is visible while the rest is enveloped in the underlying granitic mass, which is still compact or has become more or less friable and pulverized. The weathering consists of a disintegration of the granite, which becomes like a coarse sand, and which is called *granitic gravel* (*arène granitique*), whereas the portions of the rock forming the knobs are provisionally preserved. If the gravel is eroded by running water, the knobs are isolated in the terrain. The observed transitions reveal that the pheno-

menon starts and progresses along the networks of parallelipipedic
fissures existing in all granite. It is more accentuated in the intersections
of the fissures; also the summit of the parallelipipeds become rounded
and the final form will be that of a knob. Eventually these will
weather in their outward parts and will be broken down to a sandy
state.

In ordinary granites the knobs are roughly spherical; they are flattened in those granites of marked gneissic structure. Some exceptional
granites are peculiarly sensitive to weathering for unknown reasons; if
they are laid bare by deep excavations in fresh rock they disintegrate in
a few months. Rapakivi is a particularly remarkable case which seems,
however, to be unrelated to weathering but due to an inherent
instability.

The depth of weathering is determined by the easy penetration of
water into the fissures of the granite, of the order of some meters to
some tens of meters. Deeper down the fissures in the granite are generally too tight to permit circulation of waters. This weathering is
generally present everywhere, so that completely fresh granite is found
only in deep cuts where erosion is rapid enough to uncover fresh
material. When running waters move the gravels, sorting will take
place, producing beds of quartz sand still more or less feldspathic, and
beds of alluvial clays.

Evolution of the constituent minerals

Microscopic studies can follow the evolution of the minerals during
weathering. The quartz stays practically unchanged. The feldspars,
which lose their crystalline transparency to the naked eye, becoming
milky, then powdery and flour-like, show under the microscope a
pigmentation of microscopic flakes, first disseminated and then more
and more densely spaced. Finally all the feldspar is reduced to a non-
cohesive cryptocrystalline aggregate. These flakes seem to be either
of kaolin or of sericite. The reasons for the kaolinization or sericitization
of feldspar undoubtedly depend on the composition of the microsolutions responsible for the weathering. Perhaps more acidic water
(inclusions of pyrite, infiltrations of peaty water) favour the formation
of kaolin, and more alkaline water, sericite. Of the two feldspars of
granite, potash feldspar and plagioclase, one is generally attacked much
more rapidly. It is most often the plagioclase, although there is no
general rule. In an orthoclase shot through with stringers of microperthite, one will see, for instance, that the stringers are sericitized, but
the surrounding crystal is unaffected.

J. de Lapparent (1923) thinks that the weathering of feldspars at the surface does not produce kaolin, but probably an aluminum hydrate, whereas at a greater depth the conditions would be different, orthoclase being little altered and the plagioclase transformed into sericite. Concerning kaolinization, according to him it would appear only in the case of alteration by emanations of mineralizers or hydrothermal solutions. It is difficult to determine whether an orthoclase is pigmented by kaolin or by aluminum hydrate. But where kaolin deposits are concerned, and among them deposits formed at the expense of feldspathic rocks altered in place, it is possible to dispute whether the origin of their alteration was atmospheric or hydrothermal. Observations can be presented in favour of both hypotheses, and it seems probable that both cases can occur in nature and that the alteration to kaolin can be produced by weathering.

Cordierite tends to weather much more readily than the feldspars. This mineral also sericitizes, but in a different manner: the sericite flakes are typically oriented in a network controlled by the cleavages of the cordierite, or are disposed along microfissures in this mineral. The granitic cordierites are particularly unstable.

Biotite to the naked eye loses its brilliant lustre. First it becomes bronze-coloured or golden brown because of exudations of iron oxide, then it turns green, becoming opaque: it is transformed to chlorite. The microscope sometimes reveals the development of fine needles of rutile in the chlorite. Muscovite remains unchanged. Hornblende turns green and bleaches, or breaks down into chlorite and epidote. These minerals, together with zoisite, also form here and there at the expense of other minerals such as plagioclase.

Most of the accessory minerals in granite: tourmaline, rutile, garnet, zircon and apatite, resist weathering and are encountered in small amounts in the granitic sands. They are then referred to as the heavy minerals of the sands.

Occasionally some neogenic quartz, calcite and neogenic alkali feldspar form as small formless areas (*plages*) at the expense of the granitic minerals.

The weathered granite no longer exhibits the beautiful crystallinity of the fresh rock. The neogenic kaolinization and sericitization, epidote and zoisite form cryptocrystalline aggregates. Only the chlorite is visible in distinct lamellae several millimeters in diameter, directly substituting for those of biotite; but at the same time it occurs as felty aggregates of extreme fineness. These findings are not surprising, because the products of weathering form in cool aqueous environments, as do the sedimentary rocks where cryptocrystalline textures are very typical.

Complexity of weathering

Weathering cannot be reduced to an individual reaction between the minerals of the rock and infiltrating water, by which these minerals would be decomposed and impoverished in their most soluble chemical constituents, alkalis and lime. There is an interaction between the minerals which evolve; the rock reacts as a whole; it undergoes a veritable metasomatism.

Striking evidence in this regard is the formation of sericite, potash mica, at the expense of plagioclase and cordierite. The immobilized potash comes from elsewhere, probably from biotite. The microsolutions circulate between the crystals and within them along tiny fissures, often invisible under the microscope. Frequently, for instance, zoned plagioclases have their centres altered, whereas their outer parts are still fresh and of a homogeneous aspect.

Furthermore the surrounding rocks have some influence in regulating the chemical nature of the infiltrating water. This is P. Termier's opinion (1898), based on his study of the weathering of basic dykes, lamprophyres and other varieties which cut the Pelvoux granite in the Alps. In these dykes the calcic plagioclases are transformed into anorthoclase and albite without destroying the original crystal edifice. The other calcic minerals weather in their usual way, also losing their lime. The reason for the general elimination of lime from these rocks is the action of rain water which has first encountered the Pelvoux granites and gneisses, has attacked them and is charged with alkalis but not with lime. Then encountering the basic rocks whose outcrops are very much less extensive, the water removes their lime but not their alkalis. The rain water indeed seems to have deposited some alkali in the basic rocks. These reactions correspond to delicate equilibria which often change with time. When the Pelvoux was still enveloped in its blanket of calcareous sediments, it was in contrast a source of lime. In the future, when it will have lost its alkalis and will be reduced to quartz, clay minerals and some chlorite, its waters will dissolve in their turn the alkali silicates from the basic rocks. Even though this example concerns basic rocks, it is evident that it illustrates a general case.

Other modes of weathering

The mode of weathering of which the broad aspects have been described is the one normally found in regions of temperate and humid climate, and which acts at the present time over the greater part of the Earth's crust not covered by the seas. There are other types of alteration, which it will be recalled are related to climatologic factors or to ascending material, that is, non-meteoric.

Lateritic weathering. It operates in some tropical countries and transforms all kinds of rocks to laterite, a mixture of aluminum and iron hydrates and clay minerals, typically brick-red in colour. Granite does not escape this weathering and becomes lateritized if the climate is favourable.

Taffoni weathering. In a particularly dry climate, under perhaps the influence of salty winds, the progressive disintegration of inclined slopes of rocky outcrops gives rise to the formation of taffoni. Taffonis are rounded cavities, reaching sometimes one meter or more in diameter and with more or less hemispheric shape. The process is not restricted to granites, but is found in these rocks, for example in Corsica or in southern Morocco.

Weathering in urban atmospheres. In cities or in the neighbourhood of industrial centres, weathering is of a special type due to the particular chemical composition of the rain water and flowing water (J. Allan Howe, 1902).

Hydrothermal alteration. Alteration caused by hydrothermal solutions in the neighbourhood of metalliferous veins occurs in a very different manner and is moreover of varying kinds. In particular it often impregnates siliceous rocks with pyrite and various other minerals, which gives them a characteristic stamp.

Autopneumatolysis. An alteration of the minerals of granite, sometimes difficult to distinguish from meteoric alteration, eventually affects entire massifs and seems connected to the conclusion of the same phenomena which produced the rock. By analogy with the effects observed in volcanic flows, an autopneumatolysis is invoked, that is, release of terminal pneumatolytes which profoundly modify certain minerals in the rock.

An extreme case is the formation of greisen, which has been discussed in connection with the "late pneumatolytic front" in chapter 6. Greisen is a transformation of granite by destruction of feldspars and formation of muscovite around pneumatolytic veinlets. Perhaps the very common sericitization of cordierites and andalusites of many granites and migmatites is due to a similar phenomenon.

Autopneumatolysis is elsewhere reduced to an autohydration. Saussuritization, which is a cryptocrystalline development of epidote, zoisite, and micaceous or chloritic minerals, is a common alteration of plagioclase in some granite massifs. The phenomenon has been attributed by P. Michot (1948) to an adjustment to conditions of equilibrium in the environment, essentially because of the depth in the crust at the end of the formation of these granites. The phenomenon would fit such an explanation.

THE CRUSHING OF GRANITES

Description of Granitic Mylonites

By the term *mylonites*, as I understand it along with Pierre Termier, is meant all the crushed rocks regardless of degree. Some authors reserve this term for complete crushing, in other words, ground-up rocks. But in nature the ground-up rocks are intimately associated with those of less deformation and the two types are difficult to separate, so that a comprehensive term is necessary and the term mylonite is convenient.

In the most advanced cases, the crushing of granite forms a kind of paste which surrounds uncrushed fragments, which are contained in the groundmass as formless nodules. But nearby the granite is only laminated and shows a series of types expressing a lesser degree of deformation. A crushing process in granitic bedrock seems thus to be complex and without the continuity and regularity which might be expected; mylonitized rocks of all degrees are combined there; they assume a general arrangement in great masses of slightly crushed material, coarsely lenticular, which envelops fairly narrow bands of completely ground-up rock. We have on a large scale, in kilometers or hectometers, that which we see under the microscope on the scale of millimeters or less.

The important mylonitic zones which can be followed for tens of kilometers are grossly linear, comprising skeins of crushed bands, some meters thick, interrupting and succeeding each other, surrounded by rocks slightly crushed or intact. The whole of the mylonitic zone is often a hundred meters thick or more, and has thus a chaotic aspect, elusive to follow in the field when outcrops are scarce. The deformation overall is irregularly diffuse, creating bundles of linear "scales" compressed against each other. It goes without saying that such major tectonic mishaps are not confined to granites, but can occur in any formation. Nevertheless, they are particularly conspicuous in granitic rocks because of their rigidity and their homogeneity.

On account of the numerous varieties of granitic mylonite, expressing stages of attenuated deformation, it is useful to classify these rocks in the following way, according to the intensity of the crushing. This will permit us at the same time to define their details of texture:

1. Laminated rocks;
2. Deformed rocks;
3. Crushed rocks, with or without lamination;
4. Powdered rocks, or mylonites with nodules;
5. Ground-up rocks, or homogeneous mylonites.

In the first two types, the quantity of finely ground material is less than that which under the microscope forms intact or only displaced slabs or fragments. The lamination amounts to a schistose structure mechanically imposed on the mylonite: there are mylonites with or without lamination. In type 3, the quantity of ground material is higher than that left intact. In type 4, the crushing has produced a brecciated arrangement, visible to the naked eye; the scarcely crushed nodules (relics) are surrounded by a ground-up matrix and the mylonite sometimes resembles a sedimentary conglomerate. In type 5, the crushing is complete, fine and regular; the appearance is as homogeneous as that of a quartzite or the groundmass of a porphyry.

In the lowest grade (type 1) a crude schistosity with undulose surfaces first appears. In section it appears as veinlets of darker material, more or less compressed and sinuous, which enclose quartz and feldspars drawn into almond-shaped masses. Under the microscope, the crushed material forms capricious trains following one general direction. It consists of a breccia of tiny debris of quartz and feldspar, of the order of size of a hundredth of a millimeter, mixed with a fine tangle of phyllitic material. The debris are irregular in size and shape. The uncrushed portions are pulled apart and broken up in place, the streams of pulverized material intruding them, shearing the edges of the feldspar crystals, and detaching fragments. The plagioclase grains are often twisted; the twisting, revealed by the distorted polysynthetic twinning, may reach $10°-25°$. Muscovite clusters are cut up and mangled. Quartz is broken into splinters elongated in the direction of the thin streaks of ground-up material.

If there has been no lamination (type 2), the rock is penetrated by friction surfaces of irregular direction, often curved or intersecting, coated with a greenish or ferruginous polished patina. The microscopic aspect is similar to the preceding type, but without any dominating direction for the thin streaks of ground-up material.

In the crushed rocks (type 3), the schistosity is very fine if there is

Fig. 31. Bent and broken feldspar in mylonitic granites of the Marche and Haute. Vienne, France.
a and b. Albite (X40). c. Sheared albite (X60). d. Microcline (X20). e. Feldspar (orthoclase?) (X 20). f. Broken albite (X 30). g. Albite (X 60). h. Albite with fractures invaded by secondary albite. i. Microcline (X 40). j. Albite (X 40). k. Albite (X 150).

lamination. If there is none, the friction surfaces become correspondingly multiplied, enclosing portions where the grains become more mixed and tend to fade into the ground-up paste of the mylonite.

The nodular type (no. 4) is remarkable for its lack of petrographic homogeneity. The nodules, which are little-crushed portions of very diverse size, are embedded in a kind of greenish or brown paste, with a sandy or clayey feel, depending upon the fineness of the grinding. They are limited by shiny surfaces, which are friction surfaces, but these are discontinuous, and often the nodules fade out directly and insensibly into the paste on one side or another.

At the stage of most advanced grinding (type 5), the rock can no longer be recognized by the naked eye because of its apparent homogeneity resembling a sedimentary or volcanic rock composed of indiscernable grains. Microscopic investigation reveals small fragments similar to those in the thin streaks of ground-up material in the foregoing type, some tenths of millimeters overall in size; it is a confused microbreccia, more or less phyllitic, distributed in streaks which vaguely cut each other, sometimes almost invisibly.

It is interesting to study the evolution of the granitic minerals during crushing: they show a lack of important recrystallization comparable to those of metamorphism. Biotite resists very little and transforms, when lamellation begins, to chlorite and ochreous products. In certain cases its transformation to a felt of tiny flakes of a greenish secondary biotite has been described. Muscovite is resistant chemically but it is pulled apart and scattered. The feldspars are preserved almost intact longer than quartz; they are the dominating constituent of isolated debris in ground-up paste. This is probably because of their greater elasticity, which moreover is shown by the twisting of plagioclases. Quartz, which in intact granite formed juxtaposed grains whose complicated outlines were interlocked irregularly, is disarranged at the least deformation; the size of these accumulations diminishes by fragmentation; they are distributed in small slivers elongated in the direction of the lamination.

These slivers of quartz appear in fact to be considerably recrystallized, for they show a regular arrangement in small domains. The tendency to recrystallize is affirmed sometimes even more strongly: the tiny grains in rows grade into each other to produce elongated bands with blurred borders and undulose extinction under polarized light. Sometimes the quartzose plates become fibrous (chalcedony) or spongy and blurred.

A little albite or secondary potash feldspar sometimes cements fractures in the feldspars of the granite. As for the sericite, unaltered in the ground-up paste, it derives, evidently in large part, from shredded muscovite. It also develops from the alteration of the feldspathic dust of this paste. Exceptionally it crystallizes in tiny cracks or at the boundary of any sort of debris.

The recrystallizations as a whole are fairly similar to those of weathering. The mylonites are certainly more prone to weathering than ordinary rocks near the surface of the earth. It is nonetheless probable that deformation suffices to render some minerals unstable, and that biotite, for instance, chloritizes by crushing, even at depths far from meteoric activity. The mylonites do not resemble the products of general metamorphism. They carry the imprint of mechanical action, which irregularly deforms their innermost structures, and not the imprint of a constructive recrystallization. The gradations which have sometimes been described between a mylonitic series and a metamorphic series without doubt derive from crushings generally little accentuated and in part "healed", which one may meet in a series of regional metamorphism and which depend on stress effects during this metamorphism (chapter 11).

A particularly strange and undoubtedly rare case of granitic mylonite is the *pseudo-tachylite*, where the thermal effect of the crushing has been strong enough to fuse or pulverize the rock, producing veinlets resembling a glassy basalt (tachylite) and injecting fissures sometimes only a millimeter wide. According to C. E. Wegmann, "one can imagine that they were introduced in a state of fine dust, such as one may find in connection with strong explosions". First pointed out by W. Hammer (1914) in the Tyrol, under the name *Gangmylonit*, this phenomenon was called pseudo-tachylite by S. J. Shand (1917). Hall and Molengraaff (1955) discovered it in the Vredefort granite in South Africa. Wegmann has encountered it in the Dent-Blanche nappe in the Western Alps. P. Bearth (1933) has given a summary of those from Silvretta in the Tyrolean Alps. Other cases have been described in the Hercynian chain of Central Europe and the Caledonides of Norway.

Comparisons with mylonites of other rocks

Granites and similar rocks (other plutonic rocks, compact gneisses) lend themselves above all to studies of crushing. The crystalline and regular texture of the rocks displays well the successive stages of the phenomenon from the beginning, when the crystals are only bent and cracked to the stage of grinding, when the "relics", still easily identifiable, are embedded in the completely ground-up paste, which itself has no longer any characteristics of a granite. The dimensions of the grain of most granites in the order of millimeters are optimal for the microscopic study of the crushing of constituent minerals. Very fine-grained rocks lend themselves less readily.

On the other hand, the broken minerals of granite do not recrystallize much in the course of crushing; their mylonitic aspect is not obliterated microscopically. This would not be the case in crushed limestones or even quartzites, where the calcite and quartz easily recrystallize at low temperatures, healing the tiny fractures. However, the massive quartzites in the lower Trias in the Penninic zone of the Alps produce powdery mylonites having the consistency of a quartz sand. Finally, in finely bedded or schistose sedimentary rocks, the gliding between beds partly absorbs the deformation and dissimulates it. The same is true for the rocks in which there is a more or less argillaceous cement. However the presence of crush zones will be revealed in stratified rocks, by incoherent glidings chopped by small faults on the scale of some meters (the scale of "small tectonics").

Other kinds of crushing

In the different cases which follow, one finds crushing outside the phenomenon of mylonitization, that is, crushing in the true sense of the word. But it is evident that transitions exist.

Protoclasis is a crushing of some minerals in granite, while other constituents are unaffected. This seems to be a consequence of a deformation contemporaneous with the consolidation of the rock and before its completion. The phenomenon is not regarded as an incipient mylonitization, because the massifs as a whole may show signs of protoclasis without being anywhere crushed in the true sense. The most common case is that of the undulose quartz in some circumscribed massifs of granite.

Synkinematic crystallization occurs in some anatectic granites and *a fortiori* in very heterogeneous migmatites. It is revealed by a partition texture (*cloisonée*) where biotite flakes are drawn out in the interspace between feldspar crystals and calls to mind the arrangement of the crushed streaks of muscovite and chlorite in typical laminated mylonites. These deformations connected with the crystallization of constituent elements of the rock have a symmigmatic (p. 49) or synkinematic (p. 36) character.

Lastly *epimetamorphism*[1] of a granite, which is attended by more or less accentuated lamination with the crystallization of chlorite and colourless mica along the growing metamorphic schistosity, can produce rocks resembling those of an incipient mylonitization. Their texture, however, is much more regular due to the arrangement of the neogenic crystallization.

The geological significance of granitic mylonites

Granitic mylonites are found along faults, or in the great linear crush zones developed at the expense of pre-tectonic granites, and lastly along marginal or internal crush planes in some syntectonic granites (Stratiform granites, chapter 3).

[1] Metamorphism of the upper zones of general metamorphism.

Faults do not in general show a very strong development of mylon-ites, the compression not being intense enough, particularly along vertical faults, the most common case. The mylonites are localized and discontinuous. Alteration due to circulating waters in fissures is more usual along faults than is mylonitization.

The great crush zones in granitic or gneissic terrains are characterized by their great length, which may surpass 100 kilometers, by their relative continuity (in the sense indicated at the beginning of this chap-ter), by the contrast in the geological characteristics of the two regions from one part to another, and finally by the inclination of the crushing or lamination surfaces. They may represent exposures of the base of the great overthrust nappes (*nappes de charriage*) or of important tectonic surfaces of a different character (roots of a bundle of folds in a rigid basement; tectonic "scars" between old resistant blocks; zones of lateral thrusting between rigid blocks of major structures). In that case they involve the rigid, long consolidated granites.

The crushing of the granites of Corsica along the boundary of the Alpine part of the island should be mentioned. It marks the exposure of the upper part of the autochthonous massif which has supported the advance of the Alpine overthrust nappes. The dislocations of Alpine age in the granites of ancient massifs of the Alps and the Hercynian axis of the Pyrenees are deep ruptures of the basement and equally produce mylonite zones. The Argentat crush zone separating the Limousin gneisses from granites and crystalline schists in the southern part of the French Massif Central constitutes a remarkable example because of its dimensions (fig. 32). It is certainly an important tectonic boundary (E. Raguin, 1927).

The marginal or internal crush planes of syntectonic granites form a third category. It is conceivable that, unlike the foregoing cases, they are connected with the *mise en place* of the granite. They mark the direction of fissures belonging to the system of fissures of the granite tectonics of Cloos, but their crushing is unusually strongly pronounced. The relative displacement in the separated blocks may be quite important. These mylonitic surfaces are in harmony with some bands of fluidal granite, with streaks where the grain and the structure of the rock contrast from one to the other. The whole alternate or are aligned longitudinally. There is an agreement with the tectonic axial directions of the complex of the orogenesis of the region. All these signs indicate that such granites are syntectonic or even synkinematic, that is, emplaced during the phase of orogenic displacement. Some layers in the already consolidated granite give rise to crushing and there have undoubtedly been repeated stages of movement and granitization. One can take as an example the Carboniferous granites with white mica of the Central Massif, or certain syntectonic migmatites.

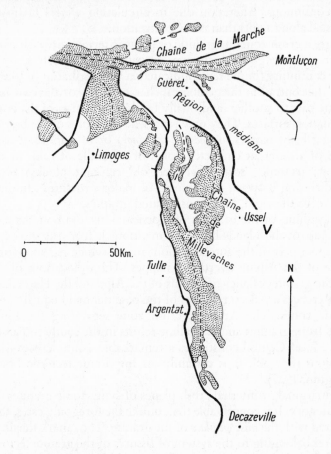

Fig. 32. Bifurcation of the branches of the Hercynian chain in the southern part of the French Massif Central.

The Argentat crush zone borders on the west the Millevaches chain. Syntectonic granite massifs with colourless mica are dotted. The axis of the massif is drawn with dashed lines and the mylonite zones with solid lines.

Chapter 11

GRANITIZATION
AND METAMORPHISM

The notion of plutonism as envisioned along the lines of the "trans-formationist" or "metasomatist" unites this phenomenon with general metamorphism[1] and calls for a rapport between the two classes of fact. The *factors* which one envisions for the development of metamorphism can thus be of interest from the standpoint of plutonism. Perhaps in both cases there is only a difference of intensity and degree between these contributing factors. General metamorphism reflects a tendency towards a grandiose readjustment to a physico-chemical equilibrium. Now granite itself has a form of equilibrium of the crustal materials of a certain depth. However we will see that the relationship between the two phenomena remains obscure.

DEFINITIONS OF THE THREE TYPES OF METAMORPHISM

Metamorphism is a recrystallization of geological formations, which transforms the pre-existing rock without the loss of the rock's solid state for even a moment, at least not completely. The diagenesis of sediments and the consolidation of a liquid magma do not come under this definition. Customarily we also exclude weathering of rocks at the Earth's surface. Metamorphism is a progressive phenomenon, which in its early stages leaves a great part of the original constituent elements of the rock unchanged, but which in more advanced stages ends by com-pletely remodelling their texture and mineralogical composition.

There are three types of metamorphism:

1. Under the influence of neighbouring plutonic rocks, the enclosing rocks are affected by *contact metamorphism*. The recrystallized zone is

[1] Translators' note: Raguin uses the adjective "general" rather than "regional", etc., in this context, as explained below.

called the "aureole" of the plutonic rock. The phenomen is also called *exomorphsim*. It was studied in chapter 6 in the case of granites, around which it is particularly accentuated and interesting. It will not be dealt with further.

2. In the domain of anatexis, vast expanses of rocks appear to have been finely injected *lit par lit* by granitic or aplitic material and transformed into "embrechites" or "anatexites", which are some of the varieties of migmatites. These rocks can more generally be termed *gneiss*. The gneisses of this sort have an infinitely greater development than those often encountered at the inner edge of the granite contact in the contact metamorphic aureole. Anatexis was described in chapter 4.

3. Some series of rocks, several thousand meters thick, have re-crystallized far from plutonic rocks without revealing any clues about the causes and mechanisms of the phenomenon. To these transformed formations the terms *crystallophyllian formations* or *crystalline schists* are applied, which emphasizes the development of schistosity in this type of metamorphism. J. Jung and M. Roques call these crystalline schists *ectinites*, after a Greek word which underlines the role of internal stress during their genesis. The phenomenon has been called general metamorphism, dynamometamorphism, regional metamorphism, dislocation metamorphism, etc. I will keep to the term *general metamorphism*, which implies no hypothesis or theory; it indicates only that the bulk of the layers of a sedimentary series and the associated plutonic or effusive rocks have been affected by the transformation.

The crystallophyllian formations have a zoned structure with parallel zones, each of which corresponds to a certain mineralogical association; and there are generally progressive transitions between the zones. Unlike the marked heterogeneity often found between successive sedimentary beds, this structure indicates a migration of chemical material. In the beginnings of the phenomenon, the average chemical composition of the formation remains practically unchanged. In the more extreme developments the metamorphic formations converge to a gneiss, rich in feldspar, and much richer in alkalis than the average sediment. This fact indicates an addition of chemical substances which are incorporated in the rock. "The metamorphosing action," writes Pierre Termier, "proceeds unevenly to different stages in the series, which as a whole become crystallophyllian. The metamorphism behaves like a spot of oil which spreads in a pile of cloth, and spreads unevenly according to the permeability of different material in the pile." This notion of a slow propagation in all directions starting from a central region is explained if one admits an addition of metamorphosing material to this region, material diffusing upwards and towards the margins. A. Harker notices that in most advanced grades of metamorphism the schistosity fades, at the same time as the zoning becomes more pronounced, no doubt the result of freer diffusion. The diffusion increases with the intensity of the phenomenon.

The layering of the crystallophyllian formations, parallel to their mineralogical zones, are *most often* parallel to the primary stratification of the beds before that transformation. They sometimes reflect this stratification in detail, as for example cross-bedding. This circumstance indicates a rearrangement in place of the elements of these layers.

However the crystallophyllian layers are, in some regions, parallel to a schistosity which cuts across the sedimentary stratification. According to C. E. Wegmann (1931 b) this is the case in the Casanna schists of the Great Saint Bernard nappe of the Western Alps. The same relationship is found in the Caledonian chain of Scandinavia.

As in the aureole of contact metamorphism, one can define as a first approximation three grades of increasing general metamorphism, those of the phyllites, the mica schists and the gneisses. These different facies, however, are far thicker, more varied and largely crystalline in general metamorphism and their textures often show special features.

Among the phyllites, chloritic and sericitic schists are well-developed. The nodular or spotted types are rarer than in contact metamorphism.

The mica schists comprises rocks essentially formed of quartz and mica; but also of calcareous schists in which calcite is associated in abundance with these two minerals. The *schistes lustrés* of the Alps represent the classic type. The hornfels facies rarely occurs.

Within gneisses, one finds intercalations of amphibolites. Pyroxenites and pyroxene gneiss in general are associated with cipolins. Eclogites, which are very rare, are beautiful rocks consisting of pyroxene and garnet, associated with some amphibolites.

The Various Categories of Gneiss

Of the three grades of metamorphism, the extreme is a zoned or foliated rock, basically composed of quartz, feldspar and mica, called a gneiss. Given the unlimited diversity of the gneisses, explained by the diversity of the original material and of evolution, this term is a veritable "sack-name", which has to be amplified as exactly as possible in each case.

As defined, *orthogneiss* and *paragneiss* are due respectively to the transformation of eruptive rocks (plutonic and volcanic) and sedimentary rocks. Very often, however, it is not possible to apply this distinction to a particular gneiss. The recognition of the original material that has undergone metamorphism is rarely achieved without the evidence provided by lateral gradations into less or unmetamorphosed representatives of this material. This class of observation is difficult in regions of general metamorphism, where the formations have been folded subsequently, torn apart into discontinuous or imbricated scales and where it is no longer possible to trace a given layer for any great distance. If the origin of a gneiss is most often obscure, it may still be classifiable according to its texture and mineralogical composition in the categories indicated below.

The migmatite gneisses, which are neither orthogneisses nor paragneisses, form a separate category. They comprise the facies of *embrechites*, if they are homogeneous, and the facies of *epibolites* or *injection gneisses* if they contain concordant veins of granitic material alternating more or less regularly with layers of mica schist. The gneisses of contact aureoles are of the same genre, but of a very restricted development in comparison to the great domains of the migmatites. The term "injection" is somewhat figurative, because it far from necessarily signifies a penetration of a myriad of pre-formed granite veins between the layers of sediments. However, in most cases it seems to reflect a more or less large addition of material. In the migmatites of the French Massif Central, M. Roques (1941) has estimated that the addition is of more than 50 per cent, comparing the chemical composition of these rocks with the corresponding rock association outside the granitized zone. But even in this case, it would be an exaggeration to believe that all the material of the multitude of aplitic, pegmatitic and granitic veins injecting the rocks was supplied from without; that the only components representing pre-existing material are the more or less insignificant, sometimes discontinuous and deformed micaceous septa preserved in the injection gneiss. Some authors, such as Holmquist (1916), think that these feldspathic veins in many regularly banded injection gneisses are only exudations of material almost *in situ*, mobilized by the metamorphism. K. R. Mehnert (1953) has calculated that in the heterogeneous migmatites of the Black Forest the average chemical composition indicates no addition in spite of the numerous interstratified granitic veins. Often the truth lies between these two extremes. But it is difficult to separate the two chemical actions, additions and rearrangement in place. As the injection gneisses are normally related to great masses of anatectic granite, they touch upon the problem of the genesis of granite: are they to a considerable extent formed from material brought in from elsewhere, or are they almost entirely formed in place? We will return to these questions in chapter 17.

FACTORS IN GENERAL METAMORPHISM

The factors which may contribute to metamorphism are the following: mechanical factors (field of applied forces, intimate deformation of material, tectonic crushing or stretching); physical factors (temperature, contact-reactions and intergranular microsolutions); chemical factors (migration of chemical substances). The method of study is mainly based on the geological observation of the phenomena and their interpretation in the light of the basic principles of physics, chemistry and mechanics. But the use of such principles is uncertain and deceptive: there is the "impossibility of experimenting under physical conditions which are not completely different from natural conditions. The scale of geological phenomena surpasses ours infinitely in time and space". (Pierre Termier, 1932). The different factors listed above probably interact more or less with each other in general metamorphism. But one must realize that our understanding of the role they play is rather vague. We do not know which is the dominant factor in metamorphism, although each one probably has some effect when considered by itself.

The Structure of Metamorphic Rocks and the Field of Applied Forces

Zoning and schistosity are the essential characteristics of the crystallophyllian rocks, even when they derive from originally massive rocks. Examples are the amphibolites derived from gabbros and the Penninic orthogneisses derived from granites, in the Franco-Italian Alps. One orienting factor has necessarily presided over the metamorphism: that is the combination of stresses distributed in the volume and produced by forces developed in the earth's crust.

As A. Harker states, all textures found in contact metamorphism are also found here, but they are modified by the influence of this state of directed stress which did not play any role, or had only a slight influence, in contact metamorphism. There is a strong tendency during formation towards a parallel arrangement of the crystals, producing *schistosity*, that is, a cleavage of the crystallophyllian rock. Elongated or platy crystal forms are favoured. Harker indicates, according to Trueman, that the length of the biotite lamellae in the crystalline schists is on the average six times their thickness, while in eruptive rocks it is about one and a half times. That of hornblende, according to Leith, is equal to four or five times its thickness in the crystalline schists, as opposed to two and a half times in eruptive rocks.

In many places, several schistosites have been superimposed. Wegmann (1931 b) has described very suggestive examples from the Casanna schists of the Western Alps.

When the degree of metamorphism increases, the schistosity tends to decrease, because the hydrostatic pressures assumes more importance relative to the stress, and because minerals with more isotropic forces of crystallization in the crystal, such as the feldspars, widely develop. At the same time, those with a high force of crystallization are more apt to develop across the schistosity. However, schistosity may sometimes be preserved in the deepest facies. According to Wegmann the granulites (in Eskola's sense, p. 14), are often much more schistose than the rocks above them; this is due either to conservation of the schistosity through a progressive metamorphism, or to movements and deformations contemporaneous with the stage of granulitic metamorphism and not healed because of a lesser ability to recrystallize in a water-poor milieu.

In crystallophyllian rock, *granoblastic* and *diablastic* textures are encountered once more, where the factor of orientation is less pronounced. Much more widespread (and it is understandable from the foregoing) are the *lepidoblastic* textures or the orientation of flaky minerals parallel to the cleavage of the rock, and *nematoblastic* texture, characterized by the orientation of rodlike minerals elongated in one direction and parallel to the cleavage. Lastly, the *porphyroblastic* and *poeciloblastic* variants are encountered as in contact metamorphism.

In order to explain the mode of action of the forces distributed in formations during the course of recrystallization, Riecke's principle has been applied, according to which if a crystal in a saturated solution is affected by a force in a particular direction, its solubility increases proportionately to the square of the stress. The environment must be represented as an aggregate of crystalline grains, compressed one against the other, in which the interstices are filled with microsolutions. "The most compressed parts of the grains are consequently dissolved, while the less compressed parts grow in circulating solution. In this way the grains will be markedly shortened by dissolution in the direction of greatest pressure, and elongated by growth in the direction of less easy expansion" (F. Becke).

J. Jung and M. Roques relate to this subject the suggestive phenomenon of "impressed pebbles" (*galets impressionnés*) of the Alpine

Molasse, which penetrate each other without rupture, by partial dissolution at the points of contact under the influence of relatively weak
compression of however long duration.

These observations explain the flattening of crystals along the planes
of schistosity in metamorphic rocks. But they do not explain the crystallographic orientation which many of these crystals show relative to these

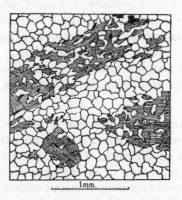

Fig. 33. Micrograph of a poeciloblastic texture (simplified drawing after A. Harker).
Porphyroblasts of amphibole in a background of quartzite.

planes, an orientation which is very obvious in mica. Petrofabric
studies under the microscope have made it possible to verify the same
properties for other minerals such as quartz, calcite and feldspar. The
phenomenon has been reproduced experimentally by F. E. Wright
(1906), who obtained oriented pyroxenes through the crystallizing of
glass under directed pressure. Another effect like that of Riecke's
principle may also intervene in the following way. As Pierre Termier
has emphasized, the foregoing phenomenon is a matter of each mineral
during formation tending to orient perpendicular to the directed pressure one of its planes of higher lattice density. Now when a crystal
grows freely in its mother liquid, those are the planes which develop
preferentially (Bravais' law). They often represent planes of cleavage.
As Harker says, "we can imagine that the force of crystallization is
larger along a cleavage than across it". Thus the fact referred to by
Pierre Termier would correspond in total to an economy of energy
expended: the crystals orient themselves in the rock in the course of the
metamorphism because they have less resistance to overcome by
developing perpendicularly to the direction of greatest pressure. This

G*

simple scheme is known moreover to be only an approximation: B. Sander's petrofabric analysis show that there can be several preferred directions in metamorphic rocks other than the main schistosity.

Some authors, however, think that the orientation of crystals during metamorphism does not arise out of these effects of stress, but simply from a diffusion and an addition of material more readily in predetermined directions such as original stratification or microfractures which follow that of the schistosity. E. Friedel, who is of this opinion[1], cites in its support the crystals of so-called "deformed" rock salt, which can be observed in salt marls. These directions of easy diffusion may also correspond to glide planes, as will be seen later.

If, in the general case, it is oriented recrystallizations which produce the crystallophyllian schistosity, in certain cases, writes M. Roques (1941)

> one sees superimposed on this first a mechanical phenomenon which can sometimes be intense. It is exerted particularly upon the residual minerals in the rock. These minerals are broken. The debris gives the impression of having been slightly stretched. The stretching is moreover contemporaneous with the recrystallization. The fragments of the residual minerals have been healed by recrystallizations even during the course of their crushing because the newly formed minerals themselves sometimes show traces of mechanical action. It must also be observed that some abundant recrystallizations are seen at the extremities of the stretched minerals, spread in the plane of schistosity.

He recalls the very curious case of large garnet or staurolite crystals in mica schists, which have sometimes been rotated during their growth. "In certain cases a mechanical schistosity participates in the formation of the crystallophyllian schistosity to the same extent as the schistosity of recrystallization."

Distributed Deformation

It is understandable that some observations of the foregoing variety have directed research towards the study of the intimate deformation of metamorphic rocks.

The forces acting on a homogeneous solid body, develop at each point stresses of variable intensity, according to the directions in space: the extremity of a vector representing the stress acting on a small unit

[1] Oral communication.

plane, constructed in the imagination within the solid and rotating around the point of application, describes an ellipsoid (stress ellipsoid). This state of stress may result in a deformation of the material. It is possible to picture the phenomenon by imagining a small sphere at each point of the solid: it will become an ellipsoid (deformation ellipsoid).

A specific case is that where one of the axes of the deformation ellipsoid is equal to the diameter of the sphere, and where the deformation of one small element is thus parallel to a unit plane. Perpendicular to this plane, which is a principal plane of the deformation ellipsoid, are revealed two planes relative to which there exists a maximum tangential deformation, and these are the cyclical planes of the ellipsoid. At the beginning of the deformation they form an angle of 45° with the principal planes; they are apt to rotate simultaneously and proportionately to the establishment of the deformation of the environment when this has a finite amplitude. But generally the speed of rotation is different and the less mobile of the two will be the most effective. These planes are predestined to rupture and gliding. It could happen in nature that one of the two remains fixed in space and in relation to the material in motion if the deformation assumes a finite amplitude, that is if the deformation is reduced to a simple gliding along this plane (deformation of a pack of cards pushed obliquely along its edge).

Many petrographers invoke these *gliding surfaces*, oblique to the principal stress, to explain the formation of schistosity in metamorphic rocks: to attain a state of equilibrium with a minimum expenditure of energy it is necessary, they think, for the crystals to develop parallel to gliding surfaces. Moreoever active chemical solutions can move more readily along these surfaces than any others. Since a single cleavage develops much oftener than conjugated double cleavage it is assumed that the least variable gliding surface in the rock would be the only one effective.

As the principal planes of the stress ellipsoid coincide with those of the deformation ellipsoid in an isotropic environment for a small deformation, and as the schistosity developed according to Riecke's principle must be oriented in the principal plane normal to the greatest stress of the stress ellipsoid, there is disagreement between the two theories: a stretching schistosity normal to the compression and a schistosity of gliding (shearing). U. Grubenmann and P. Niggli (1924) admit that the crystallization of the schistosity may take place either along a principal plane of the ellipsoid (case of weak deformation) or along the shear plane (case of strong deformation). Moreover, they remark, the ellipsoid tends to rotate its greatest axes parallel to one of the shear planes in the case of very strong deformation, where it becomes more and more elongated. This would remove the contradiction and in the case of strong deformation, the schistosity would result from a *differential movement distributed throughout the whole rock mass following very closely the planes of shear.*

J. Goguel (1945) has shown that laboratory experiments and many observations in the field of various kinds support an interpretation of schistosity as being in the plane normal to the maximum pressure. Moreover, the extrapolation indicated above, made by G. F. Becker, of the properties of a small deformation by gliding parallel to one plane to a deformation on a large scale of the same type, is based according to Goguel on a mechanical analysis tainted by errors.

However, natural conditions are more complex than simple mechanical schemes. The stretching of stratified geological formations would often seem accompanied by sliding of the beds past each other. B. C. King and N. Rast (1955) have observed in the crystalline schists of the Scottish Highlands numerous tiny hinges or drag folds in the order of centimeters, which have been almost obliterated by a general crushing expressing this relative movement of the beds of the formation. The case may be quite common, but its recognition is difficult because of the obliteration of the significant structures.

It is thus probable that both influences exist but new petrofabric studies would be necessary in order to determine the relative effectiveness of the two. It is conceivable that the schistosity by stretching (laws of Riecke and Pierre Termier) is the more common case, and that in certain zones shearing schistosity is superimposed upon it.

Geological Conditions Favourable to an Efficaceous State of Stress in Metamorphism

It would *a priori* be tempting to assume that orogenic forces have been able to produce the state of stress and deformation of which I have pointed out the traces in the development of metamorphism. Many authors actually have recourse to this mode of explanation. We will see that this often seems in disagreement with the observed facts.

To be sure the deformations accompanied by crushing and stretching are highly distinctive in the structure of mountain chains. They have not however given rise to important recrystallizations in their vicinity; they have not provoked metamorphism. This observation, made by Pierre Termier as long ago as 1904, has since been confirmed. At most some marmorization of limestones and some hardening of shales is to be observed.

The crushing of the old granites of the autochthon of Corsica below the overthrust nappes did not result in gneiss; its mylonitic granites are always crushed granites. This is a striking example of a general rule in the mylonites. Yet the mylonitic deformation is often of a surprising intensity. P. J. Holmquist (1926) cites a quartz grain of 0·2 mm whose extremities have been twisted through 30° in a Scandinavian sandstone-quartzite mylonite.

In the French Alps (Briançonnais, Maurienne, Tarentaise), the over-thrust nappes have produced the superposition of large massifs of metamorphosed formations (*Schistes lustrés*, prasinites, Permo-Coal measures gneiss) on the Eocene flysch, fine grained limestones of the Foraminiferous Cretaceous and other Mesozoic fossiliferous or dolo-mitic limestones. The contact is abrupt without lithological transitions. In spite of the intensity of compression, in spite of the heterogeneity favourable for chemical reactions in these piled-up strata, the meta-morphism of the underlying series is nil, or restricted to an initial stage without the destruction of fossils. More generally there is some inde-pendence between the overall structure of the chain of mountains and the exact distribution of metamorphism.

Moreover, if a part (principal?) of the metamorphism is earlier than the overthrusting of the great nappes, another notable part is later than these orogenic movements. R. Michel (1953) has shown that albite, widely developed in certain layers of the *Schistes lustrés* of Maurienne, was formed after the deformation. The same is undoubtedly true for the glaucophane.

According to J. Jung and M. Roques (1936):

if crystalline schists are found in zones of the Earth's crust affected by deepseated and intense tectonics it is only a special case, for the crystalline schists are so widely and typically developed in zones which have suffered only insignificant tectonic deformation.

They cite several regions in the southwestern part of the French Massif Central. "This fact is still more obvious if one refers to certain beautiful crystallophyllian series which are subtabular over enormous areas, as for instance in Oubanghi-Chari". They also note, following Pierre Termier, that in general the crystallophyllian schistosity coincides with the primary stratification of the rocks: a fact that is not conceivable if the layers in general were folded before or during the metamorphism, but which instead suggests a metamorphism before the folding.

Aside from tectonic movements, what other causes can be invoked for the systems of vertical pressures or horizontal stretching which intervene in general metamorphism? J. Jung and M. Roques state that the simple weight of the layers, no matter what their thickness in geosynclinal accumulation, cannot produce at any point in the crust a vertical pressure, but only a hydrostatic pressure. The weight of an imaginary vertical column would certainly lead to vertical crushing and transversal shearing, if the column were unsupported laterally. But the effect is neutralized by pressures from adjoining columns, the imaginary columns being embedded in the Earth's crust. In order to explain the state of stress in the layers,

> one must abandon this hypothesis and return to that of an extension in the horizontal plane. Thus general metamorphism by stress is due to tangential stretching of the rocks, under a hydrostatic pressure created by the weight of the overlying bedrock. Agreed then, according to a more general definition: in the interplay of stresses which affect the Earth's crust, the formation of crystalline schists represents stretching, and that of mountains compression of deep-seated layers (Jung and Roques, 1936).

It is obvious that a stretching of the elements in a rock horizontally will produce the same effect as a compression of these same elements vertically. What can such a stretching represent from the point of view of general geology? Is it a kind of compensation in connection with compressions produced elsewhere? The answer is obscure. Apart from the orogenic stretchings due to the translation of overthrust nappes, the only geological phenomenon which seems to me likely to produce horizontal extensions on a grand scale is the tendency of the batholithic massifs to rise. We have seen that the warping of the vaults of great radius of these massifs often gives rise to numerous tension fissures and that the linear structure of the granites disclose even during the plastic stage of the environment an overall stretching often little inclined. Is this an indication that the movements of a subjacent granite massif produce favourable stress conditions in the metamorphic series?

Other phenomena on a greater scale, and, to be sure, hypothetical, can be imagined: convection currents under the Earth's crust or else the evolution of the asthenolith. This term refers to a mobile zone under the crust, by fusion and differentiation of material below the future orogenic edifices, according to the views of R. W. van Bemmelen (1936). C. E. Wegmann[1] suggests to me another possible cause of displacements of

[1] Private communication.

the *infrastructure* (chapter 12) which would operate at a level much less deep than the convection currents of Kraus and Griggs and the displacements of the asthenolith. The movements of the infrastructure, which end in granito-diapiric tectonics, seem mainly vertical (uplifts of Fennoscandia, the Vosges and the Black Forest, the Hercynian massifs of the Alps). There is a possibility of horizontal stress of regional scale caused by unequal vertical movements of great blocks of the crust under the sedimentary and metamorphic zones.

Nonetheless, even if there may well exist metamorphic series outside the tectonic zones of maximum degree, where the deformation is intense and which constitute the whole or an important part of mountain chains, I think that there are also cases of metamorphism more directly connected with orogeny. In fact, in certain cases the crystallization seems due to intimate gliding or lamination of the beds of the rocks, as petrographic study under the microscope strongly suggests.

Other Physical Factors of Metamorphism

Among the physical factors, there is temperature. Some hundreds of degrees suffice in ore veins for the hydrothermal solutions to produce a varied metasomatism and the precipitation of minerals. These temperatures can easily be reached by geothermal heating in the interior of geosynclinal series. At a depth of 3,000 meters the temperature will be about 100°. Nevertheless heating is not alone a sufficient condition for metamorphism, because there are many thick geosynclinal accumulations free of metamorphism, such as those of the Jurassic and Cretaceous of the Dauphinois zone of the French Alps. The same applies to the thick series which occur in many of the coal basins of the world.

Another factor, already mentioned, resides in the actions of intergranular contacts. They are evidently accentuated by crushing, possibly by distributed shearing in the heart of the terrain, as P. Niggli has emphasized. These facilitate chemical reactions between neighbouring particles. The possible heating due to this deformation has a similar effect. According to Niggli, the deformation results in a state of instability which is favourable to a later transformation of the rock assemblage, as is observed in metals and alloys, which is taken advantage of in metallurgical processing. Some metals, deformed when cold and then heated, crystallize better than if heated without deformation.

The Chemical Factors of Metamorphism

In the recrystallization of a rock without passage through a molten state, some chemical transport over short distances is necessary. These transports are comparable to the diffusion which metallurgists observe in metallic alloys. Observations of the same order have been made by R. Perrin (1934) in the coatings of metallurgical furnaces. In a coating with magnesia in contact with molten iron containing some manganese and titanium oxide, he established a migration of these elements into the magnesia, independent of each other and for different distances, however small.

In Nature, where important quantities of water impregnate rocks and play the role of "mineralizers", activating reactions, effects of this type are amplified. Lenses of pegmatite or quartz of some decimeters are frequently observed in gneiss or mica schist respectively, far from any eruptive source. These lenses are attributed to an "exudation" of chemical elements from the surrounding rock.

J. Jung (1928) has verified the unequal diffusion of Fe, Ti, Al and Mg around inclusions of gneiss enclosed in metamorphic limestone in the Vosges. The metamorphism has produced in them a true fractional distillation of these elements, which have emigrated for increasing distances in the order indicated around the inclusions, in an interval of some centimeters. This was prior to, on a small scale, the setting forth of the "basic front" by D. Reynolds. The elements mentioned are relatively very little volatile. Others are much more so and there are good reasons to believe that in particular alkali silicates and borates are capable of migrating over vast distances in the development of feldspars and tourmalines.

Some migrations on a large scale seem to take place in metamorphic series, although it is scarcely possible to define their magnitude. For instance, in the series of *Schistes lustrés* of the Alps, the sandy schists and the limy marls which constitute the major part of the Alpine geosynclinal sedimentation have been transformed into holocrystalline rocks with muscovite, chlorite, quartz and calcite, with feldspar (orthoclase and above all albite) and tourmaline. These last minerals, usually of microscopic dimensions, are common in most layers of the series even far from intercalations of greenstones and orthogneisses found in this series. Even if the alkalis in the argillaceous portions of the sedimentary rocks occur in quantities sufficient to supply material for the formation of neogenic feldspar almost *in situ*, it is doubtful whether they would suffice for the mineralization of the whole assemblage. Geochemical data are missing. Authigenic non-metamorphic feldspar has been found in small quantities by F. Grandjean (1910) in several limestones of the Paris Basin. Observations by M. Topkaya (1950) have shown also the development of authigenic minerals (quartz, feldspar, tourmaline) in some non-metamorphic Triassic limestones of the Alps. It is noteworthy that for tourmaline the presence of boron in important quantities in marine clays is common. According to Rankama and Sahama (1950) the content is clearly larger than in igneous rocks, as V. M. Goldschmidt has already verified.

Thus it is difficult to appreciate directly the importance of chemical migrations over a great distance and for great quantities of material. However we will see below that the zoning of the great metamorphic series imposes the idea of such migrations.

Diffusion of chemical substances of "filtering columns" (*Colonnes filtrantes*) remains rather tenuous, so that the chemical composition of the modified rocks is often only slightly changed. A paragneiss often retains the chemical characteristics of a sedimentary rock; an ortho-amphibolite that of the original gabbro.

The filtration of these chemical substances across great thicknesses of strata is difficult to conceive. R. Daly (1933) writes: "Anyone who has seen a high-powered well of natural gas blow off obtains a lively sense of the highly impervious character of even sedimentary rock" (p. 308). However, the gas appears in general to have the pressure of the column of water between the earth's surface and its point of accumulation, which implies at least a slight long term permeability. According to E. Friedel:

> Observations made in the potash basin of Alsace show that the marls and clays do not offer any resistance to a slow propagation of fluids. We call them impermeable only because they do not allow a rapid passage. But if one takes a slab of impermeable marl of the potash mines of Alsace and keeps it in a dry place, it will in some weeks exude its entire content of salt water, covering itself with an effervescence of salt. This salt water has no difficulty circulating in the marl. It can perfectly well happen, moreover, that a formation is more impermeable for gas than for a liquid, if the cavities in it are of capillary dimensions and if the rock is wet.[1]

It thus seems that in the case of metamorphism the "time" factor is actually of significance in explaining the propagation of "filtering columns" by microsolutions.

Some authors envisage a chemical diffusion in the ionic state propagating through the crystal lattices, at least for high grades of metamorphism. It is doubtful whether this process is effective over great

[1] Unpublished communication.

distances and in any case we lack the physical bases to evaluate its possibilities.

REARRANGEMENT OF MATERIAL DURING GENERAL METAMORPHISM

Zones of Isometamorphism

If a rearrangement of material operates on the scale of a visible or microscopic crystal, and on the larger scale of a sedimentary bed transformed into a layer of crystalline schists, it effects at the same time a grand rearrangement embracing the whole metamorphic series and permitting the classification of the crystalline schists of an individual series from top to bottom in several successive facies. Grubenmann's celebrated classification of the crystalline schists is based on the notion of chemical equilibria. According to Grubenmann and Niggli, and their school, metamorphism is a change of chemical equilibria. For an initial rock of given composition there result several possible mineralogical associations, depending upon conditions of equilibrium, in other words, several possible metamorphic rocks: the series of these metamorphic rocks constitutes what Jung and Roques call a "sequence" of metamorphism characteristic of the initial composition. One can calculate *a priori* the possible mineralogical associations in the sequences and in the field one can find these associations, or rocks showing a tendency towards them.

The principal factors of equilibrium are temperature and pressure. More simply one can say that the essential factor is the *depth* at which the metamorphism takes place, because temperature and pressure increase with depth. This is schematic and the "depth" of metamorphism is only symbolic. Metamorphic "depth" may be very different from geometric depth, if the physico-chemical conditions of the deep zones have been transferred to relatively superficial levels through geological evolution, for example, if the geothermic gradient is found steepened.

The first idea of two zones of metamorphism was conveyed by J. J. Sederholm (1891). It was taken up by F. Becke in 1904. U. Grubenmann (1906) adopted it and added an intermediate zone. It was thus possible to classify the metamorphic terrains according to three depth zones characterized by physio-chemical equilibria, i.e., mineralogical equilibria determined for each of the principal sequences. These are three *zones of isometamorphism* with their characteristic *index minerals*. Broadly these zones resemble the three zones of phyllites, mica schists and gneisses already defined above as a first approximation. They are called *epizone*, *mesozone* and *catazone*. The same prefixes can be applied to the word metamorphism, and one can speak of epimetamorphism, etc.

Another celebrated classification is that of G. Barrow, even earlier than the works of Becke and Grubenmann, and later expanded by C. E. Tilley. It permits a more exact subdivision of zones in certain favourable regions, such as the Highlands of Scotland.

If a very great precision is not required, and a metamorphic assemblage of very great thickness is considered, where a statistical approach to the most common minerals can be made, Grubenmann's zones with their index minerals work out very well. But we must not look for great exactitude, because the limits are not clear cut and there are recurrences of metamorphic facies. Thus Lacroix has established that the application is practical for metamorphic rocks of Madagascar. He has discovered in different regions the same series of schists, quartzites, limestones and plutonic rocks, in one part in a slightly metamorphosed schistose facies, and in another in a gneiss facies. The first series belongs to the epizone, the other to the mesozone of Grubenmann.

However, as J. J. Sederholm has remarked, temperature, pressure and chemical composition alone do not control the metamorphic facies; original differences in texture and mineralogical composition also have great influence and dominate the state of equilibrium more or less completely during the the development of the rock. This renders the strict application of the theory difficult. M. Roques notes that for different sequences the zone limits of Grubenmann do not coincide at all; one may for instance find serpentine of the facies of the uppermost zone in an environment of gneiss in the facies of the intermediate zone.

J. Jung and M. Roques (1936, 1952) have rendered practical the use of isometamorphic zones by field geologists who must, whenever possible, trace out the limits and exact outlines of the crystallophyllian rocks on geologic maps. They define five zones and employ other index minerals, chosen in such a way that as few as possible are involved, and appearing in the most common sequences, and finally characteristic and abundant enough to be of use in the petrographic diagnosis of the rock, if possible with a hand lens or the naked eye. It is the aluminous sequence (argillacous schists) which serve the purpose. They distinguish the following zones, from the top downwards:

1. Zone of upper mica schists (with chlorite and muscovite)
2. Zone of lower mica schists (with muscovite and biotite)
3. Zone of upper gneiss (with feldspar other than albite; muscovite and biotite)

4. Zone of lower gneiss (with feldspar other than albite; and biotite)
5. Ultra-lower zone (with cordierite without biotite).

These zones are thus based on the stability of the feldspars and the micaceous minerals (micas and chlorites). Experiment shows that the change in these index minerals is not instantaneous from one zone to another, but marked enough to map the crystalline schists.

From a general point of view, some important facts become apparent with the notion of isometamorphic zones. They show, in the genesis of metamorphism, an alkalinization more pronounced at depth, a distribution of chemical substances in minerals stable at higher temperature, and an increase in grain size of crystals, all things being equal. They indicate that metamorphism rises from depth, where the rocks are "more metamorphic". They are also *the best indication of a migration of alkaline substances* on a grand scale. A statistical study by P. Lapadu-Hargues (1945) confirms this migration.

When one tries to grasp in detail the growing development of metamorphism, one observes an overlapping in the appearance of neogenic minerals which make their debut successively, their formation continuing side by side. Such are the beginnings of metamorphism in the *Schistes lustrés* of the French Alps (E. Raguin, 1930).

A more detailed analysis has shown in certain metamorphic series the replacement of the minerals of one phase by those of the following phase, through a displacement of isometamorphic zones. For example, J. Cogné (1953) has shown that the biotite schists of southern Brittany have suffered a second metamorphism following a different plan with albitization and glaucophanization. This is an example of *retromorphosis* (retrogressive metamorphism), that is, a rearrangement according to a new, less powerful or "deep" metamorphic grade than the first. This concept, also called *diaphthoresis*, was introduced in 1907 by F. Becke. Its importance is great, notably in Alpine geology. In these modifications of equilibrium intervene variations in stress conditions, or so it seemed to him. Thus was foreseen the *rhythms of metamorphism* (J. de Lapparent, 1935). This introduces to metamorphism, as in other geological phenomena where analysis is possible, the idea of the division into multiple episodes, covering undoubtedly considerable periods of time.

Eskola's Metamorphic Facies

Another classification of metamorphic rocks, also based on the concept of equilibrium, has been established by P. Eskola, accentuating a type of characteristic rock in each category of equilibrium. Without specifying the subdivisions and leaving out the glaucophane schists (following Turner and Verhoogen, 1951), one can enumerate the seven following facies:

1. The sanidinite facies (maximum temperature, minimum pressure)
2. The pyroxene hornfels facies (high temperature, medium pressure)
3. The amphibolite facies (moderate temperature, medium pressure)
4. The albite–epidote amphibolite facies (moderate temperature, lower than the foregoing, medium pressure)
5. The greenschist facies with chlorite (low temperature, medium pressure)
6. The granulite facies (high temperature, high pressure)
7. The eclogite facies (high temperature, very high pressure)

In each one of the facies it is possible to catalogue the stable mineral associations depending upon the chemical composition of the rock, and to enumerate the petrographically-varied rocks which are part of the facies[1]. These notions have great theoretical interest, but are difficult to apply in a complete description of a geological district because the typical mineralogical associations often contain less common minerals which are only occasionally represented in the series. Certain facies occur, however, in a very limited way: the sanidinite facies (inclusions in volcanic rocks); pyroxene hornfels facies (contact metamorphism); eclogite facies (rare occurrences).

But the interesting point of this classification is its justification of the possibility of applying the "phase rule" to petrogenesis. It gives a more precise definition of the equilibrium conditions in major portions of the Earth's crust. Finally *most of the plutonic rocks fit into it as metamorphic rocks*. Thus granite seems to belong essentially to the amphibolite facies. Nonetheless, P. Michot (1948) has shown that, depending on the case, granite may have been crystallized with the imprint of a shallower facies, which shows up in the type of endometasomatic saussuritization of the feldspars. Such cases of disequilibrium in the granite massifs relative to their settings may signify an important transfer of material in conformity with the opinions of the "magmatists" concerning the emplacement of granites.

The Base of the Metamorphic Series

In the zone of "lower gneisses" (*gneiss inférieurs*) of general metamorphism, for the most part more coarsely crystalline and of a more massive

---

[1] The term granulite designates the fine gneisses with little mica of deep metamorphism.

structure, all things being equal, the distinction between orthogneisses and paragneisses is effaced in the development of uniformity or a variability stripped of definite character. What is more, the distinction between these ectinites and some homogeneous migmatites also becomes more and more blurred.

At higher levels the filter columns of general metamorphism differ considerably from the granitic injections by the tenuity of additions and by the absence of veins of pegmatites, aplites and quartz, diffused as very thin seams in the injection gneisses, In the lower gneisses of the ectinite series, some feldspathic layers form along the schistosity, sometimes cutting it, formed by an exudation of local material or by a freer and more capricious, and also more important, concentration of added material. *There is a convergence of the lower gneisses and the migmatites at a deep level.*

Often the difference between the two types of rock will be subtle; possibly this difference will only be perceived in the field because of transitions or recurrences. Write Jung and Roques (1936):

> It may be added that the phenomenon of migmatization only becomes perfectly clear on the regional scale, and that neither isolated samples, nor thin sections can make diagnosis possible. The study of migmatites is above all a field study.

In several regions where metamorphic series have been well studied, it can be stated that broadly the ectinites lie above the migmatites. "Probably pneumatolysis is intense enough everywhere in the lower part of the crystallophyllian series to bring about the formation of migmatites" (Jung and Roques, 1936). But understandably the migmatite front is not necessarily parallel to the zones of isometamorphism (isograds): in the French Massif Central it rises to higher and higher zones from north to south.

The superposition of the ectinites over migmatites may be objected to on the basis of the example of the Alps, where the ectinites are so well developed, although migmatites of the Alpine cycle have seemed to be absent until quite recent studies. However, the accessible thickness of the Alpine metamorphic series is not very great if one unfolds the overthrust nappes. Furthermore, the observations of M. Reinhard (1935) and his collaborators tend to make one think that the role of the Alpine granites is less trifling than it had once appeared. We know today that the granitic "hearths" in the cores of the Tessin nappes are associated with typical migmatites whose petrofabrics are identical to those of Alpine metamorphic rocks of the region as a whole (E.

Wenk, (1953). These are the granites and migmatites of the Alpine orogeny. The same is true of the Tauern. C. Exner (1948, 1951) has found some gneiss with large porphyroblasts of Alpine microcline near Bad Gastein. In the crystalline massifs in the centre of the Tauern, F. Karl (1959), developing an old idea of B. Sander's, has shown that there are Alpine gneisses and granites, associated with augengneiss and much older granite gneisses. Both at Gross-Venediger and between Hochalmspitz and Ankogel he has discovered tonalities similar to the Peri-Adriatic late-alpine tonalities, such as in the Adamello. The difference between the first and second rests in the late Alpine metamorphism which has affected the first (*Tauernkristallisation*). This metamorphism displays itself above all in the formation of numerous microscopic inclusions of clinozoisite, geometrically arranged in the core of the plagioclases of the rock. In the Peri-Adriatic tonalites a late hydrothermal phase has started the same transformation. It is known on the other hand that great areas of Alpine granite in Bergell (Bregaglia) have a migmatic structure.

However, it must be noted, as we have seen in chapter 4, that the migmatites themselves sometimes have a floor, that they do not necessarily pass downwards into the anatectic fundamental granites. In this case they have been injected in some kind of stratiform deposit by tangential tectonic movements, or else they may have been superposed on more rigid zones and apparently less deformed, as certain ultra-deep-seated gneisses (Noe-Nygaard and Berthelsen, 1952). But it appears as if the passage downwards toward the anatectic granite is the most common case in the zones of great orogeny.

CONNECTIONS BETWEEN GENERAL METAMORPHISM AND GRANITE

1. A first essential fact is the granitic affinity of the crystalline schists of general metamorphism recorded in the basal gneisses of several series of strong metamorphism, where chemical diffusion is broadly active. On the scale of orogenic structures it is less probable that general metamorphism is independent of plutonism. Their differences are only evident in block tectonics. Pierre Termier has admitted that general metamorphism surmounts and envelopes the great zones of granitization. For C. E. Wegmann "the orogenic infrastructure", the zone of granitization with migmatites, supports the folded and faulted "superstructure" with a transition zone between them of general metamorphism.

2. The application of the concept of "metamorphic facies" in the

sense of Eskola is convenient for both metamorphism and plutonism, which indicates a certain parallelism between both phenomena. Temperature and pressure are not the only determining factors, because the difference between plutonic and metamorphic rocks remains even in the same facies.

3. A third fact is the special mechanical state reigning in the formations in the course of their recrystallization and expressing itself by the extraordinary efficacy of the system of distributed stresses and by a widespread intimate deformation. This mechanical state seems mainly to be related to the pre-tectonic conditions, but is prolonged and changed during orogenic movements. On the other hand, it seems more and more as if the mechanical factors have played a great role in the development of plutonism. One meets again the parallelism emphasized above. Perhaps one could use as an argument the phenomena of horizontal stretching observed in the vaults of the great granite batholiths, and conclude from it that the granitization has created a state of stress in the strata during the metamorphism.

4. In conclusion, one ascertains a rather mysterious relationship between granite and general metamorphism in connection with orogeny but at different times and following different rhythms. One may suspect that for the development of granitization and metamorphism the "factors" are of the same nature but act in different proportions and with intensities which are not of the same order of magnitude.

Chapter 12

GRANITE AND OROGENY

Some decades ago it was not considered absurd to regard the studies of lithology and orogeny as completely separate domains in which knowledge of one could be conveniently ignored in the other. The recent evolution of ideas[1] which has reconciled the theory of the plutonic rocks, and particularly of the granites, with the phenomena of metamorphism, has radically modified this point of view.

Very particularly under the influence of C. E. Wegmann's school, the kinematic and chronological factors of granitization have come into their own: there is no doubt that granitization and orogeny are two great geological phenomena which affect one another and often depend directly one on the other.

The study of the connection between granite and orogeny is carried out by means of *structural analysis*, a method made notable by Wegmann. It consists of a kinematic interpretation of the petrographic and structural criteria available on all scales, from that of outcrops to the great tectonic assemblages on the one hand, and to the microscopic on the other. This kinematic interpretation emphasizes evolutionary aspects, in other words, the relative chronology of the criteria studied.

A. Demay (1942) has stressed the importance of microtectonics on the microscopic scale. He has emphasized that the intimate details of texture of migmatites or of some gneissic granites are in harmony with the structures of greater magnitude. However, everything is not found on the microscopic scale and the results of this magnitude must be combined with the study of movements on greater scales "in the same way as histology cannot resolve the problems of comparative anatomy" (Wegmann). This poses the question of the use of microscopic petrofabric analysis (chapter 7). Where it has been carried out, it seems to me that it has not directly provided results applicable to structures of a higher order, for the more one goes into detail, the more

[1] See in particular: R. Perrin and M. Roubault, 1951.

complexity appears, and the more interpretations become the subjects of caution, particularly in migmatite terrains. The effectiveness of petrofabric analysis (*structurologie*) is affirmed, particularly for macro-structures, statistical examinations of microscopic structures serving mainly in an auxiliary way or as a control.

The harmonization of the different orders of magnitude is not a matter of similitude. As Wegmann expresses it (1947): "The pheno-mena resulting from different orders of magnitude are not, from the kinematic and dynamic point of view, larger or smaller replicas for which the same reasoning would be applied without modification". By combining the techniques appropriate to the different orders of magnitude, it is possible to go much further than if only one technique is used by itself.

We are going to examine the categories of criteria which may be significant for the various major types of granites.

ANATECTIC GRANITES AND SYNTECTONIC MIGMATITES

If one could obtain a representation of the astonishing chemical mobility which has controlled the development of anatectic granites[1], the image obtained of the emplacement of these granites would still be incomplete. In fact, along with the chemical mobility *á tache d'huile*

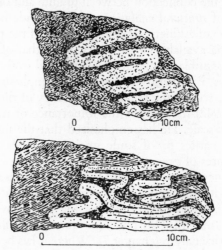

Fig. 34. Ptygmatic folds (drawings after J. J. Sederholm). Aplite veins in fine-grained gneiss.

[1] To which we will return in Chapter 17.

(by the oil spot mechanism), there has also been a tectonic mobility of equal importance. The phenomena of deformation in anatexis correspond to very special types of movement, plastic and very free movements *seeming* to be produced in a semi-fluid environment, or rather in an environment which locally shows an irregularly distributed partial fluidity. These movements were not overlooked by J. J. Sederholm: for him the emplacement of the Finnish Precambrian granites, separated by great periods of erosion, were related to orogenic movements, and corresponded broadly with periods of deformation. Nevertheless it is to C. E. Wegmann that the credit must go for the more precise evidence of the tectonic role of anatexis.

I mentioned *seeming* above. Actually the kinematic image will not suffice to prove fluidity, no matter how free its style may be, because flow movements are possible in crystallized material, such as can be seen in glaciers.

Fig. 35. Aplites in gneiss with ptygmatic folds (drawing after a photographic figure by J. J. Sederholm). The size of the figure is about 2 m.

Among the phenomena studied by Sederholm are the curious and common little *ptygmatic folds* of veinlets of granitic material in the heart of migmatites. Let us visualize for the moment aplite or pegmatite veins, some centimeters thick for example, squeezed into tight folds of an amplitude of some decimeters, folds repeated over a small distance, but preserving nonetheless strange, well rounded flexures in the hinges, without thinning or rupture. Never are there proportionally stronger mechanical changes in the sections where the veins are most strongly curved: they are as thick after bending as before. The picture invokes the impression of a fluid non-elastic milieu and a liquid filling in the course of the folding; but this is probably only a too simplified view. These folded veins are found cut by straight veins of the same fillings, and large crystals of feldspar common to the veins of both types are found at their intersections. At other times the material of the ptygmatic folds is diffused through the neighbouring rocks, forming recti-linear zones of nebulites later than the folding. There are also cases where the ptygmatic veins branch and where the different branches have been independently folded, cases where they are torn apart passing through a zone which was a little different from the surrounding rocks. These aspects signify, according to Wegmann, that the movement has been slower in some zones and faster in others.

According to the various indications mentioned above, the ptygmatic folds are proof of deformational movements in the environment during the granitization itself, in other words, when this environment was at the maximum state of "mobilization".

Many other phenomena of "small tectonics" have been analyzed by C. E. Wegmann. The effects of fluidity interwoven in the nebulites (dictyonites of Sederholm), the intimate more or less incoherent

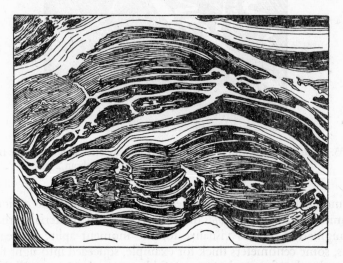

Fig. 36. *Boudinage* and *lit-par-lit* injection in amphibolite (drawn after a photograph figure by C. E. Wegmann). The size of the figure is some meters.

wrinklings of the embrechites (symmigmatic folds of M. Roques), "healed" shear fractures and other diverse criteria, are attributable to small imbricate movements in the mass in the course of granitization. Certain eruptive breccias (agmatites) where the fragments seem frayed express the stretching undergone. Other breccias have been formed by tension and extension of the rock, the tears produced being immediately filled or replaced with aplite or granite. Stretching is also reflected in linear or fluidal structures of the veins, in *boudinage* of more rigid layers between more plastic layers (C. E. Wegmann, 1932). The minerals developed in the veins or in the metamorphic aureoles (feldspar, garnet, andalusite, etc.) are often broken and drawn out, without the rock which encloses them itself being deformed, when it concluded crystallization later. For instance, in the intense injections of pegmatites in the environs of Helsinki, the early veins show a typical stretching of the garnets, a stretching which disappears in later veins of the same complex.

In the "eyed" embrechites in the famous section of the Gorges d'Héric of Montagne-Noire, France (Jung and Roques, 1952) or in those of Aston, Ariègeois Pyrenees, the gross feldspar nodules are sheared by symmigmatic slip planes into two, sometimes three fusiform elements, buckled, and closely packed together. A phase of lamination has followed the formation of the porphyroblasts. In the first section (Héric) skeins of aplitic veins intersect systematically in a small angle the schistosity of the migmatite. The phases of different depth, with modification of the stress field, have evidently succeeded each other.

All these effects of deformation, so common in anatexis, are not distributed at random. They occur in Finland in the orogenic zones and in more or less clear conformity with the tectonic style. For instance I have noted, during a trip through this country, the manner in which the ptygmatic folds conform to the schistosity of the rocks and with the tectonic directions. One sees sinuous veins straighten from one locality to another in order to conform with the schistosity, or even more, packets of little folds of these veins, folds whose hinges cut the schistosity but whose straight limbs conform to it. In this case, if there is only one schistosity, the general lamination was probably formed at the same time as the granitization or a little before it. It cannot have been formed later, because the material of the veins is massive; and if it were formed a long time earlier, in a previous cycle, the extraordinary tightness of the ptygmatic folds would have been rearranged along another probably different orientation. The schistosity often appears to be a little earlier than the orogeny. If the migmatization is connected to the schistosity or is a little later, it is bound up with a first phase of the corresponding orogeny. It is usually possible, however, to trace several successive phases and we will review below some examples of this kind.

The mobility of the migmatites is also connected to the displacement of chemical fronts. When this is great, aspects of diapirism are manifest in correlation with an increased mechanical mobility. *Migmatic diapirism* has a universality well-emphasized by C. E. Wegmann (1930): that of batholiths is only a special case of the upper levels of the superposed tectonics. Figure 27 illustrates the phenomenon for the Caledonian migmatites of Greenland (J. Haller, 1955).

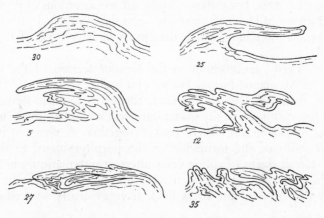

Fig. 37. Structure of migmatite massifs. The Caledonian metamorphic complex of north-east Greenland (drawn after J. Haller, 1955, simplified). The figures give the dimensions in kilometers of the structures.

The tectonic role of the migmatites is equally evident on a still greater scale. Wegmann has delineated in several parts of Finland the tectonic structure of Precambrian orogenic edifices, thanks to undulatory movements along the axes of these edifices. These undulations have caused the regular, approximately cylindrical surfaces of the tectonics to emerge obliquely on the nearly horizontal erosion surface, so that the tectonic forms can be reconstructed with the aid of stereograms. He has thus shown that these structures usually have a tangential style and have similarities with the Alps. The localization of the granites can now be clarified. In southwestern Finland, the oldest ones outline a maze of numerous sheets appearing to follow the tectonic surfaces of a

Precambrian chain which extends into Sweden. Their development, according to Wegmann, would even have accentuated the important axial depression shown by this orogeny at the outlet of the Gulf of Bothnia. He has been able to make observations of the same kind in the younger Precambrian chain of eastern Finland. Such an arrangement of the migmatites is analogous to the disposition of synkinematic granites which will be discussed below. But the scale is much vaster in the migmatites. There is, however, continuity between the two categories.

MIGMATITES IN AN IMMOBILE ENVIRONMENT

Migmatites may perhaps exist characterized by another evolution than the orogenic evolution. The great migmatitic complexes here in question are situated in the very old Precambrian basements and maintain over great areas a subhorizontal style. One such complex is found, according to Jung and Roques (1936) in Oubanghi-Chari in central Africa.

This suggests a tranquil migmatization on a supra-orogenic spatial scale, and probably of a duration much longer than an orogeny, in any case of a depth of formation much greater than that of the spindle-shaped anticlinal migmatites or that of the granitized zones of tangential displacements in chains of Alpine type later than the Precambrian. Moreover, the undisturbed aspect of these crystalline layers would arise rather from the obliteration of the transitional stages by means of continuous recrystallization over long periods.

If this hypothesis were confirmed, these deep migmatites could represent the result of the chemical migrations and differentiations imagined by R. W. van Bemmelen (1936) at the limit of the crust and the mantle of the globe, and propagated more or less upwards. What he calls an *asthenolith*, following Bailey Willis, would develop there, or a zone of great mobility in the depths of orogens, the locus of the initiation of the deformation of the Earth's crust proper.

SYNKINEMATIC GRANITES

Lenticular circumscribed granites, concordant to the planes of movement of orogeny, are involved under this heading. Their axial elongation is along the tectonic axis. Their texture is often oriented, with zonar variations of structure, resembling healed surfaces of separation and strung-out inclusions. Stretched schistose septa are interlayered.

Mylonite zones concordant with the assemblage indicate a prolongation of movements at certain points after consolidation.

The plate-like form of these granitic masses, similar to thick sills, is remarkable. They are thus generally *stratiform granites*. This form resembles the lenticular intrusions of Greenstones in the orogenic zones, intrusions which are often considered synkinematic. This type of granites may seem rare at first sight, because they are difficult to recognize, if the granitic sheets are little inclined and their thicknesses surpass the depth of erosion in the valleys.

Naturally granites of stratiform aspect also exist, composed of cupolas of great batholiths formed in place without movements. In most cases, however, it turns out that such granites, first considered to be batholiths, are flat bodies. The celebrated granite of Orijärvi, Finland, long regarded by Wegmann as a tongue of stratiform granite, despite Eskola's opinion that it was an anticlinal batholith, has recently been established by drilling to have a floor under which the sulphide ore minerals of the Orijärvi mine have been found. The same can be said for one of the granites of the Bavarian Forest, considered by H. Cloos as stratiform and floored, and under which a boring has recently found the graphitic beds known laterally beyond the granite.

When the structure of the assemblage stands on end there can be no doubt and the disposition can be studied in the section cut by the topo-

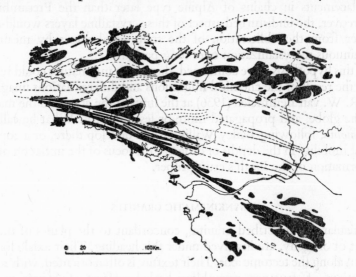

Fig. 38. The granites of Brittany (after Ch. Barrois). Black: granite. Dotted lines: synclinal axes.

graphic surface. In the orogenic zone of the French Massif Central, for example, the Carboniferous granites with white mica of the Mille-vaches Plateau are often on end, those of La Creuse are little tilted, whereas those of La Marche are steeply inclined. The granites of southern Brittany (fig. 38), which extend along the axis of the zone of the Millevaches Plateau and of La Creuze, seem equally synkinematic (Ch. Barrois, 1930).

In the Caledonian orogeny, some platy bodies of granite occur in sections of the Scandinavian Alps (fig. 39). In the Precambrian chains, C. E. Wegmann has set forth some examples, particularly among the Finnish granites of the first cycle. Some sheets of this type occasionally occur as a late phase of the syntectonic migmatites: thus in the neigh-bourhood of Helsinki, where they assume the facies of pegmatites dis-posed in great concordant intrusions (Wegmann and Kranck, 1931).

Some synkinematic granites in the form of phacoliths deviate from the typical stratiform type.

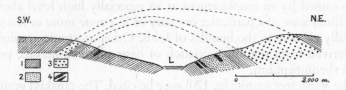

Fig. 39. Section through the Sulitjelma ore deposits (Norway) (after F. Carlson). 1. Mica schist. 2. Amphibolite. 3. Granite. 4. Pyrite. L. Langevand Lake.

POST-TECTONIC GRANITES

This case is very common and most batholiths belong here: these are massifs of intrusive character in folded belts and *a little later than the folding*. It would perhaps be better to say "late tectonic". Even though they are distributed in swarms along tectonic axes, they do not seem to have participated in the tectonics at their contacts. Actually instead of being injected concordantly in the layers like the foregoing category, they often cut the folds, either transversally or from below upwards, and entering indiscriminately synclines or anticlines. If account is taken of the mechanical forces brought into play for the emplacement of batholiths (chapter 7), it can be admitted that this emplacement is facilitated in periods of orogenic relaxation shortly after folding.

Such are the Hercynian granites of the Pyrenees for the most part, those of Morvan and the Vosges, and several of the circumscribed

H

massifs of the Massif Central. The Tertiary granites of the Alps are the same. The large batholiths of the American Cordilleras may also be cited, such as the Sierra Nevada in California. It can even be added that most of the batholiths of the "eruptive belt" of the Pacific seem to belong here, as do the tin-bearing granites of Malaya, and those of Cornwall of the Hercynian cycle.

These late granites are often granodioritic, but produce differentiations in the direction of more acidic potash-rich rocks, in the course of successive episodes of granitization.

ATECTONIC GRANITES

Circumscribed granites unrelated to an orogeny seem to be rare apart from generally small bodies and above all apart from the subvolcanic granites.

Putting aside these last, each atectonic granite poses a special problem. Their atectonism, which can be more apparent than real, could have been caused by an emplacement at an especially high level above the mobilized zone of a particular orogeny or in a zone more or less shifted laterally relative to the bundles of folds. Other atectonic granites may be derived from the differentiation of basic plutonic massifs, possibly with rheomorphism.

The Vredefort granite (p. 120) may be cited. The rapakivi granites of Finland and Sweden, referred to as atectonic, are laccoliths according to Sederholm.

With regard to the subvolcanic massifs, they evidently are related to fracturing of the crust which has given rise to volcanic eruptions. No direct relation to an orogeny can be seen in the same region. Their lack of internal Cloosian tectonics has been underlined in chapter 7. Their peripheral dislocation is a special case of movement en masse of granite massifs.

CONNECTION BETWEEN GRANITIZATION AND OROGENY

Plutonic Evolution in Orogeny

R. A. Daly has made an inventory of the granites of the world and has concluded that they are generally localized along orogenic zones. This is a very broad picture, for batholiths may be situated at a fairly great distance laterally with regard to the corresponding orogenic belt.

For example, following a remark by K. C. Dunham (in M. H. P. Bott and D. Masson-Smith, 1956), the granites (quartz monzonites) of the Basin and Ranges, U.S.A. are not situated exactly in the folded Cordilleras, but are all situated away from them in a parallel zone. Thus in New Mexico they are found in a series which comprises the whole of the succession from the Cambrian to the Cretaceous only some thousands of feet thick, without geosynclinal facies, unfolded, the only structures being some post-granitic faults.

Furthermore, for Daly the emplacement of granites followed more or less closely upon the great orogenic movements. Actually it is often contemporaneous with or earlier than these movements. Emplacement shows a strange and varied evolution during the course of the phases of an orogeny. In this evolution, four cases can be distinguished: (1) a succession of chemically and structurally diverse granites; (2) migmatization preceding the granites; (3) broad-scale differentiation beginning with the basic rocks; and (4) repeated alternations of volcanism and plutonism. This evidence of differentiation has already been partly alluded to in chapter 8.

Without knowing the reasons for this diversity, we must content ourselves with a review of the four categories:

1. The succession of the dominantly sodic granites (granodiorite) with abundant oligoclase, followed by more potassic granites (monzonitic granites) with abundant microcline, is commonly observed: the Archean basement of Nigeria (King and de Swardt, 1949); Finland (W. A. Wahl, 1937). H. H. Read (1949) emphasizes this succession in attributing to the first granites a more metasomatic and a more autochthonous character than those which followed. This is on a grander scale the law discovered for the large composite batholiths (chapter 8).

2. A vast development of migmatites inaugurates the cycle and replaces the granodiorites mentioned above. Phases of successive granites then follow. Such is the case in the Hercynian chain of the Pyrenees, where the initial migmatization probably is not due to an unfinished granitization but to mechanical conditions (kinematic or dynamic), having prevented homogenization. It is a question of a migmatization of short duration, embracing only a restricted part of the duration of the orogenic cycle, and having been able to proceed upwards fairly close to the Earth's surface.

3. In broad-scale differentiation the initial rocks are gabbros, associated possibly with ultrabasic rocks. The Caledonian chain of Norway has been cited in Chapter 7. In the Urals the gabbros and peridotites have been followed by granites and syenites, and even nepheline syenites at Kushva.

In the Hercynian chains of Morocco (the Mesteta of Central Morocco,

Jebilet, the Western High-Atlas), a gabbro-granite series is seen. In Central Morocco thick doleritic dykes precede the batholiths of straight granite, such as at Ment. In the Jebilet a swarm of small gabbro massifs seems to precede the granite massifs. In the High-Atlas, some massifs and dykes of gabbro and dolerite, deformed by folding in the Erdouz, precede the granitic batholiths, like the one of Azegour, which metamorphose these basic rocks.

4. In the Hercynian and Alpine chains, the alternation of periods of volcanism and plutonism is well known. We will return to their study in the next chapter.

Structural Analysis and Superposed Tectonics

Applying structural analysis in some mountain belts deeply eroded to various tectonic levels, C. E. Wegmann (1953 a and b) distinguishes from lowest to highest levels a migmatite zone (in the broad sense) and a zone of folded unmetamorphosed sedimentary formations. In this upper zone, the sedimentary formations may be associated with an old crystalline basement which supports them, a basement which has acquired its crystallinity in previous orogenic cycles, and has not been modified by the migmatites related to the mountain chain in which it now occurs. The two zones are separated by a more or less thick transition zone, where non-magmatic general metamorphism develops. The lower zone, that of the magmatites and intrusions, he named the *infrastructure* of the orogenic edifice. The upper zone is called the *superstructure* (fig. 40).

Between the infrastructure and the superstructure, both strongly deformed by orogenic movements, there is a complete disharmony in the style of deformation. Above there may be Jurassic-type folds, flat overturned folds or nappes of Alpine style. Below in the domain of the migmatites there may be vertical uprisings more or less folded and more or less abrupt of diapiric character, or else tighter folds, overthrusts but rarely at low angles. In the infrastructure actually the syntectonic ascent of mobilized material gives to the deformation a more vertical style, at the same time as semifluidity confers in detail a turbulent aspect. Note that the notions of the infrastructure and the superstructure are different from those of an *ancient basement* (*socle ancien*) and *cover* (*couverture*). The old basement of an orogen may be taken into the infrastructure if it is granitized anew, or left instead in the superstructure if it is not granitized. Whereas the basement and the cover are separated by a stratigraphic discordance, the infrastructure and the superstructure are

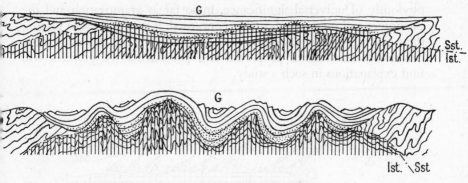

Fig. 40. Infrastructure and superstructure (after a drawing by C. E. Wegmann). The first section represents a geosyncline before the folding and shows the basement S and the geosyncline G.

The infrastructure (Ist) is marked by vertical lines. The base of the superstructure (Sst) is affected by general metamorphism indicated by dots. The second section represents the same arrangements with moderate folding.

separated by a tectonic disharmony. The distinction between the two phenomena is sometimes very delicate.

In some cases it is possible to photograph the superstructure-infrastructure boundary, as in the cliffs of Norwegian fjords and above all those of Greenland. In other cases it must be reconstructed like a puzzle, as in Finland or in Sweden (Wegmann, personal communication).

In this theory, granitization is *a normal and syntectonic process in the deepest part of the orogens.*

Always stressing the evolutionary point of view and carrying his analysis still farther. Wegmann defines *superposed tectonics* (*tectonique superposée*), which is the interplay between two kinds of structures attributable to different epochs in the same region. "Superposed structures are only exceptionally of the same style. In most cases they are distinguished by their geometric character and by the nature of transformations" (Wegmann, 1947). It is thus a question of superposition in time. It is also, very often, a superposition in space for the upper levels are deformed at the same time as the underlying basement already tectonized. The second tectonics affects the upper strata; in the deeper levels it is "superposed" in time on a first tectonics. The study of superposed tectonics reconstructs the evolution of an orogenic domain in a manner as precise as possible both in time and in space. It is obviously of universal significance. In so far as granitization and the phenomena of metamorphism are concerned, it is of interest in placing them in the broad geological context, which is at the same time chronological. General properties and peculiarities of granites will find explanations in such a study.

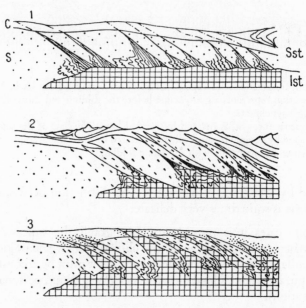

Fig. 41. The infrastructure in successive phases of an orogeny (after a drawing by C. E. Wegmann).

1. The basement (S) begins to break up into large scales separated by slip zones whose widths increase downwards near the infrastructure (Ist) indicated by cross-hatching. The cover (C) is weakly affected.

2. The basement is broken down into great scales between which the rising infrastructure is intercalated.

3. The material of the infrastructure gains in height and width partly in the state of magma. It influences not only the basement but also the cover.

F. E. Suess stressed the difference between *"tectonics by intrusions"* (*tectonique par intrusions*) due to generalized granitization, and tectonics due to tangential displacements, which is that of edifices of folds and nappes (F. E. Suess, 1926). Tectonics by intrusions consists of the lack of obvious plan and definite direction, which in contrast is what is found in mountain chains. Gneisses with extremely variable and in detail capricious orientations yield overall to the outlines of granite massifs. Different facies repeat themselves in a multiple and complicated fashion. The formations have been blurred by recrystallization. Some such regions become rigid very quickly in the orogenic evolution and incapable of deformation, at the most all they may do is act *en bloc* and crush and laminate their borders. For F. E. Suess granitization extends progressively during several geological periods in the regions of *Intrusionstektonik*, whereas orogenic deformations are always much briefer. On this basis he has presented an overall scheme of the Hercynian-Variscan edifice of Central Europe, where the Bohemian block represents the type of region of Intrusionstektonik.

For him, tectonics by means of intrusions and tectonics by tangential displacements would function in different regions. In fact the difference depends on the tectonic depth and the number of superposed orogenies in the domain. *Intrusionstektonik* seems to me to involve certain parts of a deep infrastructure, where several superposed tectonics occur together.

A Demay (1942) has defined under the name of *"deep tectonics"* (*tectonique profonde*) "that which appears at the base of a tectonic edifice, in the vicinity of active magma of the same orogenic periods, or at least in a zone under its influence". To my mind this involves a special case of the infrastructure, with a more or less universal rheomorphism and at a level which is too deep for any kind of tangential movements.

Examples of application

C. E. Wegmann (1935 c) distinguished in his studies of the Caledonian orogeny of Northeastern Greenland a superstructure formed of Eocambrain (*antécambrien*) and old Palaeozoic rocks, folded little, if at all, metamorphosed, and below an infrastructure where the base of these formations has been migmatized over a great thickness, and has been intensely mobilized and deformed. In this infrastructure, is disclosed a superposition of the Caledonian migmatization on the orogenic elements of an ancient basement older than the sedimentary formations above it. According to the relics of palingenesis it was formed of zones of granite and gneiss. The rejuvenation of these elements, folded transversely to the later Caledonian folds, has given rise to a series of transversal culminations of these folds.

Another example of superposed tectonics has been given by Wegmann (1931) from Finland in the orogenic arcs of Helsinki-Nordjöskatan and Nordjöskatan-Viksund, each one about ten kilometers in length. In this complicated history he distinguishes the following phases:

A. Deformation of a schistose series containing intrusions with plagioclase phenocrysts;

B. Intrusions of gabbros in lenticular bodies with intrusive contacts. Intense deformation, particularly along the borders, displayed by stretching of igneous breccias, by a lamellar or linear texture of the marginal portions, by recrystallized hornblende streaks and by leucocratic streaks. The deformation is much later than the intrusions and began at comparatively low temperature as revealed by the lithological facies;

C. Emplacement of synkinematic granites and new deformations. Their texture is stretched, with oriented crystallization following the plane of the differential lamination and showing great variations related to the degree of lamination. There is no assimilation and little or no pegmatites;

D. Phase of release (*detente*) at a shallow depth, with fractures filled by basic dykes. Probably a long time interval. The formations are then brought anew to deep level conditions, perhaps by the deposition of a new sedimentary series, or possibly by tectonic subsidence.

E. New foldings, much more intense, with important translations, and strong migration of which the most extreme result in the Hangö granite. Extraordinary development of pegmatites individualized in veins or pockets. The pegmatites occur in several cycles and the main folding took place during the phase of pegmatites. But already in the migmatites, the dictyonites show several phases of lamination. The differences of degree of migmatization express the different amplitude of relative movements, for the slip planes are the zones of more active migmatization. The massive bodies of ancient gabbro exert a protective effect against the general deformation, and the old tectonic structures are thus reflected in the heart of the new structures.

A great local variability has been abundantly produced in this superposition of tectonic events. The rocks are far from uniform: the intensity of variable movement, activation of mobility and influx of granitic solutions, do not coincide. The three variables evolve independently up to a certain point. Further if one takes into account the differences of material, the result is a collection of varieties.

Finally there is the example of superposed tectonics of the Osi district in Nigeria (King and de Swardt), with two successive and independent migmatizations in the formations of the base of the ancient platform of West Africa.

CONCLUSION

Granitization, it seems to me, extends largely in space beyond the orogenic zones, which themselves extend beyond the bounds of geosynclines. It also extends out in time. Anatexis, as J. J. Sederholm has in some degree suggested, is a planetary phenomenon.

However, a coincidence of anatexis and orogenesis is very often confirmed. The traces of deformation in most migmatites are striking. The activation of the chemical fronts following surfaces of deformation is manifest on all scales. Reciprocally the chemically-mobilized environments yield very readily to tectonic solicitations. Finally orogeny may raise the migmatite massifs and the mixed environments in the course of granitization, by a diapiric effect in the broadest sense of the term.

H*

Chapter 13

GRANITE AND VOLCANISM

Eduard Suess wished to show the relationship between surface volcanism and the emplacement of plutonic rocks at depth through the examination of a more and more advanced *denudation series* of eruptive assemblages in different settings. He described a succession of phenomena between volcanic manifestations such as "bodies of cinders of the present time" and the granite massifs which he considered the deep hearths of volcanism. This was a somewhat theoretical view of an idealized linking up of fragmentary observations, the direct relationship not being in fact observable. The case of subvolcanic granitic massifs described in chapter 3 seems to be very special, and moreover their interpretation is ambiguous. It is possible that the evolution of great granitic massifs is completely different (Cloos and Rittman, 1939).

The parallelism in chemical composition between the families of plutonic rocks and those of lavas has been noted for many years. From this arose the idea of a correspondence between the two great divisions, the magmas being the same but the mode of consolidation different. It should be noted, however, that according to the average analyses of a great number of rocks of different provenance a lava is generally a little richer in silica, soda and potash, and a little less rich in iron oxides, magnesia and lime than the corresponding plutonic rock of the classification. R. A. Daly explains this fact as due to a greater abundance of gas in the magma chambers at the base of volcanoes, all things being equal: whence the lowering of the temperature of solidification of the magma and the prolongation of differentiation. This operates in accordance with a common rule in the direction of an increase in silica and in alkalis.

The chemical parallelism remains a strong argument for the connection between surface volcanism and the deep plutonic intrusions. It is accompanied moreover by a certain mineralogical parallelism. However, arguments of a geological nature relative to the structure itself of eruptive assemblages or to the distribution of the products of eruptive phenomena in space and time are of greater weight. These arguments will be reviewed under the following headings:

The subvolcanic granite massifs;
Volcanic facies in the margins of granites;
Volcanic affinities of the dyke suites of granites;
Is metallogenic volcanism of granitic origin?
Relationships of granites with earlier volcanic formations.

Leaving aside the problem of the evolution of other plutonic rocks such as gabbros, which may be very different, we will restrict ourselves to granite, and possibly to similar rocks often related to it by simple differentiation: diorite, syenite and monzonite. Examples including these rocks may be actually as convincing as if they were one of the varieties of granite.

THE SUBVOLCANIC GRANITE MASSIFS

This case is specific and very likely exceptional. As H. Cloos has noted, these massifs are located in rigid regions of great linear fractures and are related to the fissure volcanism of these regions, whereas the important batholiths are as a rule in orogenic zones. But the link between granite and lavas in the subvolcanic massifs must still be elucidated.

For Clough, Maufe and Bailey, a sinking down *en masse* of a cylindrical column of the solid crust, whose summit would be found at some depth below the surface, would be produced. In the void thus formed the granitic magma would be emplaced. A repetition of the phenomenon would give rise to the observed descent of the massif relative to its settings and the intrusion of successive granular rocks in a concentric arrangement and in peripheral circular dykes.

R. Daly (1941) envisions the descent of the less important blocks:

Clough, Maufe, and Bailey have suggested that a batholithic chamber may be formed by the sinking of a single subterranean block whose height is nearly as great as the whole thickness of the earth's crust. It is at least possible that the sunken block at Glen Coe is merely part of the relatively thin roof of a batholith ... The existence of the "cauldron" does not compel the view that the great chamber beneath was opened by similar down-faulting *en bloc* (p. 196).

It would involve the local caving in of the roof of a batholith.

The magmatist's interpretation just mentioned is undoubtedly attractive. It is certain that concentric dykes, generally of porphyries, suggest a fluid magma. By extending the argument, the massifs of granular rocks in annular zones, sometimes separated by screens of older rocks, appear to be controlled by the same mechanism as the dykes. Nevertheless these rocks cannot be consolidated in the same way as true magmas. Otherwise why the difference from neighbouring volcanic rocks?

A direct relationship by gradual transition between granular rocks and volcanic rocks has not been observed, except perhaps for the unique case of Erongo, but only successions of the two. The volcanic phenomenon conditions the emplacement of plutonic masses but perhaps does not initiate it. When the volcanic caldera is displaced laterally several kilometers in successive phases, the emplacement of the granular rocks is displaced as well, with its suite of circular peripheral dykes as on the islands of Mull and the peninsula of Ardnamurchan in Scotland.

Let us recall, however, that according to Cloos and Chudoba (1931) in the case of the Erongo granodiorite massif of South-West Africa the plutonic material would pass to lava flows "like the stem of a mushroom passing to its cap". "There is no doubt that here we come upon the passage of an abyssal rock body to its corresponding flows."

One of the most recent discoveries in this field is the Messum complex, also in South-West Africa (Korn and Martin, 1954). It belongs to a SW–NE alignment comprising several subvolcanic massifs, the most important of which is the Brandberg, and Messum is situated some tens of kilometers from it. Erongo is situated on another parallel alignment. The body belongs to the volcanism at the end of the Karroo. Messum is a subvolcanic massif of 15 km in diameter. Surrounded by basic lavas which have a steep dip towards the circular fault bounding the massif, it consists essentially of granites and diorites with a central navel of foyaïte. Large inclusions of gabbro in the form of discontinuous circular segments are found in the outer half of the width of the granitic annular zone. The central foyaïte is intrusive in volcanic tuffs also present in the central part. The gabbros in contrast and the granitic rocks have a stratiform structure with dips towards the centre. The succession of events would be as follows if we restrict ourselves to the principal rocks to the exclusion of the various dykes: lavas, gabbros, granites and the first periods of subsidence, foyaïte and the second subsidence. The plutonic rocks would be in part magmatic and in part metasomatic. The granite shows no sign of Cloosian tectonics, in keeping with most subvolcanic granites.

All these volcanic complexes show different possibilities of caldera formation. Erongo—a shallow wide caldera in a large plateau volcano. Brandberg—a deep very regular caldera without appreciable volcanic activity. Messum—repeated deep subsidence and strong volcanic activity. The group forms a rather representative cross-section, on the whole, of present-day caldera types. The plutons which are now exposed are the lower levels of great calderas. Many a present day caldera may conceivably have the structure of a Brandberg or a Messum complex at depth (Korn and Martin, p. 115.)

The existence of granitic rocks in subvolcanic massifs is a particular case of a more general situation. The various granular rocks, and not only the granitic and syenitic ones, have often been emitted under the same conditions. For example, in the volcanic archipelago of the Canaries, some granular rocks are known. According to J. Bourcart and E. Jérémine (1938);

> they have been found in La Palma in the Angustias ravine (gabbros and altered dolerites), and on Grand-Canary in the form of sills (syenites) in the rhyolites of the Tejeda valley, and some dykes (gabbros) at Laguna. Elsewhere they are found only in sparse blocks (at Gomera) or as inclusions in tuffs (at Teneriffe, Grand Canary and La Palma). Some very different rocks have been recognized among these inclusions: syenites, nepheline syenites, monzonites, gabbros, essexites, theralites, pyroxenites. Most of these inclusions have been torn from granular rocks now covered by extruded lavas. Only at Fuerteventura have crystalline rocks been found in direct contact with other rocks.

There syenites and gabbros form a massif of some kilometers and cut a series of older basaltic rocks. E. Jérémine described the metamorphism of the basaltic rocks by the syenites. A more recent succession of basaltic and rhyolitic lavas has been poured out next. In this regard the authors recall that on Tahiti, on Réunion, in the Hebrides and several other volcanic islands, *the granular rocks are intrusive in the volcanic series*.

TRANSITION FROM PLUTONIC TO VOLCANIC ROCKS

We have seen in chapter 5 that some granitic massifs develop progressively near their border a microgranitic facies through the decrease of their grain size and the appearance of phenocrysts, including even bipyramidal quartz. In spite of this texture calling to mind that of volcanic porphyries, we have tended to regard it as an effect of convergence and to assume that no truly volcanic phenomenon has been connected with it.

It happens, however, that this porphyritic facies has a great extent compared to that of granite in the true sense, that it grades at least locally into facies more clearly volcanic, and that some incontestable volcanic formations are to be found in the immediate geologic settings although not always directly connected.

In northern Morvan, north of the French Massif Central, Alb. Michel-Lévy (1908, 1937) has shown that the vast Dinantian granite of Lormes is linked by an imperceptible transition to "a thick assemblage of often fine-grained granular rocks sometimes with two stages of crystallization". These rocks constitute the vault of the granite for tens of kilometers in all directions. They grade into rhyolitic dykes penetrating Dinantian sedimentary formations or volcanic tuffs. In part they have remelted the dacitic tuffs of this stage which at the same time bear the imprint of granitic contact metamorphism.

In Kabylie de Collo, Algeria, M. Roubault (1934) has shown the connection of the Tertiary granitic massif with microgranites and even with rhyolites by imperceptible transitions. These rocks occupy stretches of several kilometers in the hills to the west of Collo Bay forming numerous small peaks (volcanic necks) which pierce the Eocene marls farther west. These necks often have characteristic "organ" structure indicating crystallization at shallow depth.

Some relations of the same genre but of a much greater extent are known in the volcanic formations of Eocambrian age in Sarrho, Morocco (E. Fauvelet and J. Hindermeyer, 1952). The enormous stretches occupied by rhyolitic ignimbrites, rhyolitic and andesitic flows and tuffs, reveal in several regions very special granites, which are connected with the volcanic rocks by intermediary granophyres. Alkalic and leucocratic, they consist of orthoclase, albite, little developed chloritized biotite, and accessory green hornblende.

The mode of association between these granites and the rhyolitic flows of the lower complex of Precambrian III assumes diverse aspects:
1. The rhyolitic carapace of the granitic massifs of several square kilometers with contact surfaces of great radius of curvature, but showing local irregularities (contacts en baïonette or saw-toothed). The contact zone, varying from some decimeters to tens of meters,

is composed of porphyritic and micropegmatitic rocks. In some zones (over 100 m) the lavas seem to be ploughed up by the granite, without the contact being faulted.

2. Infiltration of granular rocks in the volcanic flows generally aligned in the direction of the flows. They are connected to an important granite massif or form small isolated masses which at times surpass a kilometer in size.

3. Veins of aplite or microgranite cutting the rhyolite flows in all directions, or else occurring in discontinuous bands within the lavas with large phenocrysts of feldspar, locally anastomosing in small granular masses.

Whatever the nature of the contact between the alkaline granites and the lavas, these rocks form an inseparable assemblage of comparable if not identical mineralogical composition. The innermost mechanism of the transformation to rhyolitic magma of such hearths in granite is obviously not known. (Choubert, Fauvelet, Hindermeyer, 1952).

The most important development known of the rhyolites, that of Yellowstone Park, U.S.A., is interpreted by R. A. Daly as a "deroofing" of a granitic batholith whose summit reached the surface. Similarly the Bushveld "red granite" of South Africa, contains a rhyolite of effusive facies. According to Daly (1914);

In the basin of the Fox River, Wisconsin, the granite of a preCambrian batholith is gradually transitional, through a massive rhyolite porphyry (keratophyre) into a rhyolite in which all the evidence of former flowage and rapid surface cooling is apparent. The areas of granite are contiguous and the areas of keratophyre lie in a zone bordering the granite on the east and south, while the rhyolite areas lie in an outer zone beyond the keratophyre and farthest removed from the granite (p. 122).

Is this an example of local destruction of the roof?

The rapakivi granites of Finland are accompanied by true rhyolites. These rocks, granites and rhyolites, are characterized by their peculiar feldspathic ovoids (p. 69). Their peculiarities affirm their unity of origin, even if the granite and the rhyolite are not contiguous.

F. Bederke (1948) indicates, in the Sudetens and Erzgebirge in Hercynian Central Europe, a series of examples of granites and volcanic flows or intrusions which resemble facies of one and the same origin. The most striking case would perhaps be the connection of the prophyry stock of Eisenkoppen near Altenberg to the Riesengebirge granite outcropping some kilometers away. This rhyolite porphyry grades at depth to a microgranite, which resembles in a striking manner certain facies of the above granite. Orthite is encountered in both rocks. The metalliferous veins of Altenberg, satellites of the porphyry, are of the same paragenesis as those of Riesengebirge.

DYKE SUITES OF GRANITE AND THEIR VOLCANIC AFFINITIES

As has been seen in chapter 9, certain granite massifs are rich in lamprophyric dykes. Still more common are the dykes of microgranite encountered towards the periphery of many of the massifs, in the granite or outside of it. The phenomenon is so common that it seems superfluous to give examples; the examination of geological maps is sufficiently demonstrative. It should be noted, however, that the fact is, all the same, not absolutely universal. For instance the Quérigut granite in the Pyrenees is accompanied by hardly any microgranite, although it has produced quantities of aplites and pegmatites.

In contrast to pegmatites, which can degenerate into hydrothermal veins, but cannot feed volcanic vents, the porphyritic lamprophyres or microgranites of the suites of granite massifs sometimes have obvious volcanic affinities. This is the case, as we have seen, with the andesite dykes in the granite of the Central Pyrenees. The microgranite dykes often grade towards their walls or their extremities into rhyolites with more or less glassy groundmasses.

Let us examine the factors which may produce the arrangement and overall structure of the dyke suites of granitic massifs, to see in what measure they may represent the deep roots of surface volcanism.

The geological mapping of M. Boule of the Margeride granite near Entraygues, in the southern part of the French Massif Central, shows a close grouping of thick, grossly parallel, rhyolite dykes (fig. 42). Other thinner dykes of microlithic andesite are associated with them. There are at times petrographic transitions from one type to another. The age is probably Carboniferous, pre-Stephanian. The dykes, enclosed in large part in granite, extend into the mica schists to the north. They can be regarded as zones of departure for the magma, still not very concentrated but already well established in its volcanic facies. Is it possible to affirm that these dykes in effect attained the Earth's surface at the time of the formation to produce a volcanism? They are pre-Stephanian because fragments of them are encountered in the coal-bearing conglomerates of Decazeville. Now no lava flows, nor pyroclastic deposits of pre-Stephanian age exist in the neighbourhood, either because erosion has destoyed them, or because they were never there. It is thus impossible to draw a definite conclusion. However the actuality of volcanism is favoured by arrangement of dykes, with maximum frequency and size within a restricted zone, their penetration far from the granite and lastly their rhyolitic character.

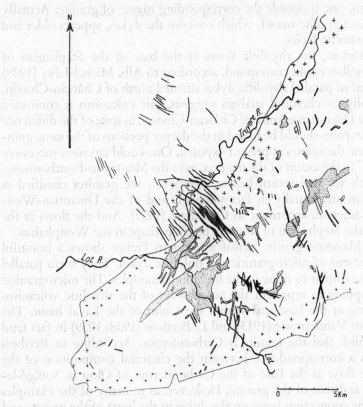

Fig. 42. The southwestern end of the Margeride massif (after the mapping of M. Boule, Figeac sheet of the Carte Géologique de France). Black: porphyries. Dotted: granite with white mica. The crosses indicate the margin of the normal granite massif.

Approaching surface volcanic structures, dykes of magma must decrease in number and increase in thickness. The sheaf of rhyolite dykes around Aubusson, in the centre of the Massif Central, seems to represent this stage (fig. 30). It connects directly, according to L. de Launay (1901) with vast flows or laccoliths near the topographic surface of the epoch, the assemblage outcropping for nearly 40 km from the environs of Château-sur-Cher to those of Gouzon. These rocks are Dinantian in age, associated with sandy sediments with anthracite and with pyroclastic intercalations. Their remarkable variability of texture seems to indicate a consolidation near the Earth's surface. At this level of thick dykes, close to their junction with superficial volcanic manifestations, one is outside the corresponding masses of granite. Actually the Guéret granite massif, which contains the dykes, appears older and of an anatectic facies.

In Morvan, the rhyolitic flows at the base of the Stephanian of Montreuillon could correspond, according to Alb. Michel-Lévy (1929) to a sheaf of parallel rhyolitic dykes situated north of Château-Chinon. If actually, as chemical analysis suggests, this volcanism is connected with the Dinantian granite of Château-Chinon, in spite of the difference in age, its roots should be found in the deeper portions of the same granite, below the masses at present exposed. One could envision successive "pulses" in the ascent of the magma, as in the Montagne-Bourbonnaise, to which we will return below. Moreover, the granites classified as Dinantian are actually in fact younger, and of the Dinantian-Westphalian interval, according to C. Barrois (1927). And the flows at the base of the Stephanian of Morvan began perhaps in the Westphalian.

The Mayenne granite massif in western France shows a beautiful development of microgranitic and doleritic dykes. They form parallel networks similar to those of the foregoing examples. The microgranitic dykes appear to represent the access ways of the rhyolitic volcanism occurring at the base and within the Culm of the Laval basin. The studies of Vandernotte (1913) and L. Berthois (1938, 1939) in fact tend to establish that the granite is Carboniferous. According to Berthois there is a correspondence between the chemical composition of the rhyolite flow at the base of the Carboniferous of Clou in Soulgé-le-Bruant and that of the granite. However, as in many of the examples cited, the connection between the dykes in the heart of the granite and the flows cannot be observed.

According to the foregoing examples, the porphyritic dykes, enclosed within the interior of certain granite massifs and possibly representing the access ways of a volcanism subsequent to the emplacement of the granite, are arranged in great parallel sheaves. They are related to the fissuring of the granites during consolidation. Their disposition is often transverse relative to the elongation of the granite massifs, which often coincides with the direction of the tectonic axis of the corresponding orogenic cycle. The directions transverse to the tectonic axes often mark important faults. This explains the extent of these dykes and makes possible if not probable their propagation up to the surface at the time of their intrusion.

At the level of these dykes, the well-individualized porphyritic magma contrasts sharply with the granite. But how does it appear at the original base of these dykes? They emanate from the late consolidated, deep portions of the massif. Sometimes deep sections of erosion reveal at the centre of the batholith a more acidic granite slightly differentiated and obviously later. It is without doubt such zones that produce the porphyries, although I do not know of any precise observations in this respect. The microgranites vary readily over very short distances within the same dyke, from an almost granitic texture to a clearly porphyritic texture. At their base they could grade into granite dykes, the limits of which undoubtedly disappear rapidly downwards into the heart of the almost as recent granite which encloses them. If they become porphyritic higher up, it is because of sudden cooling in the already consolidated portions of the massif and above all because of their poverty of mineralizers. At the final stage of consolidation, the granitic emanations have already been given off, or at least all have been localized in the pegmatites in such a way that the mobilized environment where the dykes feed is no longer saturated with them. In this way one would see the obliteration of the roots of post-granitic volcanism in the heart of late portions of consolidation of the granite massifs. *But all this is hypothetical rather than an objective establishment of fact.*

METALLOGENIC VOLCANISM

If by taking the point of departure of our studies deep in the crust we have realized the possibility of a granitic origin for some volcanism, is it not possible reciprocally to start at the top of the crust and arrive at similar conclusions? Metallogenic volcanism seems to provide arguments in this regard.

Metalliferous deposits of straightforward volcanic character, i.e., metallic concentrations directly related to outpourings of lava or to fumaroles, are rare. This is undoubtedly due to the premature and rapid release of mineralizers as volcanic gases. Beyond some concretionary cassiterite in the rhyolites of Bolivia, Mexico and Nevada, and the sedimentary deposits of volcanic submarine exhalations, there are few worthy of mention. There exist, however, in many districts of recent volcanism important hydrothermal veins arising from thermal activity whose origin is deeper than the base of the lava flows. *These metalliferous zones are concentrated in the regions of volcanism, without having been*

directly produced by surface volcanism. Hydrothermal veins of different
types are involved in this aspect, from the epithermal (Japan) to hypothermal veins (Braden in Chile), and including the intermediate mesothermal ones (tin-bearing veins of Bolivia).

In contrast, many important volcanic regions are impoverished in
metallization. Such are the volcanic regions of East Africa, of the
Auvergne, the Rhine, the North Atlantic, and in general the zones of
fissure eruptions. On the other hand, there are volcanic systems
favoured by metal deposition, such as the Carpathians, New Zealand,
Japan, the Andes, and the Rockies. It is obvious that non-metallogenic
volcanism is related to the great linear fractures of the rigid crust and
metallogenic volcanism to zones of Tertiary orogeny. Now the batholiths of plutonic rocks are situated along the orogenic zones; their
ability to produce metallic deposits, at more or less great distances in
space and time, is one of the best established facts of metallogeny. One
is thus led to relate metallogenic volcanism to the batholiths, which are
generally invisible or whose connection with volcanism is not obvious
or straightforward, although close.

A remarkable case is that of the tin veins of Bolivia (Ahlfeld and
Muñoz Reyes, 1939). They are localized in fractures in a series of small
rhyolitic or dacitic volcanic masses, or in fractures in the adjoining
sedimentary formations along the Cordillera Orientale of the Andes.
North of the region granitic batholiths appear along the same zone. The
aureoles of these granites are sometimes slightly tin-bearing. From the
geological conditions and the chemical composition of the rocks, there
is little doubt that the alignment of the granites continues at depth under
the string of volcanic structures; and one may believe that these
represent surface manifestations of the great phenomenon of the
emplacement of the Andean granites. The hydrothermal veins are
deeper, as is revealed by the mining operations, than the volcanic
structures and do not derive directly from them, although all are closely
connected with these structures. The hydrothermal metallogenic
activity and volcanism derive in some way from deep-seated events
which have prepared for or followed the emplacement of the granite.

This example, like all the others to which we have just referred, leads
us indirectly to *the idea of a connection between plutonic and volcanic rocks.*
To be sure this connection does not necessarily indicate that volcanism
originates from plutonism; the opposite is possible, we shall return to
that. This is a completely different matter from the case of subvolcanic
granite massifs, which are situated precisely in the domain of fissure
volcanism and which are only exceptionally metallogenic.

If the examples above are related to the Mesozoic and Tertiary orogenies (Alpine chains, the orogenic belt of the Pacific), it must similarly be the case in the Hercynian cycle which has been so rich in granites. At the end of the cycle, Permian volcanism developed.

Volcanic phenomena attained a remarkable intensity in the Permian. The principal centres of eruption are in Saxony, Thuringia, the Saar basin, the Vosges and the Black Forest, the Autun basin, the Brive basin, Esterel and the southern Tyrol. The porphyry flow of Bozen is certainly the thickest and most extensive known in Europe (E. Haug, 1911).

This flow extends from Lugano westward as far as Sesia. This Permian volcanism also seems to have been metallogenic, because the Permian sand and clay sedimentation in lagoons of these regions everywhere shows signs of metalliferous impregnations, often of copper. If the metalliferous material were brought in by meteoric, vadose, or tele-thermal waters, this must be due to the chemical erosion of the hypogenic deposits of this epoch, such as those of galena and barite connected with Permian lavas of the environs of Lugano, or the similar ones rich in fluorite of Esterel, southern France. Part of the deposits of the Permian lagoons may be from sedimentary exhalation, in other words, directly connected with volcanism.

RELATIONSHIPS BETWEEN GRANITES AND OLDER VOLCANIC FORMATIONS

The Dinantian Tuffs and the Granites of the French Massif Central

The Dinantian tuffs of the northern Massif Central are rhyolitic, trachytic and above all dacitic. They sometimes contain corresponding lava flows or sedimentary intercalations. The extent and thickness of these tuffs, half marine, half continental, is very great. Remnants preserved from erosion have been found from Morvan in the north to Beaujolais in the east, and Creuse in the west; their original extent must have been at least 25,000 sq. km. To the west, the tuffs rest directly on the gneissic or old granitic basement; in Bourbonnais and Beaujolais on greywackes of the Culm. In northern Morvan they have no other sub-strata than the Carboniferous granite which has eaten into their base. Their determined thickness in the Sichon valley near Vichy amounts to several thousand meters according to J. Jung and his collaborators.

In Morvan, Alb. Michel-Lévy (1908, 1929, 1930, 1937) has shown that the granite of the large Château-Chinon massif, which rose in places far into the cover of tuffs, has in part reshaped and metamorphosed these tuffs. A microgranitic facies forms its roof and margins. The chemical composition of the granite is the same as that of the dacite associated with the tuffs. In Montagne-Bourbonnaise, north of Forez, Jung, Chichery and Vachias (1939) describe the sequence of events in the following way. A first granite, that of Saint-Julien-la-Vêtre, in the region of Bois-Noirs, was emplaced probably in the lower Visean. "This magma solidified very slowly, because during the whole course of the middle and upper Visean, it was the secondary source of new outpourings". As a matter of fact it is the same magma which has cleared a way for itself up to the surface and has given rise to volcanism by the great sheets of Dinantian pyroclastic tuffs. Analysis reveals the chemical similarity of some tuffs with this granite. "The connection of this volcanism with the granitic reservoirs below explains the relative constancy of composition of the emanated products, their enormous regional extent and their thickness. It is a type of areal volcanism." Towards the end of the pyroclastic period, the magma was injected underground between the upper part of the consolidated granite and its cover. It thus forms the vast intrusive bodies of microgranite of the Plateau d'Urfé, whose exposure covers about 150 sq. km as the sole formation present. Finally the differentiation terminated with emission of rhyolitic dykes. The connection between these porphyries and the granite is shown by the chemical analyses and the differentiation diagram based on them. A more recent granite than all the foregoing rocks, that of Mayet-de-Montagne, probably of the upper Visean, differs on the contrary from the preceding magma by a more strictly potassic character.

Comparing observations from Morvan and Montagne-Bourbonnaise, which belong to the same ensemble, one sees that the phases of volcanism and the ascents of granite are likely to occur alternately several times, the volcanism preceding the emplacement of plutonic rocks.

The Case of Tertiary Mountain Chains

As Turner and Verhoogen have noted (1951), there is a connection between andesite-rhyolite-basalt volcanism of orogenic zones and the batholiths of these zones. But according to them in essence the batholiths precede the volcanism. Actually there is often alternation between the two activities.

In the San Juan Mountains, Colorado, a volcanic activity precedes as early as the upper Cretaceous and accompanies the orogeny of the beginning of the Tertiary (T. S. Lovering, 1933). Some intrusive rocks, ranging from gabbros to granites, and which abound along a zone extending from San Juan to Boulder (the Front Range), are present in dykes, sills and small batholiths. They consist of diorites, monzonites and quartz monzonite porphyries, contemporaneous with or alternating with the volcanic formations. This activity lasted until after overthrusts of the Front Range. The metallic mineralization of Leadville, Gilman, Central City, Nederland, etc., followed the intrusion of Eocene porphyries. All are cut by a peneplain developed before the Oligocene. In the Oligocene there was little or no volcanism. In the Miocene thick interstratified volcanic formations formed with associated porphyries or granular rocks ranging from gabbro to granite. A new metallogeny is related to them: Cripple Creek, San Juan.

The copper deposits of Braden, Chile are situated in a volcanic vent which pierces a vast intrusion of andesitic porphyry and quartz diorite, the intrusion itself being emplaced in the heart of a series of volcanic outpourings of older lavas and tuffs, probably also of Tertiary age. There are all gradations between the porphyry and the quartz diorite (Lindgren and Bastin, 1935).

This plutonic-volcanic association is also found in the Miocene of Japan. In the northern part of Honshu the dioritic to gabbroic rocks cut layers of stratified volcanic tuffs (I. Kato, 1955).

In the Balkan chains, W. E. Petrascheck (1953) distinguishes between two great periods of effusion, in the Senonian-Eocene and in the Miocene-Pliocene. The rocks of the first effusive period occur primarily in the sub-Balkan zone (Bihar Mountains, Timak Mountains). A little later, in connection with the Laramide orogenic phase, dioritic-syenitic-granodioritic intrusions are produced, in the Bihar mountains, in Banat and the sub-Carpathian zone. They are similarly found in the Vardar zone. The locus of this activity is thus on both sides of the mass called the "Rhodope zone"! This plutonism is characterized by a rapid and very accentuated differentiation (the "banatites"). As to the second effusive period, that of the "young volcanism", it begins at the inner border of the Carpathians of Slovakia, and continues in Transylvania and along the Dinarides south of Belgrade, in Kopaonik, the Rhodope and Chalcidic. A granitic and granodioritic plutonism is associated with it, as well as the syenite of Ditro in Roumania and a great part of the intra-Dinaric granites.

Other Examples

In the Harz, in Germany, the Brocken granite was formed at the end of a long series of volcanic phases, which are arranged *en echelon* across the Devonian and Carboniferous of this region and in the Rheinische Schiefergebirge. In the Erzgebirge the Permian porphyry volcanism of Teplitz has preceded the emplacement of several granite stocks.

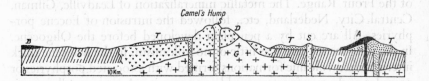

Fig. 43. Section through Mount Macedon, Victoria (drawn after E. W. Skeat and H. S. Summers). O: Ordovician sandstone and shales. G: Granodiorite. D: Dacite. S: Sölvsbergite. T: Trachyte. B: Basalt. A: Andesitic basalt.

Lastly, at Mount Macedon in Victoria, according to Daly, dacites enclose granite (fig. 43). Successive emissions of differentiated magma are involved here.

CONCLUSIONS CONCERNING THE RELATIONSHIP OF VOLCANISM AND GRANITIC PLUTONISM

The best established cases of the relationships between volcanism and granitic plutonism are those where granular rocks have come into place in volcanic formations derived from a little older magma which seems related to the granite through a differentiation, either minimal or considerable. This fact is striking in the case of *subvolcanic granitic massifs*, but we have seen that it appears to have a much wider and more general significance.

This relationship is by no means "necessary", because many granites have been emplaced without being preceded by volcanism. The inverse relation, that is to say the direct derivation of volcanism from eruptive granular rocks, can be seen scarcely ever or else poorly. The disposition of the volcanic manifestations above the zone of intrusions of hypoabyssal porphyries, themselves superposed on the batholiths, conforms to the ideas of Edward Suess expressed at the beginning of this chapter, but are nowhere apparent. However this case, where the volcanism would represent only a superficial reverberation in the development of the plutonic rocks at depth, would seem *a priori* simpler, more logical and easier to grasp. The impossibility or difficulty of placing it in a prominent position could make one suppose that it actually does not exist.

According to W. Klüpfel (1941), "plutonic rocks are never formed simultaneously with volcanic rocks, but the plutonism succeeds the volcanism". One certainly finds porphyries at the periphery of granitic massifs, but "all the observations of surface flows and of explosions of tuffs simultaneous (with the plutonism) are erroneous. The similarity of plutonic and volcanic quartz porphyries is only a phenomenon of convergence." "Plutonism is only a continuation of volcanism under other conditions". He based his opinion on the following arguments:

1. The point of departure for a true volcano from a plutonic mass has never been observed, in spite of erosion exposing zones once 12–15 km deep. Even if the granite is accompanied by porphyries on its margins, or as intrusions at some distance from it, contemporaneous volcanic explosive phenomena are not observed.

2. The observed succession is plutonism succeeding volcanism.

3. The differentiation of the magma is in an inverse sense, the magma of the plutonic rocks being first basic, then acid, and the contrary taking place in volcanism.

4. Volcanism is related to periods of fracturing of the crust; plutonism to periods of folding.

As to the third point, however, differentiation of volcanic magmas is far from being uniform, and may show in most cases recurrences. The fourth point to my mind calls for reservations, because plutonism embraces great periods of time and varying conditions. W. Klüpfel's thesis thus seems to me to be too absolute. The making of granites proceeds in some cases by successive pulses with interludes of porphyritic intrusions and volcanic activity as in the north-eastern part of the French Massif Central. Besides, the absence of pyroclastic tuffs does not prove the absence of volcanism, in other words, of manifestations at the surface: explosive phenomena are only one aspect of volcanism.

Scepticism concerning the idea of a direct link between volcanism and supposedly subjacent plutonic masses is reinforced by the existence of cases of volcanism without plutonism and plutonism without volcanism. For instance, stratiform fissure volcanism, particularly basaltic, represents a direct and rapid ascent of lava from below the crust. On the other hand differentiated fissure volcanism, such as that of the Auvergne or the African Rifts, shows alignment of volcanic centres which have given rise to emission of varying lavas over a long period of time: it seems to be a variation of the preceding case and in any case nothing indicates the presence of subjacent plutonic rocks. On the other hand, there are granites without volcanism: those whose dyke radiations consist not of porphyry but of pegmatites. In particular the anatectic granites do not seem likely to generate volcanism. In sum, *if there is no orogenic volcanism without plutonism, there is in contrast much plutonism, orogenic or not, without volcanism.*

Let us definitely remember that petrographic and chemical arguments exist in favour of a direct link between some volcanism and underlying plutonic masses. It is hardly reasonable to reduce to a simple convergence such a universal fact as the petrographic similarity of certain lavas, such as rhyolites or andesites, with peribatholitic porphyries. However, the simplicity is only apparent: even if only very little is sufficient *a priori* to pass from rhyolite to granite of the same chemical composition, we find that the granitic or granophyric intrusions have developed in volcanic rocks of completely different composition, such as the subvolcanic granitic masses of the basalts of Scotland and elsewhere.

Chemical argument to prove the correlation between a plutonic rock and a particular volcanic rock is tempting in principle. But it is not certain, taking into account the degrees of chemical differentiation which are possible between rocks of different structure in the same assemblage. It has at times been confirmed as misleading. The famous Monzoni monzonite was in days gone by regarded as Triassic, and a chemical correlation with the Triassic lavas was admitted. It is now known through structural observations that it is Tertiary.

The best arguments for the correlation of volcanism and plutonism remains the existence of recurrent phases of granitic ascension and volcanic emissions, proved to exist in many a region. Everything considered, the most frequent normal liaison seems to be volcanism-plutonism and not the reverse. The problem of the "denudations" of Suess, which have as a goal the demonstration of the connection between volcanism above and plutonism below, is wrongly proposed and misleading. If volcanism precedes, it will be obliterated at depth by the ascending granitization. If volcanism is later, an examination of the zones in the heart of the granite from whence it derived will not be convincing, because it is doubtful whether the swarms of intrusive dykes or lamprophyric dykes really reached the surface of the earth. At the present state of knowledge, the true roots of volcanism are not known with certainty, having not been obvious in a tangible way.

Volcanism and granitic plutonism thus often accompany each other, but not necessarily so. Is their possible liaison in the history of the crust accidental, or has it a deep organic cause? No definite conclusions can yet be drawn.

Chapter 14

GRANITIC METALLOGENESIS

The metalliferous deposits which appear to have been derived more or
less under the influence of granites, as indicated by their positions relative to granite massifs or their mineralogical compositions, are both
numerous and varied. Their metallogenesis in the strict sense, that is to
say, based on physico-chemical conditions, is obviously diverse. It
presents a variability comparable to that of the episodes of the evolution
of granite. Nevertheless these deposits have a fundamental unity and
merit study as a group.

ESSENTIAL CHARACTERISTICS

1. Metallogenic granites usually belong to the category of circumscribed granites rather than to that of the anatectic granites. This fact
undoubtedly reflects the more intense, more concentrated, and locally
greater, chemical evolution leading to the formation of the granites of
the first category. In the second, phenomena are more diffuse, in other
words, less apt to produce concentrations of metalliferous compounds.

One aspect of the intense chemical migrations in the circumscribed
massifs is the differentiation often found in the granitic rocks. This
explains why in granitic metallogenesis true granites are often not
involved, but rather dioritic, monzonitic and syenitic rocks, namely
"granites" in the widest sense, following the convention adopted at the
beginning of this book. "All of the types of deposits found in genetic
association with quartz diorite, granodiorite and quartz monzonite are
also found with granite" (A. F. Buddington, 1933).

However, certain authors think that migmatites have sometimes
created metalliferous fronts, ahead of the migmatization front. According to N. H. Magnusson (1948), the Swedish anatectic granites were
responsible for numerous pyritic deposits with zinc and lead, such as
Falun and Ammeberg, localized in a magnesium aureole in front of these

granites. A similar theory has been presented for a great part of the metallogenesis in the Austrian Alps, particularly for siderite and magnesite around the Alpine gneiss of Hohe Tauern (E. Clar, 1953), and similarly for the siderites of the Pyrenees, around Canigou and in Ariège related to Hercynian migmatites (E. Raguin, 1953). V. Duhoux (1949) interprets the gold deposits of the NE part of the former Belgian Congo as related to the migmatite front which mobilized gold dispersed in the old pregranitic schists of the region.

2. Mineralizers play an important part in granitic metallogenesis. They are displayed in the paragenesis of the pegmatitic type (pneumatolytic minerals) or of the aureole type, or of both types combined. As an example of the first, those with fluorine-bearing mica (tin) may be mentioned, as well as those with tourmaline, e.g., gold veins of Brazil, and with scapolite, e.g., iron ores of the Urals. As examples of aureole types, the metasilicate and garnet gangues of the copper, lead and zincores of the Basin Ranges, U.S.A. suffice. A granitic massif with a metallogenetic character generally has a contact metamorphic aureole developed extensively and intensively.

Just as metasomatism is an essential phenomenon of the aureole, it is equally important in the formation of metallic concentrations in the neighbourhood of granite. Such deposits in the aureole are regarded as "pyrometasomatic".

3. There are gradations from granitic deposits to hydrothermal deposits, and some hydrothermal deposits actually form part of the granite aureole. The relationships of their positions are sometimes conclusive in this regard.

In normal non-metalliferous aureoles, it is known from the work of A. Lacroix that some fissures are filled with pneumatolytic and even strictly hydrothermal minerals. It is equally well-known that the complex pegmatites terminate in hydrothermal fillings of geodic (vuggy) facies, and that common pegmatites degenerate into quartz veins.

The aureole in its periphery passes into hydrothermal veins. The hydrothermal manifestations, however, can also prolong in time the final phases of granitization, not only outside but even in the stockworks and impregnations in the granite itself. These manifestations can still be followed by emissions of porphyritic dykes emanated from a late active deep zone of the granitic edifice, as in the deposits of the Basin Ranges. The best arguments for the *juvenile*[1] character of most

---

[1] I refer to as *juvenile* materials emanated from depth. The term was created by E. Suess for waters of volcanic origin. W. Vernadsky (1924) adopted it for elements and minerals stable in the magmatic zone of the globe.

hydrothermal veins is their dependence on granitic massifs. W. H. Emmons (1933) stresses the importance of this category of veins:

> The systems of metallic veins have been deposited by ascending thermal solutions which have risen from these great irregular bodies of intrusive magma called batholiths. It is probable that 95% of these vein systems are connected with acidic or "granitic" batholiths and probably less than 5% with basic intrusions.

The latter control, above all, deposits of other types (segregations). The interpretation of batholiths as "bodies of magma" is today a little out of date, but this changes nothing of the description of the deposits and their connection with the batholiths.

4. The granitic metalliferous deposits sometimes represent metallic concentrations brought in by agents of the granitization and emplaced in the layers where there were no metals before, and sometimes a re-working almost in place of metal compounds pre-existing there. Initially pure limestones, enriched with magnetite (Urals) or with copper sulphides (Bingham, Utah), represent the first case. The öolithic ferruginous limestones, recrystallized with similar magnetite (Diélette, Normandy), represent the second case. There are certainly also intermediate cases. One may ask, for instance, whether pyrite deposits are not sometimes formed by the combination of imported sulphur (hydrothermal sulphide solutions) and autochthonous or almost autochthonous iron.

ORIGINS OF THE METALS OF THE DEPOSITS

Even if the metalliferous front is later everywhere than the other fronts of metamorphism of the granitic aureole (chapter 6), it does not signify that the metallization was a phenomenon of the end of the granitic evolution involving the entire massif. The metalliferous concentrations had to progress to the margins of the granite simultaneously and proportionally to its ascent. It would be improbable that they would surge out all at once, coming from great distances at the moment the activity of the environment was on the point of stopping. Furthermore, lamprophyres, definitely terminal phenomena, are rarely connected with metalliferous activity.

It seems that more often the effects of the aureole are not terminal phenomena, but marginal phenomena connected with the whole evolution of the granitic body, and particularly its ascent. All known granitic bodies actually must be fixed at different stages of evolution;

all have not attained the "normal final stage", in other words that stage due to autonomous causes, because all natural phenomena encounter accidental factors. Now for all known granites, the effects of contact metamorphism are of the same kind, whatever the stage attained. Diversities of the aureoles either accentuated or unobtrusive at various points around a particular massif have, it seems, a local character related to the surrounding conditions, rather than to the chronology of the emplacement of the granite.

Aside from the concentrated metals, there are also dispersed metals in granite. They are either contained in essential minerals of the granite, or as very fine autonomous inclusions composed of metallic compounds, either oxides or sulphides. Thus iron occurs as magnetite, ilmenite or pyrite. The formation of metallic grains represents the beginnings of metallogenesis. It can be said that this formation is normal in the evolution of granites, and even that it is an early feature, because these discrete grains are in general among the first elements to consolidate in the succession of minerals in granites.

The analogy between the marginal metallic concentrations and the bodies of common pegmatites representing satellites of the granite is strict from the point of view we have chosen. Now these pegmatites seem to be connected with the whole evolution in the same way as other phenomena of the aureole. If the marginal concentration of metals appears less normal than the formation of pegmatite bodies or pneumatolytic fillings of fissures, it is only a matter of quantity and proportion. The process appears to be the same for metals and pegmatites, and can be presented in the following way. Metallic "clouds" are driven away with the mineralizers to which chemical affinities unite them, with due regard to the mobility of the mineralizers. These metallic clouds, which together form the metalliferous front (p. 96), are most often redissolved in the advance of the granite. Their material can be taken as well from the enclosing rocks as from the underlying mobilized environment. The mineralizers being essentially heterogeneous in composition and distribution, irregularity of metallic concentrations ensues, resembling that of the pegmatites. When the phenomenon stops the supply of metals remains in place, held in "containers" or "traps" depending upon circumstances, as we will see below.[1]

This concept of the mode of perigranitic metalliferous concentrations approaches that of C. J. Sullivan (1948) or D. Guimaraes (1949).

The old term "gite" mineral (literally mineral lodging, home) also corresponds to the idea of a receptacle.

According to Sullivan the metal deposits are concentrated, during the formation of a granitic rock, in inverse ratio to the amounts in which they can be incorporated in the ordinary minerals of the granite. The metallic ions, thus concentrated, have been *rejected*, as it were, by the granite. This would depend particularly on the ionic radii and charges. Offhand these points of view could explain the singular concentrations of lead, zinc and copper, metals rare in the Earth's crust with respect to its average chemical composition, but nevertheless accumulated in enormous tonnages in some perigranitic deposits.

"The ability of a particular plutonic rock to concentrate a particular element", writes Sullivan, "depends on the lattice structure of the crystals of the plutonic rock, the ionic radii and valences of elements susceptible to concentration". Elements of the same ionic radius tend to substitute for each other in the crystal lattices; elements with high ionic charges (valence) tend to replace those of lower charge; a higher degree of substitution is possible at high temperature than at low temperature. He observes that it is the rocks rich in quartz (granites) which are most amenable to this mode of concentration by the rejection of ions. "The quartz crystal has a very closed lattice which because of the small size and high valence of the Si ion makes solid solution difficult (of other ions in the lattice)". The rocks rich in quartz thus reject many metallic ions.

According to Sullivan, copper, silver and gold enter the lattice of minerals of plutonic rocks with difficulty, because of their weak charges, and in the case of gold because of its large ionic radius. Nevertheless, he does not explain why lead and zinc are not captured in the lattices of granitic minerals, because lead can replace potassium in potassium feldspars and biotite, and because zinc can replace bivalent iron and magnesium in the ferromagnesian minerals of rocks (Rankama and Sahama, 1950). It seems to me in fact that these elements, as well as copper, more than anything else stay with the pneumatolytes, particularly with sulphur; the rejection of the excess of pneumatolytes by granite, rather than the rejection of the metallic ions themselves allows these metals to be driven out of the granite.

Overall, these theories, although they are based on ionic diffusions over large distances (a process about which agreement is far from unanimous), conform with the facts. The migration of solutions rendered mobile by pneumatolytic elements might, however, be considered to play definitely the same role as such ionic diffusions. The idea of a generally insignificant transport of metals and their rearrangement by granitization, with possibly local concentration, is very alluring, but difficult to prove in actual cases. A better knowledge of the distribution of dispersed metals in the rocks of different categories would furnish in the future the necessary information for such a study. As the essential chemical elements of granites have been found present in place and as granite can have been created by differential anatexis (p. 5) or metasomatism, so the metals of the granitic deposits could have a prior existence as well in the same domain.

G. Fischer (1951) has objected to the theory of rejection of metallic ions because a granite massif succeeding a migmatization would find the space despoiled of such metals and would no longer be able to engender metallic deposits. One often nevertheless finds the opposite, particularly for the pneumatolytic ore minerals of the tin group. He gives as examples the tin deposits of the Erzgebirge. He stresses the post-granitic character of the deposits associated with the granitic massifs (greisen altering the granite near some tin deposits). He notes that the pneumatolytic deposits are always local concentrations related to the morphology of the roof of the granite (cupolas).

To my mind, the post-granitic character is more apparent than real, as I have tried to demonstrate in the preceding pages. For the remainder, the observations of G. Fischer lead to the thought that the role of the pneumatolytic and hydrothermal solutions remains great, even admitting the alluring theory of the elimination and rejection of metallic ions by the mobilized environment in the course of granitization. This rejection could be accomplished at different rates and during different periods of the prolonged evolution of a granitic terrain.

MODE OF DEPOSITION

In ideal circumstances of homogeneity the metallic substances would radiate evenly through the aureole and beyond it, and no metalliferous deposits would form through the granitic metallogenesis. These latter are due to traps which have produced an accumulation and halted the migration of the pegmatitic fluids and hydrothermal solutions. Various modes of deposition can be observed:

1. Veins and masses formed by filling derived from pegmatites. They occupy scattered cavities in the granite (miarolitic cavities) existing at the end of the formation of the granite. Yet again Cloos's fissures in the granite and outside the granite, namely in spaces created at a terminal stage of the evolution of the granite massif by this evolution itself, as has been shown in chapter 7. In both cases they are open places,

I

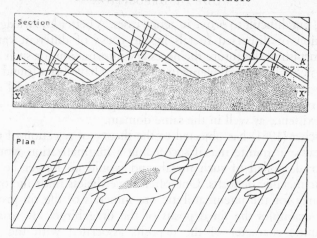

Fig. 44. Schematized section and map of cupolas of a batholith (after W. H. Emmons).

The map is drawn at the A–A′ of the section. The granitic massif is shown dotted, except the uppermost part above the "surface limit " X–X′, which has been left blank and which constitutes the "hoods" of the cupolas. The lined area represents the enclosing formations. The metalliferous veins intersect the hoods and propagate outwards.

appearing unexpected in some way, and which it is natural to see filled up by the residual material of the granite.

2. Veins arranged systematically around the periphery and the summits of batholithic cupolas. The cupolas, or protuberances of the roof of the batholiths, show a pronounced fissuring which extends outwards. They are a zone of accumulation of ascending mineralizers and consequently of metallic concentrations (fig. 44).

3. Impregnation of the granite itself or its immediate margin, either early, at the moment of the consolidation of the rock (magnetite), or later, as hydrothermal stockworks profoundly altering earlier consolidated granite (pyrite). This last mode seems to be connected with an aborted rejection of mineralizing fluids, which do not seem to have been able to escape from the margin of the massif and which spread through fissures in the granite at a temperature already quite low.

4. A suite of metalliferous stratiform bodies in the surrounding rock, particularly in limestones; columns of impregnation in favourable rocks, such as certain hornfelses. The deposits may be hundreds of meters from the granite. They result from easier egress passages where mineralizers have been channelled over a long distance, controlled

either by physical properties or the chemical constitution of the rocks.

5. Vertical mineralized chimneys, with or without volcanic manifestations, which precede the granite or alternate with pulses of granite. When volcanism occurs, it seems to be a question of abnormal and accidental phenomena in the emplacement of the granite (e.g., the copper deposits of Cananea, Mexico). If volcanism has not occurred, it is a question of an intense and localized rejection of mineralizers in hydrothermal solutions (tin-bearing pipes of Malaya, according to Lacroix, 1933). The chimney may show indications of collapse, as in the open stopes of mine workings, an effect possibly attributable to dissolution at depth (Wolfram deposits of Puy-les-Vignes, France, according to M. Wepp, 1950).

ARE THE METALLOGENIC GRANITES OF A SPECIAL NATURE?

One can discover, as in the following example, that there is something peculiar in the petrographic characteristics of the granites which have engendered particular types of metal deposit.

The little Montmins granite massif, near Echassières in the northern part of the French Massif Central, is accompanied by a series of quartz veins with wolfram which radiate north and south of the massif, passing from granite into the surrounding mica schists (fig. 45). This mineralization is pneumatolytic: tourmaline, fluorine, with some iron and copper sulphides, stannite, lepidolite, and exceptionally autunite, accompany the wolframite or appear separately in some veins of the same group. The texture of the granite is exceptional. Of coarse grain and porphyritic, it is rich in muscovite which is the dominant mica; its quartz is bluish and idiomorphic; rose-coloured orthoclase and pale green sericitized albite give the rock a pleasing appearance. Under the microscope, the muscovite often shows a micropegmatitic association with feldspar. Even though the granite tends towards a pegmatitic aspect, true pegmatites are almost absent from the massif and the aureole is almost insignificant. The mineralizers seem to have remained for the most part diffused in the batholith, apart from the final phase of quartz veins with wolframite and the release of solutions which by their ascent have kaolinized important portions of the massif.

Another example is that of the Azegour granite in the Atlas of Marrakesh, Morocco. It has produced impregnations of scheelite, molybdenite and chalcopyrite in vesuvianite-bearing garnetites within limestones metamorphosed by the aureole of this granite. Again it is a matter of a coarse-grained granite which is, however, poor in mica.

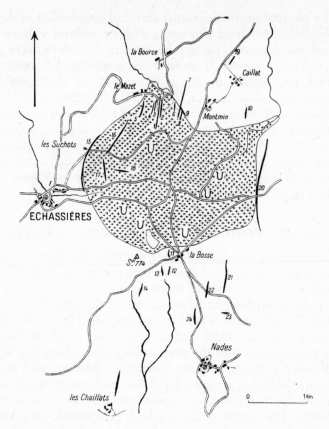

Fig. 45. The Montmins granite massif (Allier) and its veins. The kaolin quarries are
marked by the symbol U. The main veins are designated by numbers.

The feldspars are perthitic orthoclase and oligoclase. Their rose colour
is due to schillerization. Sometimes the microscope reveals a little
micropegmatite along the borders of the quartz and the orthoclase and
a little myrmekite between the two feldspars. The massif has a very
pronounced aureole, but few true pegmatites. The abundant mineralizers have diffused in a regular fashion around the massif, and the
residual solutions have mineralized the hornfelses of the aureole.

The two preceding granites properly attract attention, not being
rocks of common aspect, and one might *a priori* suspect that they were
capable of producing mineral deposits of interest. However it does not
seem that one could go very far in this direction in making an inventory
of the metallogenic granites based on their textures and their most

apparent characteristics: *the method is not sensitive enough*. In contrast a detailed chemical-mineralogical examination, including even the study of traces of certain elements, could give suggestive results. An example of this method is given by J. Westerveld (1936), who has compared the granites of the tin-bearing arc of Malaya with some others of classic tin-bearing regions.

The granites of the great tin deposits are, according to him, of a very uniform type and of an everyday appearance. Concerning the granites of Malaya, Indonesia, Cornwall and Saxony, he establishes that they are biotite granites, often porphyritic, with sometimes a little muscovite. According to their chemical analyses, they could be classified as the monzonitic granites of French terminology. However, their micas and particularly their accessory minerals reveal some peculiarities.

There are some indications of a higher content of rare elements which distinguish them from common granites: there is an exceptional content of rare earths in the granites of Malaya; small quantities of tin in the black mica, in the quartz and the feldspar of the Banka granites; some traces of Li, Sn, Bi, Cu, Co and U in the zinnwaldite mica of the tin-bearing granites of Saxony, and of Ga, Sn and W in the biotite of the granite of the East Pool mine near Redruth, Cornwall.

He gives a table of the amounts of oxides of the elements Y, La, Ce and Nd of various granites from Indonesia. These amounts range from $0.005-0.01\%$ even though the average amounts of the same oxides in the Earth's crust are of the order of $0.002-0.005\%$ (Westerveld, 1941).

Recently J. Jedwab (1956) has measured the concentration of Li in the feldspar and Sn in the feldspar, biotite and muscovite of two adjacent granites in Brittany, one of which contains quartz veins with tin, the other none. He finds much higher averages of these elements in the first granite. Nonetheless the spread in the figures is important and the number of analyses is small, so that the results are not absolutely conclusive. This type of investigation, however, merits universal application.

The geochemistry of the granites was first approached by K. Rankama (1946) from a different angle. He has shown that the contents of trace elements in granites of lesser and lesser antiquity seem to show an increase in the elements Li, Be, Rb, Cs, Ba, the lanthanides, Ta and Pb. He calls these elements "granitophile" because of their tendency to become enriched in granites during the evolution of the earth.

The study of the geographic distribution of such elements during a particular epoch, namely in "metallogenetic provinces" (or better still in geochemical provinces), should moreover lead to fruitful results. It would be necessary to study the regional clarkes[1] of the different elements particularly within granites. Their variations according to region should provide insights into certain questions and above all the pattern of the irregularities of distribution of the great global concentrations of certain metals: tin in South-East Asia, silver in the American Cordilleras, copper in Central Africa, etc. L. de Launay has envisioned a primary preferential distribution of certain elements at the time of the first formation of the Earth's crust. It will be perhaps possible, if this distribution is linked to geographic variations in the corresponding clarke, to analyze the geological factors of this clarke without going so far back.

PRINCIPAL PARAGENESES

In a general way, the *gangues* of the deposits with granitic affinities comprise pneumatolytic minerals and the silicates of the contact aureoles in the deposits close to the granite. Some hydrothermal minerals of the lowest temperatures, such as barite, calcite, dialogite and fluorite are found in more distant deposits. The fluorite is, however, also pneumatolytic. Quartz is found in all categories and it grades into the jasperoid facies in the low temperature deposits. The carbonates, particularly siderite, may appear even close to the granite. The metallic part of the paragenesis presents the following varieties:

1. *Magnetite*, with some sulphides (pyrite, pyrrhotite), apatite and silicates. Segregation deposits or metasomatic bodies close to the granite particularly in limestones.

2. *Cassiterite, wolframite, scheelite*, gangues of quartz and pneumatolytic minerals. This type is associated with pegmatites and developed particularly in pneumatolytic quartz veins.

3. *Molybdenite*, with other sulphides (chalcopyrite), in impregnations or quartz veins in the aureole.

4. *Sulphides, pyrite dominant*, often cupriferous (inclusions of chalcopyrite), with or without magnetite, pyrrhotite, mispickel, precious metals. This type is found very close to the granite or forms veins and bodies farther away in the surrounding formations ("porphyry" ore minerals of the U.S.A.). It constitutes on the other hand late impregnations in the granite itself.

[1] The *clarke* of a chemical element is its average content in the crust.

5. *Sulphides, pyrite subordinate:* Deposits of chalcopyrite, sphalerite, galena, with precious metals, in silicified gangues: metasomatic veins or bodies of mesothermal facies, rather far from granite (thousands of meters), such as the important deposits of the Western U.S.A. Other deposits of this type, where the tourmaline is formed in abundance in the gangue, have in contrast a hypothermal facies, such as some gold-bearing chalcopyrite ores (gold deposits of Ontario).

6. *Stibnite* in quartz veins. This type is found farther from the granite, or is later if it is enclosed in the granite itself.

THE GRANITIC DEPOSITS IN THE METALLOGENIC CLASSIFICATION

Inclusion deposits. This group involves normal but accessory mineralogical elements of the granite, substantially more abundant than in ordinary granites: cassiterite, monazite. However, this concentration becomes of commercial importance only if the rock is transformed into eluvium, exploitable directly or providing material for nearby alluvial deposits.

Segregation deposits. Thick metallic masses, localized in the plutonic rock or close to its border, have been concentrated and crystallized by the complex of the same mechanisms of formation as that of the plutonic rock itself. They represent extreme cases of differentiation. Lindgren gives as examples the deposits of iron segregations in the American Adirondacks, the involved rocks being granites and syenites, sometimes massive, sometimes gneissic.

The mechanism of segregation must to my mind be taken in the broad sense of chapter 8. If the granitic rocks are often formed by metasomatic processes and not by crystallization from a magma, their differentiation must be conceived of as a migration of chemical fronts rearranging or accentuating the heterogeneities of the pre-existing formations in place; the concentration of deposits could be accomplished in a similar fashion to that of the pyrometasomatic deposits. The distinction between the two metallogenic types (segregation by differentiation and pyrometasomatic type) tend to diminish or to correspond to a difference in intensity of the phenomena. Perhaps the segregation type is much better defined in the basic plutonic rocks (chromite, ilmenite deposits) than in the granites.

Pyrometasomatic deposits. They occur in metamorphic contact aureoles and are often a little later than the silicates of metamorphism. However there are recurrences of these minerals, as also synchronous crystallizations and intergrowths of amphibole and chalcopyrite, garnet and

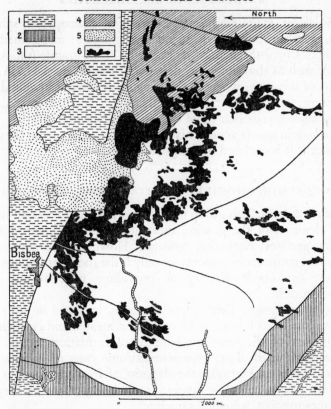

Fig. 46. Map of the cupriferous pyrite deposit of Bisbee, Arizona. (Drawn after J. B. Tenney, XVIth Inter. Geol. Cong.).
   1. Precambrian schists. 2. Cambrian. 3. Devonian and Carboniferous. 4. Cretaceous. 5. Granitic porphyry. 6. Ore masses projected onto a horizontal plane.
   The mineralization comprises late pyritic concentrations in the porphyritic stock and pyrometasomatic vein masses some distance out in the Palaeozoic formations.

magnetite, etc. The role of the mineralizers is attested to by the gangues of tourmaline, mica, apatite and scapolite. The introduction of metals by granite is often manifest, as is the release of carbon dioxide gas in the calcareous rocks partially transformed into hornfelses.

There is sometimes a relationship of deposits to porphyritic facies of granite: as Bowen (1933) notes the conditions of rapid crystallization liberate more of the volatile elements, which in a gradual crystallization would have been absorbed and fixed in the pneumatogenic minerals of the rock, principally micas.

Pegmatite deposits. Among the complex pegmatites some are tin-bearing. Others contain columbo-tantalite, beryl and lanthanide minerals.

Pneumatolytic deposits. There are in some granites fissure fillings or impregnations of pneumatolytic minerals without the formation of true pegmatites. These are concentrations of tourmaline, topaz, apatite, fluorite, cassiterite, muscovite or lepidolite.

The quartz veins with cassiterite, wolframite or molybdenite derive from pneumatolytes generally independent of pegmatites.

Hypothermal deposits related to granites. The peri-batholithic hydro-thermal veins or bodies bear witness in a striking way to the importance of the renewed movement of water in granitization. The fact that sedimentary formations with a relatively high water content, particularly in clay minerals, are found replaced by granitic rock of the batholith which is much less rich in water, obviously implies an important elimination of this fluid. Water is a mineralizer of major importance.

Among the hypothermal veins, those which have a granitic origin are localized not far from the border of the granite or arranged around the cupolas of the batholith. Some have a more or less pneumatolytic paragenesis, i.e., they are transition. Others contain minerals characteristic of high temperature of formation: pyroxene, garnet, pyrrhotite, magnetite. The temperature, according to W. Lindgren, could be of the order of 300–500°.

The mineralizers are driven out of the batholith before the complete consolidation, C. N. Fenner (1933) established, because there is an accumulation of metallic compounds near the cupolas. It cannot be a question of late hydrothermal solutions injected through fissures of the cooled and rigid mass, because the shape of the batholith would not in that case have an influence on the localization of the veins. Here the question arises of the relationships between the hypothermal fluids and the pegmatites, because these latter represent the residue of mobilized material emitted before the crystallization was achieved. The idea that the hypothermal fluid itself is only a residue of the pegmatites after crystallization of the feldspars is supported by the following argument: the degeneration of the complex pegmatites in the hydrothermal facies, with replacement of the primary minerals, development of some metallic sulphides and various gangue minerals. Connection between some tin-bearing quartz veins and cassiterite-bearing granitic pegmatites, and the continuation of the same veins in regions remote from the granite in the form of common sulphide veinlets, containing for instance lead-copper.

The idea that hydrothermal fluid apart from the restricted case of the

I*

complex pegmatites is independent of the pegmatites is supported by two facts. In the great vein districts, pegmatites are not particularly abundant, as might be expected under the other hypothesis; rather they are often conspicuous by their absence. On the other hand, C. N. Fenner observes that in many sulphide deposits, particularly those pyrometasomatic, great quantities of elements such as Fe, Mg, Cu, Pb, Zn, have been introduced, which suggests an agency of transportation very different from that of the pegmatites, where these elements scarcely ever appear.

Mesothermal deposits related to granites. Here more distant veins are involved than in the foregoing category or else internal stockworks in the granite itself which have had a destructive effect on the minerals of the rock. In the first case, one often observes a *zoning* in the distribution of the deposits. For example, quite close to the granite there are deposits of magnetite, pyrite, pyrrhotite with chalcopyrite with hypothermal gangues. Farther away, some hundreds or thousands of meters, there are veins or bodies of sphalerite or galena essentially mesothermal according to their paragenesis. Still farther away, manganese or hematite deposits occur. The deposits of the Basin Ranges in the U.S.A. serve as an example (fig. 47).

In the second case, also found in many mines in the western United States, the granite, already cooled and intimately fractured, is not in equilibrium with the solutions and is profoundly altered. Even if the mesothermal deposits are later than those of the foregoing categories, relative to the emplacement of the granite, there can be new pulses of magmatic character and certain porphyries associated with the batholiths may cut these veins.

Long distance hydrothermal deposits. What share does granite have in their origin? It is undoubtedly not exclusive, but is it dominant? It is a question of mesothermal or telethermal veins (lead-zinc type of Missouri and Tri-State). There is no longer either a granitic paragenesis, nor any visible spatial relationship to granite. The distinction from purely vadose water is vague. One could either envision simply the travel of the foregoing types from far away, or a distant heating of non-juvenile material, particularly water. One could in contrast assume that the granites have nothing to do with such hydrothermal circulations. It is possible that other factors have enriched the waters of infiltration with metallic substances.

Important vein systems far from granites of the same age are known in France, for instance Cevennes, Maures, Alps. Beyond very local hypothetically possible action of granular basic rocks, some other

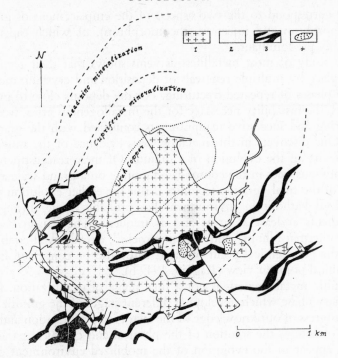

Fig. 47. Geological map of the mining district of Bingham, Utah (drawn after R. N. Hunt and H. G. Peacock, simplified).
1. Monzonite. 2. Quartzites. 3. Limestones. 4. Breccia.

possibilities could be suggested. For instance the theory of secondary hydrothermal veins of H. Schneiderhöhn (1952) envisions a renewal of the movement of metallic substances localized in the ancient deposits of the basement, under the influence of the circulation of very hot deepseated waters in a very much more recent epoch. The "pseudo-hydrothermal" deposits of P. Ramdohr (1955) would result from a renewal of movements of the same kind, more locally but very intense, by the action of general metamorphism.

CONCLUSION

This examination of metallogenesis has demonstrated a double mechanism: metasomatism and fissure filling. Metasomatism dominates close to the granite and fissure filling farther away, except in the case of limestones where metasomatism takes place very easily at any distance.

These correspond to the two aspects of the emplacement of granite: metamorphism and injection (rheomorphism), of which the first is probably predominant.

The study of most metalliferous veins shows that their formation takes place by multiple renewals of deposition and crystallization between phases of repeated fracturing. For the deposits close to granitic massifs, the instability necessary for the metallogenesis arises from the rupturing and successive readjustments connected with the granitization. One discovers in this metallogenesis evidence of the multiform complexity of the evolution of a granite. Of these readjustments the only obvious ones in the consolidated granite on a grand scale are the joints of the final "granite tectonics". But the earlier evolution of the mobilized batholithic environment has probably gone through readjustments at least as great and as frequent. The liaison between "hydrothermal fillings" and "granitic rocks", already well-established from the geochemical point of view, must also be conceived from a mechanical point of view (Raguin, 1949 b).

Granitic metallogenesis is not a final phase of granitization. It is a subsidiary phase which develops at different stages of the granitization. The progress of our knowledge of the factors of granitization and their mode of action, the solution of the physical and chemical paradoxes which appear in the evolution of the mobilized environment of the granitization, will lead at the same time to a better comprehension of the metallic deposits of granitic affinities. These are not abnormal and teratological phenomena in the Earth's crust, no more than all the other metalliferous deposits.

Chapter 15

THE RADIOACTIVITY OF GRANITE

The granites are more radioactive than other rocks. Radioactivity in nature is provided by uranium, thorium and the disintegration products of these metals, and also, to a lesser extent, by potassium. All uranium or thorium ores are at the same time ores of their disintegration products. For example, a uranium ore is at the same time a radium ore; and there is a constant relationship between the proportions of uranium and radium and also other disintegration products, provided that the deposit is old enough for the equilibrium of disintegration to be established. The radioactivity of granite is essentially due to the two series of uranium and thorium. The geochemical evolution of uranium compounds is most complex and it is to this that we will devote our attention in the following pages.

URANIUM DEPOSITS

Pegmatite Deposits

The veins and bodies of complex pegmatites of granites contain autunite and exceptionally uraninite[1] among their various minerals. Some pegmatites contain uraniferous minerals of thorium and the lanthanides. This is understandable, because granites are radioactive and because the mode of formation of the pegmatites actually makes a sort of selective variety of the granite, thanks to which diffuse substances occurring in small quantities in normal granite can be found locally in a state of higher concentration.

Autunite is found in flakes which often coat fissures or alteration zones in rocks; it even forms concretionary veinlets. It is known moreover that it can be deposited from surface waters, as we will see below.

[1] The term *uraninite* is reserved for the crystallized oxide UO_2 and the term *pitchblende* for concretionary or amorphous varieties of the same minerals.

The autunite of pegmatites thus represents an alteration phase of the pegmatite, or it may be an ultimate phase of "auto-destruction" at low temperature. Phosphorus is normal in the pegmatites, as evidenced in juvenile minerals such as apatite, manganese phosphates and occasionally monazite. It is thus not always necessary to invoke actions *per descensum* for the development of autunite.

Uraninite, less abundant, seems *a fortiori* juvenile, like the occasional uranium minerals of lanthanides. These minerals (complex oxides and urano-niobates, urano-tantalates, urano-titanates) are less easily altered under meteoric conditions. However an alteration consisting of a separation of lanthanides and uranium and favouring a formation of uraninite has possibly taken place under somewhat deep hydrothermal conditions. This would be a kind of hydrothermal degeneration of the pegmatites.

Deposits in Sedimentary Formations

A. Lacroix (1923) observed the formation of autunite[1] on Madagascar in a Quaternary deposit. The flakes of this mineral impregnate the peaty alluvium lying on granite containing pegmatites. This autunite "is concentrated in numerous shrinkage fissures, in worm holes and in the cylindrical cavities left by the disappearance of roots, which may also form geodes". Surficial waters charged with radioactive elements through the leaching of pegmatites, may thus precipitate these substances under certain conditions and particularly in a reducing environment.

The important deposits of uranium vanadates in Colorado and Utah in sandstone, principally of Jurassic age, seem to be the result of a slightly different process. Here carnotite is the principal mineral, often accompanied by vandium-bearing mica (roscoelite) and various metallic sulphides, notably copper-bearing ones. These minerals impregnate the sandstone as a microscopic felt between the quartz grains; they are certainly formed *in situ*. Petrified wood, common in these sandstones, has played a role in the precipitation of these substances, whose tenor decreases away from it. Bituminous strata have a similar effect. Impregnations occur at certain stratigraphic levels, sometimes following them closely for several hundred meters; they are also in pipes or along fissures. Although mostly of shallow depth, the ores have sometimes been followed horizontally under several hundred meters of cover. They thus do not represent the result of recent superficial meteoric circulation. Some assume that they were formed at the time of sedi-

[1] Or rather uranocircite.

mentation or a little later by meteoric waters leaching the Precambrian formations of the region which contain uraniferous veins. I prefer to think, with other authors, that *teletethermal* waters would have later produced this concentration of uraniferous material, together with those of the sulphides. This is a better explanation of the many stratigraphic levels mineralized, the mineralized faults, and the relationship with the sulphide paragenesis. Impregnations may reach up to 0.3% uranium oxide in the best ores.

Other uranium-bearing sedimentary formations are still more enigmatic. Some bituminous schists of marine facies are uraniferous. Those of Scania in Sweden contain 100 grams of uranium per ton (about 25 times the content of average granites) and 0.3% vanadium. Oil-bearing formations sometimes have high radioactivity compared with common sedimentary beds.

In the marine intercalations of the coal-bearing terrain of the north of France, G. Muchemblé (1943) has found 3×10^{-12} to 10×10^{-12} grams of radium per gram of rock, which is equivalent to the content of the most radioactive granite or ten times the content of the average granite.

The fine marine muds rich in organisms which have given rise to carbonaceous schists of the ampelite type are rocks with usually high radioactivity. From the studies of J. Joly, of H. Peterson and of Piggot, it is known that in the present-day oceans, blue oozes, red clays and Globigerina and Radiolarian oozes are radioactive (radium tenors of 3.9 to 13.1×10^{-12}).

These observations bring up the question of a concentration of uranium by living matter. We know nothing of the physical state in which uranium is fixed.

The sedimentary phosphates also contain exceptional amounts of uranium, sometimes in the order of ten thousandths, attributable perhaps to selective captivation at the expense of some kind of meteoric water. With regard to the famous gold-bearing conglomerates of the Rand, their tenor of the same order in the form of thucolite and pitchblende, is attributed by R. Ramdohr (1955) to an ancient detrital addition of pitchblende and by C. F. Davidson to a hydrothermal impregnation.

This deposit and similar ones represent great resources of uranium. However rich the uranium-bearing sedimentary beds may be, they are exceptional within the sedimentary series and represent *a weak geochemical content relative to those of the granites of the Earth's crust.*

Hydrothermal Deposits

The hydrothermal vein deposits of uranium are to date the most important sources for atomic industry, that is to say they represent the greatest concentrated tonnages. Their paragenesis is very varied and the persistence of pitchblende under diverse conditions is remarkable. J. Geffroy (1955) distinguishes four categories:

The hypothermal type is represented by the famous deposit of Shin-kolobwe in Katanga. It is one of the elements of the copper and cobalt-bearing metallogenic province of Katanga, in which other stratiform deposits of copper, following dolomitic layers in the depth, sometimes also contain a little uranium. At Shinkolobwe the deposits are strictly of vein form in fractures in silicified rock (fig. 48). Apart from copper and cobalt sulphides, the paragenesis comprises molybdenite, gold and platinum with monazite and tourmaline. The sulphides and native metals are later than the uraninite.

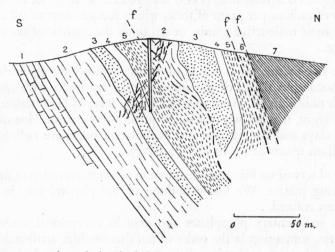

Fig. 48. Section through the Shinkolobwe, Katanga (drawn after H. Buttgenbach). 1. Dolomitic limestones. 2. Dolomitic shales. 3. Cellular rocks. 4. Foliated siliceous rocks. 5. Talc schists. 6. Siliceous talc formation. 7. Kundelungu series. ff. Faults. The stockwork and the shaft are schematically drawn.

The mesothermal type with cobalt, nickel, bismuth and silver is found in the Erzgebirge of Bohemia and Saxony: Jachymov (fig. 49) and other important vein fields. Similar deposits exist at Great Bear Lake in Canada. Cobalt and nickel occur in the form of arsenides. Gangue is for the large part dolomitic. In this type and in the following the

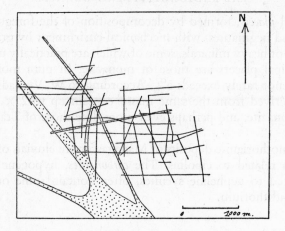

Fig. 49. Map of the veins of Jachymov, Bohemia (drawn after L. de Launay). Dotted:
Dykes of microgranite.

uranium is in the form of pitchblende and its products of supergene
alteration.

A propos this category and the preceding, it is necessary to emphasize
the *connection with cobalt*, and possibly also with nickel. There seems to
be some universality to this, the reason for which, however, is not
known.

Mesothermal sulphide type: The sulphides are the common varieties:
sphalerite, pyrite, galena and chalcopyrite.

Epithermal type: The ores have a quartz-chalcedony gangue, with
more or less fluorite, pyrite, marcasite and very small quantities of
other common sulphides. Such veins are found in the French Massif
Central.

THORIUM DEPOSITS

Granitic rocks contain thorium in the order of 13×10^{-6} grams per
gram of rock, about three times the tenor of basic rocks. This means,
as we will see, that granite contains about three times as much thorium
as uranium. Thorium seems to be contained in microscopic minerals
rich in lanthanides, which are accessory minerals in granites: monazite,
orthite, etc. It is concentrated in some pegmatites, in the preceding
minerals and in others of which some are uraniferous: niobo-tantalates,
niobo-titanates and fluosilicates of the lanthanides.

Apart from these pegmatite deposits, the most important deposits are alluvial *placers*, formed by decomposition of the foregoing rocks, granites and pegmatites, with mechanical enrichment by gravity. This is a matter of heavy minerals, some of which are practically unalterable. The principal placers are those of monazite. In pure monazites the thorium tenor rarely exceeds 5%. According to W. Vernadsky (1924): "placers derived from the same massif contain up to 2×10^6 metric tons of monazite, and perhaps even more, like those of Travancore in India".

The uranothorianite deposits of Madagascar are eluvials of pyroxene pegmatites related to cipolins. The *carbonatites*, hypogene carbonate rocks related to nepheline syenites, often contain some ores of lanthanides and thorium.

GRANITE AND THE METALLOGENESIS OF URANIUM

We will lay aside consideration of the metallogenesis of the imperfectly known sedimentary deposits of uranium. They are probably derived more or less directly from the destruction of earlier granitic or hydrothermal deposits. One event of this evolution might be the possible concentration by living material. We will occupy ourselves with the hypogene deposits of uranium. Their connection with granites, directly or through intermediate stages, seems to be well documented for a great part of them.

Direct Derivation from Granite: Uraniferous Pegmatites

Granite contains in a diffuse state four times more radioactive substances than the basic or sedimentary rocks. According to Evans and Goodman (1941), cited by J. Goguel (1948), there is an average of 4×10^{-6} uranium in granite as against $1 \cdot 1 \times 10^{-6}$ in the basic rocks. Thus 1 cubic kilometer of granite may contain on the average 10,000 tons of uranium. It should be noted that the tenors of the granites may show great fluctuations and may fall as low as $0 \cdot 3 \times 10^{-6}$. On the other hand some vast masses assay as much as 23×10^{-6}.

We know that the radioactivity of granite (apart from that due to potassium) is essentially located in the microscopic heavy minerals in the rock, such as those which produce the coronas in biotite. The photographic plate makes it possible to localize and even to estimate the content of uranium and thorium (R. Coppens, 1950). Urano-thoric minerals are mostly involved for, as Goguel remarks, the total tenors of thorium and radium often vary in the same sense. The most radioactive minerals frequently found in granite are monazite and orthite. Others may show some variable radioactivity depending on the proportions of thorium and uranium associated with the lanthanides, which they may contain: zircon, sphene and apatite. Uraninite may also occur.

Such minerals become concentrated in some granitic pegmatites, as well as numerous other radioactive lanthanide minerals which cannot be identified in the microscopic state. Sometimes they may form crystals of greater dimensions. However the uraniferous pegmatites remain exceptional even if most granites are radioactive: some flakes of autunite are common, but uraninite is rarely developed in important quantities. Even in the richest groups of pegmatites, the total concentration rarely exceeds 30 to 40 tons, according to Vernadsky, who writes: "the greatest quantity of uranium always remains dispersed in the granite mass and is not found in the pegmatites".

An obscure question is the process of concentration of the radioactive minerals in the uraniferous pegmatites in the form of macroscopic uraniferous or thorium-bearing lanthanide minerals, or in the form of uraninite. A. Fersman (1931 a) indicates that such minerals form in a phase of higher temperature of the complex pegmatites (around the transformation point of quartz, 600°) and that the evolution continues at lower temperatures, producing more oxidized coloured minerals such as autunite and also colloidal pitchblende, which is likely to continue into the hydrothermal phase. The problem of the mode of concentration is connected with that of the genesis of the complex pegmatites.

Indirect Derivation from Granite

Present-day thermal waters are often radioactive, much more so than the meteoric waters of infiltration. The hydrothermal fillings contain traces of radioactive minerals much more commonly than was formerly thought. It has been seen above that hydrothermal uranium affects a certain indifference to metallogenetic type: it occurs in three stages of the classification and under very different conditions. *Uranium thus becomes easily mobilized under hydrothermal conditions.*

The uraniferous veins, richer in content of uranium than the pegmatites, nevertheless contain small amounts relative to the quantities of the metal found dispersed in granite. Thus the famous veins of Jachymov had yielded up to 1935 a hundred grams of radium. If we take into account that at this time the ores were essentially exploited for radium, and of what was taken out 25% was lost in extraction, the

125 grams of radium correspond to 375 tons of uranium on the basis of normal proportions. If we assume that the total vein content represented four times as much material (which is probably liberal), the 1400 tons of uranium would be equivalent to the content dispersed in $0 \cdot 14$ km^3 of granite according to the figures given above. We would need seven Jachymov deposits to have the equivalent of 1 cubic kilometer of granite.

The origin of the uranium of hydrothermal veins may be *juvenile* (namely brought from depths), or else it could be provided by material extracted by leaching from pre-existing rocks. The first hypothesis, *juvenile origin deriving from pegmatites*, can be supported by the example of the tin-bearing veins of Cornwall, which are continued or cut by occasional sulphide veins, of which some are cobalt-nickel bearing with a little pitchblende. On the other hand the well-known vein systems in the Erzgebirge suggest a relationship of the uranium veins of the region with the Hercynian granites: the successive metalliferous phases of the district get farther and farther away from the granite in space and time (Schneiderhöhn, 1941). The uranium-bearing phases are rather late in this ensemble and could indicate a reverberation of the end of the emplacement and consolidation of the granite. However, P. Niggli (1929) suggests another way of looking at it. Noting that these veins are "considerably younger" than the cassiterite and pyrite-galena veins of the Erzgebirge, he does not admit the derivation of the uranium veins from the granite pegmatites. He relates them to a hypothetical basic magma, long differentiated from the granitic magma and surviving the consolidation of the granite. This point of view has the advantage of taking into account the well-known relationship of nickel and cobalt with basic magmas. But one objection is the weak radioactivity of the basic rocks. In any case the uraniferous veins of the Erzgebirge represent a metallogenetic evolution of long duration, starting with hypothermal types and terminating with different types of low temperature chemistry. This evolution seems to reflect that of the great granite batholiths, which have consolidated and differentiated at depth. Such a parallelism is an argument in favour of the hypothesis of a direct juvenile origin of the veins.

The second possible hypothesis for the provenance of uranium from hydrothermal veins is that of *leaching per ascensum* of pre-existing metalliferous rocks. These rocks would have to have been exceptionally rich in uranium, because the uranium veins with which we are concerned are rare: the leaching of any granite would not be sufficient. It would thus be a matter of a leaching of a system of old uraniferous pegmatites, or sedimentary beds of the carnotite-bearing sandstone type, or biochemical uranium-rich sediments. A granite much richer in dispersed uranium than the average granite might also be envisioned as a source. Roubault and Coppens (1955) have recently pointed out a case of dispersion of highly radioactive microscopic inclusions (probably pitchblende) in granites several hundred meters from epithermal uraniferous veins. An exact study of the granites from this point of view has still to be made; the local distribution of dispersed uranium in the granites should give information in this respect.

It is possible that these various types of leaching may occur in nature for the formation of the important hydrothermal uranium deposits. When the veins are in the granite but are of any age much younger than it, the hypothesis of leaching has much to recommend it (the veins of Limousin or Portugal). When the veins occur in schists or in gneiss, it is unthinkable that possible uraniferous sediments could have been preserved as such, and one is tempted to assume a derivation from granites or uraniferous pegmatites (direct derivation or by leaching). However, a renewal of movement, in the supposed uraniferous sediments, with reconcentration in hydrothermal facies is conceivable under the influence of general metamorphism, as P. Ramdohr (1955) has suggested for the auro-uraniferous conglomerates of the Rand. And the final leaching producing the hydrothermal veins whose origin we are discussing, should in this case be produced by the departure of concentrations which already were of hydrothermal facies.

Thus according to the second hypothesis (formation of uraniferous hydrothermal veins by ascending leaching), the phenomenon could be the result of a more or less complicated process in several stages. If the uraniferous sediments themselves are really related to surface leaching or ascending leaching from pre-existing deposits, their part in the cycle is only one more intermediate process, but not the primary origin. *And we always fall back on granite as the primary source of the metallogenesis of uranium.*

CONCLUSION

We are left with the problem of the radioactivity of granite itself. The granites harbour within themselves an average content of uranium and thorium higher than in other rocks. The corresponding amount of these metals, with regard to the immensity of the volumes of granite in the earth's crust, is a geochemical fact of the first order.

The radioactive concentrations in nature thus represent a prolongation of the influx of radioactive material related to the emplacement of great granitic bodies in the upper parts of the Earth's crust. Is this influx of radioactive material an *effect* or a *cause* of granitization? The terrestrial depths seem to be occupied by material with little or no radioactivity, according to calculations of the heat flow of the Earth (Goguel, 1948). Now the growing granites, as we have seen, are zones of intense chemical migration. If the radioactive substances are thus diffused in minimum quantities in the depths, perhaps need they only use these migrations in some way to be peripherally distributed in the crust? Perhaps on the other hand they play a causative role in granitization. Could not the hypothesis of J. Noetzlin (1940) on the priming of volcanic processes by nuclear chain reactions, related to exceptional but very local concentrations of radioactive material, be applied with still greater probability to the setting in motion of the ascent of the granitic batholiths? G. Choubert (1952) has developed the hypothesis of an active role of nuclear phenomena in granitization, while recognizing the lack of a solid basis for the idea. We had better confess our present ignorance in the matter of the radioactivity of the granitic domains.

Chapter 16

GRANITE IN THE EARTH'S CRUST

THE NOTION OF EARTH'S CRUST

The Earth's crust is the superficial zone of our planet, a zone in a solid crystalline state, which rests on regions of high temperature. The crust is called the *lithosphere*. The regions of high temperature are called the *pyrosphere*: the rocks there are probably no longer in the solid state, i.e., crystallized, or they are perhaps only partially so. The notion of the Earth's crust is based on the existence of the geothermal gradient, on the facts of isostasy, and on those of seismology.

The geothermal gradient, due to the increase of temperature with depth, is the deepening corresponding to 1°, on the average 30 to 40 meters in the zone accessible to direct measurement. It indicates a heat flow moving outwards from the very hot zones. Volcanism and the intrusions of molten magma within the interior of solid layers bear witness to this in the same manner.

The theory of isostasy, based on gravity measurements, consists in the assumption that cones with equal apical angles having their apices at the centre of the Earth contain equal masses, regardless of the altitude and the form of the surface topography.[1] According to gravity measurements, there exist regions relatively less dense below the mountains and regions with much higher density than the average of the crust at the same depth under the oceans. Consequently transportation of materials on the surface of the earth by erosion, sedimentation and orogenic movements, must be compensated by a rearrangement in a deeper zone. A discussion of the measurements leads to the idea that this compensation operates above a surface called "the surface of compensation", which can be considered, as a first approximation, as a surface of equal depth below the geoïd. Underneath the equilibrium would be hydrostatic. The depth of the surface of compensation appears

[1] A good review of these geophysical questions and a bibliography will be found in J. Goguel 1948).

to be of the order of some tens of kilometers. It is tempting to see there the base of the lithosphere. The milieu underneath would be characterized by a sudden diminution of *long-term rigidity*. As J. Goguel remarks, it is possible that this condition coincides with a disappearance of the crystalline state.

The study of the propagation of earthquakes, for the waves which travel near the surface of the globe, has revealed, according to Mohorovićić, the existence of a surface of discontinuity at 50 km beneath Europe, and according to other authors at a lesser depth elsewhere. This surface could also be related to the base of the Earth's crust. However, it corresponds to a sudden increase in the *instantaneous* rigidity underneath: which is perhaps not a contradiction.

The Elaboration of the Earth's Crust by Orogeny

The crust, such as we know it, was formed during the course of geological periods by frequently repeated orogenic foldings in one zone or another, and by intrusions of magma becoming consolidated at different levels within the rock layers.

When the crust as a whole is examined, one is struck by the quasi-ubiquity of foldings. Where the ancient formations are sufficiently denuded of more recent sedimentary covers, one can see crystalline formations outlining more or less contorted and intertwining spindles, which are the roots of ancient foldings. The case of Finland is classic, and the three Precambrian foldings of different ages revealed by J. J. Sederholm form the entire deep basement of the region. Elsewhere in cases of important zones of horizontal crystalline formations, seemingly unfolded, it may be a question of restricted lenses, which have remained rigid between the links of the network of folds. Or it is even possible that these formations were affected by an orogeny of tangential style, or by a recrystallization of horizontal style, having effaced the structure of the folded beds.

The Depth of Investigation of the Crust

Thanks to orogeny, which initiates a gigantic coming and going of material between the depths and the surface of the earth, we can see materials from regions much deeper than would be permitted by the deepest incisions of erosion across the swellings of great radius of the globe. Through the axial undulations of fold belts, these materials are carried sometimes to a height well above sea level.

In the French Massif Central, Jung and Roques (1952) estimate at

20,000 meters the thickness of the Hercynian or older metamorphic series comprising azoic superposed argillaceous schists, but not the very deep gneisses (*gneiss ultra-inférieurs*). One observes there the type of material which exists in the Earth's crust of a depth of more than 20 km, brought to the surface by orogeny. It is probable that elsewhere there exist orogenic chains of still greater amplitude. Some orders of more important magnitude, from 30–50 kilometers, are admissible as the maximum amplitude of axial undulations of the chains. Consequently, at any point on the globe, at this depth, are found materials belonging to some chain and therefore likely to outcrop elsewhere, not too far from there, if the interplay of axial undulations of this chain and erosion are favourable.

It is scarcely likely that the materials of deeper compartments would be visible anywhere, except of course for certain eruptive rocks, which did not form part of the crust, it seems, before their consolidation, and which have risen in the state of a magma. Some tens of kilometers thus represent the depth of geological investigation of the terrestrial crust. This comparatively small figure nevertheless perhaps embraces the greater part of the thickness of this crust.

The averages of analyses of rocks taken from all points on the surface of the earth, taking into account their relative extent, are thus likely to give an average chemical composition for the crust. Now the composition obtained is intermediate between granite and quartz-diorite. Indeed we will see that *granitic rocks must be the dominant material in the crust*, beneath the skin of sedimentary rocks of the surface, which is only 1–2 km thick away from the localized geosynclines, and beneath the metamorphic rocks, mica schists and gneisses, which moreover are often associated with various granites or are transformed progressively into granite at depth.

BENEATH THE TERRESTRIAL CRUST: THE SIMA

E. Suess introduced the notions of sal[1] and of sima. Under the crust, the composition of which is principally silico-aluminous (sal) is found, according to him, a zone consisting of basic eruptive rocks, of silico-magnesian composition (sima). Beneath, much deeper, he distinguishes a third zone, that of ferronickel (nife) forming the metallic core of the earth. He bases his argument on the characteristics of meteorites supposedly representative of the internal material of planets of the solar system.

[1] Or rather *sial*, the term generally used now.

This theory is perhaps not confirmed in every respect, above all, not so far as the metallic core is concerned. The argument based on the high average density of the globe carries little weight, for any material, in a suitable physical state involving a sufficient condensation of atoms, can attain an extremely high density. The argument of terrestrial magnetism to support the notion of a central sphere of iron is of no value, because at high temperature iron loses its magnetism. However, a metallic core similar in nature to the meteorites is generally admitted at the present time. So far as the sima is concerned, the geological facts also lead to the notion of a basic magma, of a sima, beneath the terrestrial crust. We will return to this.

Let us note first, along with R. A. Daly (1933) that the existence of this sima, as consisting for this author of a basaltic magma in a glassy state, would furnish the most precise definition of the crust:

> To postulate a vitreous substratum at moderate depth all around the globe is automatically to offer a definition of the earth's crust; the crust is a complete solid-crystalline shell, resting upon a complete noncrystalline shell. The latter has rigidity for small periodic stresses surpassing that of granite and is not in the magmatic state as ordinarily conceived.

We will examine *the geological arguments in favour of a basic substratum*: they are fissure volcanism, the great masses of basic rocks outside of the orogenic zones, and the swarms of greenstones of the orogens.

Fissure Volcanism

Let us summarize the data of fissure volcanism as given by A. Rittman (1936). It consists in the emission of vast flat flows of basalt which can be termed "plateau basalts". Their extent is very great. For example, the Deccan "traps" in peninsular India cover 300,000 sq. km of the surface. The distinction may be made in this volcanism between simple and composite piles, the latter being more common. The single flows of the composite pile are generally 5–15 meters thick. The thickness seldom exceeds 100 meters or falls below 1 meter. By the accumulation of numerous flows, these piles may reach a thickness of 3,000 meters. They are not poured out by isolated volcanoes, but undoubtedly along long fissures in the crust. They are emitted rapidly without differentiation, and their petrography is uniform. They are found in various regions on the surface of the globe and they have been emitted in various epochs from the Precambrian up to the Tertiary. This is a fundamental geological phenomenon: it seems to be a matter of a repeated extrusion of the basaltic substratum of the crust.

The principal plateau basalts are those of the Arctic region (coasts of Greenland and Scotland), the Mongolo-Siberian basalts, those of Deccan, the Syrian-Ethiopian basalts, those of Parana, and those of the Columbia River in the Rocky Mountains. In total, more than 2 million sq. km of the earth's surface is covered by such flows, and this is a considerable fraction of that surface (500 million sq. km).

Great Basic Masses outside Orogenic Zones

The presence of large bodies of circumscribed basic rocks within the *sialic* domains of the crust (granitic and gneissic rocks) is a fact of great importance. Melanocratic gabbros, peridotites and serpentines, and related differentiated rocks, norites and anorthosites, are involved. At least a considerable fraction of the material of these basic rocks has certainly come from the depths, as their ferromagnesian chemical composition differs from that of the surrounding milieu. On the other hand, granitic endomorphism can only produce gabbro in very limited amounts, or still less amounts of peridotites: it practically stops with the diorites. *The phenomenon thus gives rise to the idea of an ascent of material from the underlying sima.*

This important and relatively rare phenomenon seems peculiar to the Precambrian, both in space and in time. Nevertheless, this may only be apparently so, and may result from the fact that a great depth of erosion is necessary to expose these basic masses, because of the rather plate-like style which they have away from orogenic zones. The best known are those of the Bushveld, of Duluth, and of Sudbury. They have the form of *lopoliths*, that is of great tabular bodies, the bottom of which has sagged because of its weight or because of empty space beneath created by the emission of material. It is the opposite form to that of a laccolith and of much greater dimensions. Lopoliths have perhaps a root largely fissural, more or less central and probably multiple. The great masses formed essentially of anorthosite in Canada, for example, would be related to the same group of phenomena.

Bushveld. The Bushveld lopolith, in the Transvaal, mainly composed of norite, was initially 500 km long and 250 km wide. Its thickness is not known, but is probably more than 10 km. From the top downwards it comprises: rhyolite, microgranite, coarse-grained red granite, norite, with a "chilled" phase of diabasic norite at the base. The norite, which forms the main mass, shows an extraordinary differentiation of

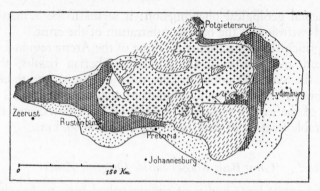

Fig. 50. The great intrusion of the Bushveld (after A. L. Du Toit, simplified). Crosshatching: Norite. Crosses: Red granite. Dotted: Zone injected by dolerites. Blank: Floor of the intrusion formed by the Transvaal series. Oblique hatching: roof of the intrusion formed by the Waterberg and Rooiberg series.

petrographically varied type, distributed as stratified sheets of some meters to decameters in thickness, with a remarkable regularity over wide areas. The granite cuts the norite.

Duluth. The Duluth gabbro,[1] north of Lake Superior, is located along the contact of the Precambrian formations of the Animikie and the Keweenaw. It is exposed for a distance of 200 km with a maximum width of 40 km. It is possible that south of the lake, the "laccolith" of the Bad River gabbro, Wisconsin, is a reappearance of the same body of gabbro on the other flank of the great synclinorium of the Lake. The Duluth gabbro is overlain by granitic and syenitic masses. The overlying stratiform basalts of the Keweenaw have the same chemistry as the gabbro and seem of the same fissure character as other plateau basalts. The conditions in total recall those of the Bushveld, apart from the presence of these basalts.

Sudbury. The Sudbury lopolith in Ontario outcrops in the form of an oval 50 by 25 km. with a thickness of 3–4 km. It has a norite or hornblende gabbro at the base, and these rocks grade upwards into pegmatitic granite. The latter forms more than half the thickness.

In these three examples differentiation is extraordinarily strong. In the Sudbury body, it extends from norite to granite. In the Duluth body it forms zoned facies or banded alternations of varied gabbros, anorthosite and troctolite. In the Bushveld, some bands of anorthosite and of norite have differentiated jointly in regularly stratified beds with multiple recurrences: some zones of metallic minerals such as platinum,

[1] See the bibliography in F. F. Grout, 1933.

chromite and magnetite were produced at several levels following layers with a thickness of only a few meters, but of an astonishing consistency over tens or sometimes hundreds of kilometers.

These differentiations have generally been interpreted as magmatic phenomena. The sinking of crystals by means of gravity, convection currents during cooling or turbulence during injection, possibly successive intrusions have all been invoked. Such mechanisms meet with great difficulties, particularly in the Bushveld, because of the extremely regular rhythmic character of the lithological facies. Let us note the many basic and ultrabasic bodies of small dimensions that exist in the world, or of kilometric dimensions, of diverse ages, with a remarkable striped structure, but less differentiated than the lopoliths; this category of rocks shows a quite special (and unexplained) ability to differentiate in regular beds.

For the Bushveld, Turner and Verhoogen (1951), who accept the magmatists' concept, write in their classic work:

> The over-all simplicity of the rock sequence and the complicated variation which modifies and to some degree obscures it are reminiscent of the variation encountered in a sedimentary series— e.g., where in a series of interbedded shales, sandstone, and conglomerates, a general downward coarsening of the formation as a whole can be detected. In the rock succession of a stratified lopolith, as in a clastic sedimentary series, we see the result of sinking and accumulation of mineral grains of varying size and density in a fluid medium subject to fluctuating turbulent flow. In spite of the relative ease with which problems of aqueous sedimentation may be studied in the field and in the laboratory, the process is so complex that reconstruction of the conditions of deposition of a given sedimentary formation on the basis of its petrographic and field characters is still attended by much uncertainty. Igneous "sedimentation" in a body of magma is subject to just as many variable factors, but experimental data are much less adequate than in the case of aqueous sedimentation. It is not surprising, therefore, that opinions differ widely as to the relative roles of gravitational settling or floating of crystals and of various possible flow movements in the magma body in bringing about the heterogenous condition of basic lopoliths.

Radically opposed is the opinion of S. van Biljon (1949). Through the observation of lateral gradations of sedimentary beds in the Pretoria series, forming the substratum of the Bushveld lopolith, into certain stratiform layers of the norite complex, he explains the whole complex as a gigantic metasomatism of sedimentary layers. If this theory is confirmed, one must maintain that the numerous dykes of gabbro and basalt accompanying the Bushveld around its margins, and around similar lopoliths, possibly would be the result of rheomorphism.

We should note that metamorphic processes have been invoked by Perrin and Roubault (1939) for the formation of granular rocks in general, including the ultrabasic rocks.

It seems to me that even in the case of the magmatist's interpretation a metasomatism after solidification and an effect comparable to differential anatexis (p. 5) would help explain the banded structure of the complex. In every respect, even if the great basic masses outside the orogenic zones were formed magmatically or metasomatically, or by the two processes successively, they are phenomena of the depths: "basic fronts" of enormous dimensions and tonnage, suggesting an emanation of sima.

Swarms of Greenstones and Granites in Orogens

The frequency of lenticular massifs of greenstones along the orogenic zones contrasts with the rarity of basic rocks of the preceding types. It is correct to add that the upended state of these massifs means that they will be exposed at almost any level of erosion and prevents their concealment. The greenstones (roches vertes) of the orogenic zones are often involved in the folding and are partly metamorphosed to amphibolites or prasinites, which reveals their early position in orogeny.

It is sufficient to cite the Caledonian chain of Scandinavia with its greenstones rich in pyrite segregations; the Hercynian chain of the Urals with its platinum- and chromite-bearing gabbros and dunites; the Alpine chain with gabbros and serpentinites along the axial metamorphic zone in the Alps of Western Europe, with chromite-bearing serpentinites extending along the Dinaric branch of Yugoslavia, Greece and Anatolia. It is thus along most orogens from different epochs of the globe. The Alpine branch of New Caledonia, where there are about twenty bodies of ultrabasic rocks covering an area of 5,500 sq. km in total must also be mentioned.

A good part of the greenstones of orogenic zones are interpreted as basic flows of a submarine volcanism. This fact is particularly clear for those of the spilite facies. But it is also true for others which are often geographically associated with them and have mainly a granular facies.

M. Lemoine (1955) has noted it for the gabbros and serpentines of

Queyras, in the Franco-Italian Alps, occupying a fixed stratigraphic level, associated with radiolarites, and locally showing pillow-lava facies. L. Dubertret (1952) has shown that the enormous masses of peridotite of Lebanon grade upwards into diabases and pillow lavas, overlain by radiolarites. J. Brunn (1952) has reported similar observations from northern Greece.

According to Brunn, the basic rocks in this country extend over an area 80 by 30 km and attain a thickness of more than 1,500 meters. Associated with the great masses of peridotite are less important quantities of gabbros, dolerites, microlithic rocks (spilites, basalts, pillow lavas), accompanied by tuffs and radiolarites. Their volcanic character is incontestable. The principal masses of peridotite are found at the base of the assemblage and show a tendency to stratification. Higher up light-coloured gabbro beds are intercalated with stratification marked by variations in grain size. Sometimes the order of the beds is reversed and these are replaced by a multitude of pseudo-veins or by magmatic breccias. Metamorphism is lacking at the roof and reduced at the walls to a slight thermal action in the Triassic or Liassic limestones forming the substratum. The absence of metamorphism in the surrounding framework opposes the idea of a metasomatic formation of the peridotites and the granular rocks. The author attributes this formation to an intense magmatic differentiation in very thick volcanic flows. The non-existence of peridotitic volcanic magma makes it necessary to assume the elimination of a very important quantity of material from a basaltic chemical composition.

Even though this phenomenon is very enigmatic, it does not seem to be an isolated case. Conditions are the same in Lebanon, according to Dubertret. In New Caledonia, according to J. Avias (1955), there is also a relationship between serpentines and peridotites on the one hand and a marine basalt series on the other: a relationship which he interprets as a strong metasomatism of the volcanic series in the solid state under the influence of a moderate to weak general metamorphism.

Despite the importance of the marine orogenic volcanic formations, this does not preclude the existence of massifs of *intrusive* greenstones in the suite of ophiolites of the orogenic zones. Contacts with hornfelses can particularly justify such an interpretation.

Besides the greenstones of the folded chains, some granites are also present. Some, synkinematic, occur as elongated vast sheets along the zones of deformation. Others are connected with differentiation of gabbroic rocks. I have cited examples in chapters 7 and 12. Still others cut the folds and are later than the main folding.

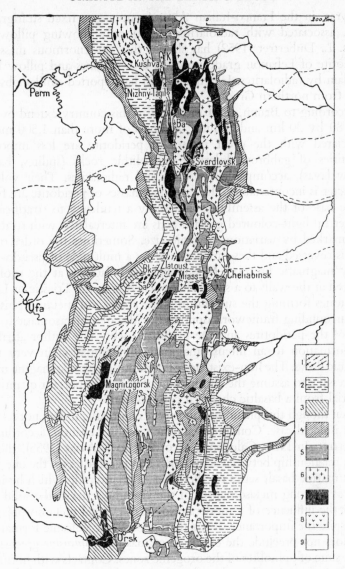

Fig. 51. Geological map of the Urals.

1. Ancient crystalline schists. 2. Undifferentiated Palaeozoic. 3. Devonian. 4. Carboniferous. 5. Intrusive rocks, lavas and tuffs. 6. Granites and syenites. 7. Greenstones. 8. Porphyries. 9. Permian (in the west) and Tertiary (in the east).

Localities—B. Berezowsk. Ba: Bazhenov. Bk: Bakal. K: Krasnouralsk. S: Saranov. Sa: Satka.

This complex evolution, magmatic and metasomatic, and this association of various plutonic rocks in which the basic element plays a very great quantitative role, suggest the idea that the great orogens involve the total thickness of the crust. The orogenies give rise to a great mixing of material between the depths and the surface of the earth, by means of which masses of sima have been introduced across the moving layers, either in the form of magmatic injections (submarine flows, intrusions) or in dispersed form by chemical migrations.

THE GRANITIZED DOMAINS OF THE CRUST

The migmatite terrains are characterized by a regional extension of the phenomena of palingenesis in the heart of the migmatites, and leading to vast anatectic granites without precise limits. The granites may grade into quartz diorite, but bodies of basic rocks are little developed in such terrains, apart from the pre-existent basic lavas (pillow lavas of the Svionian in Finland, for example) caught up by the palingenesis. Important basic intrusions of the lopolithic type in these same areas would be of a completely different geological age than the anatexis and unconnected with it. In fact the lavas taken up by anatexis are not very thick, nor are the bodies of possible gabbros enclosed in the migmatites; and no progressive gradation of regional character towards basic migmatites is visible. In migmatite terrains, one has the feeling of being in eternal granite "to endless depths", and these granitized domains give the impression, because of their extent, of a universal substratum of the upper crust.

But this is only apparently so. There is not, as far as I know, any permanent granitic *migma* in the mobilized state (more or less magmatic) at the base of the crust throughout the global periphery. The crust includes many dead migmatites; but at any moment of geological time the active migmatites (migma) have only a limited although regional extent. For example, they are lacking beneath the lithosphere in regions and at times where the fissure basaltic eruptions arose following a release in tension at depth in the crust, without emanating sialic magmas.

Migmatites seem to develop particularly along orogenic zones where gravimetric studies indicate a thickening of sial. They may also have developed in certain zones outside the orogenies and remained at depth, in accordance with the hypothesis suggested in chapter 12.

The migmatites of orogenic zones are not peculiar to the Precambrian, as Daly believed. They occur in the Caledonides, in the Hercynides and the Alpides (see p. 192). They are epochs of fluctuation

K

of the upper limit of the pyrosphere along certain arcs in the crust, that is to say, the steepening of the geothermal gradient: a considerable part of the thickness of the lithosphere became mobilized and granitized; migma developed, rose upwards and reached a level of relatively little depth. And the orogeny proceeded. The mica schists of the southern part of the French Massif Central and the lower Palaeozoic of the Pyrenees were invaded by anatexis at the dawn of the Hercynian orogeny.

Independent of granitization by anatexis, some granitic massifs in the form of batholiths intruded either inside the orogenic zones or outside them. Perhaps they originated in the migmatic domains beneath. Such granites seem to be in disequilibrium with their surroundings, as M. S. Walton (1955) notes. We will return to the question of their emplacement.

We can say that *granite is more distinctive in the lithosphere than any other plutonic or metamorphic rock, and is actually its most characteristic rock*, whereas the great assemblages of basic rocks present there an alien aspect, and seem to have come from below, at least as far as a considerable part of their material is concerned.

CONCLUSION

The crust of the Earth is influenced by the pyrosphere in two ways: either by an extension of the physico-chemical conditions of the depths to higher levels, forming migmatites and anatectic granites in the crust; or by penetration of material, and there are the three processes of fissure eruption, great emplacements of basic rocks, and orogenic intrusions and extrusions. The last two phenomena may also engender granite, by assimilation and differentiation.

If we thus keep the old term pyrosphere for the zone of general mobilization of the rocks, we signify that the fluctuations of anatexis reveal the independence of the limit between sial-sima and the pyrosphere. The first limit is below the boundary of the pyrosphere in the case of a great development of migmatites. The contrary may be the case at other times and in other places: for instance in the rigid zones where the fissure basalts do not produce material other than sima.

The limit of the solid, or rather the completely crystalline environment, is not a sphere, because the zone of migma may rise to comparatively high levels at certain periods. Neither of the two limits (the limit of the crystalline envelope, the limit of the sial) are permanent. The pyrosphere deforms incessantly in the same way as the lithosphere, says

Pierre Termier. The sial-sima limit becomes mixed by multiple and intrusive compenetrations along the zones of orogeny. Nevertheless the rock types maintain rather sharp limits, which indicates a relatively sharp chemical discontinuity between sial and sima.

Essentially granite is a mobilization or a remobilization of sial (migmatites). This does not exclude the creation of certain granites by differentiation of simatic magma from depth (Daly, van Bemmelen). Granitization is one of the principal "processes" of the Earth's crust. It reflects the influence of the substratum on the crust. It is of such importance that the main part of the crust is granitic, as a result of the adding together of the granites of all ages. The phenomenon is not uniform, nor continuous. It appears in various episodes. Of their sequences and their real significance we are mainly ignorant; and the evolution of the deep zones of the planet, which influences the evolution of the lithosphere, is unknown.

Chapter 17

THE PROBLEM OF THE FORMATION
AND EMPLACEMENT OF GRANITE

Throughout the length of this book we have seen the interaction, the "play" of seemingly contradictory phenomena during the different episodes in the formation of granite: magmatic or metasomatic aspects; displacements of material versus chemical evolutions in place; chemical variations in the environment or preservation of the chemistry of the rocks existing before the granite; static effects such as geodic crystallizations versus dynamic crystallizations under the influence of stresses; crystallizations in open spaces contrasting with blastesis in crystalline material. This plurality of aspects is explicable, once the fact is accepted, which has been amply demonstrated by geological observations, that granite is a *type of convergence*, and consequently the end point of several quite different evolutions. It is fruitless to toss into the same sack all the observations made on any and every granite; lumped together these observations are not likely to make much sense at all.

Correlations should be sought in groups of granites of the same type. Of major importance in the comprehension of the natural history of granite is the consideration of Wegmann's "tectonic levels", namely the temporal and spatial place of every granite in the structural evolution of the particular part of the Earth's crust involved. M. S. Walton (1955) has emphasized the distinction between granites in equilibrium with their geological settings from the standpoint of grade of metamorphism and granites not in equilibrium. The grade of metamorphism of various environments must therefore be taken into account.

The principal difficulty arises out of the matter of the "time factor": conditions have varied considerably in the course of the creation of any granite. A granite is built up progressively by a succession of remouldings, or "retouches", of which for example the endometasomatic modifications at the end of crystallization bear witness. This difficulty has been perceived by P. Michot (1948), who postulates equilibrium for certain massifs only at the end of their emplacement.

It would be desirable to define the successive equilibria which have reigned during the evolution of each granite and then to compare the granites which have followed the same evolution. Unhappily we are far from being able to classify with certainty and precision the granite massifs from the point of view of their evolution. One can only reckon on a blurred view of the phenomena of granitization obtained by emphasizing characteristics which seem more important or more common. Such a choice obviously involves a degree of subjectivity.

TEMPERATURE OF FORMATION

The minerals which form within a given range of temperature are referred to as "geological thermometers". The temperatures of formation, however, vary enormously depending upon the presence of this or that impurity, or this or that solvent, and the concentrations of these substances. A fortiori, in nature where precise conditions are generally unknown to us, these temperatures are very roughly determined and ought to be accepted only as very gross approximations. Direct measurements have only been possible for the volcanic flows; these have given temperatures in the order of 800–1,200°. Let us examine the indications that we can infer from certain mineral constituents of granites.

Quartz. The quartz of granites seems to have gone through the variety stable above 573°, to which ordinary quartz crystallized at lower temperatures transforms upon heating. The bipyramidal form of some of these quartzes moreover suggests it. The transformation (inversion) point of quartz is raised 0·0215° for each increase in pressure of one atmosphere. At 40 km depth, i.e., in the zones of thickened sial of the orogens, the transformation would take place at about 800°. This would be the minimal temperature of crystallization of the deepest granites. For others it should range down to 600°. In the pegmatites the temperature of formation must have been lower than in granite, because their chemical composition is richer in mineralizers, whose effect is important as we will see. The two forms of quartz may be found in pegmatites.

Tridymite and cristobalite, the states of silica stable at higher temperatures than quartz, are never found in granites, although, as S. J. Shand (1927) has observed, fragments of quartz-bearing rocks caught up in volcanic flows often have their quartz transformed into tridymite.

Similar inclusions, common in plutonic rocks and particularly in granites, never show this transformation. The natural occurrences of tridymite are in the volcanic flows; it also occurs in siliceous bricks; cristobalite, which is rarer, accompanies tridymite in some lavas.

In the laboratory, quartz heated above 1200° becomes unstable and becomes amorphous and then crystallizes as cristobalite, at least if it is not rapidly heated to 1800° where it becomes obviously liquid. J. Wyart (1945) has shown that, in the presence of distilled water at a temperature a little above the critical temperature of 374°, glassy silica crystallizes as cristobalite. Thus supercritical water has a role as a "mineralizer" in lowering the crystallization temperature of cristobalite.

According to G. Friedel (1926): "R. Weill has obtained cristobalite by the crystallization of silica in the presence of an aqueous solution of soda contained in a closed vessel at about 700°, whereas towards 500° quartz was formed". Fenner has shown that in the presence of sodium tungstate quartz is stable below 870°, tridymite between 870 and 1470°, and cristobalite above 1470°. With vitreous silica in contact with a dilute solution of potash (1/100 mol. per litre), a crystallization of cristobalite is obtained at 335° according to J. Wyart (1945). If the experiment is carried out at 340° or higher, cristobalite appears transitorily, and is transformed into quartz.

The data above indicate that alkaline solutions have an obvious influence as mineralizers lowering the temperatures of crystallization of silica, and in particular facilitating the crystallization of quartz. At the same time the complete discordance of the stability temperatures of the various forms of quartz dependent on the solvent involved is noteworthy, as is also the absence of certain modifications, as for instance tridymite in some cases. Only in a very approximate fashion can the following conclusion be drawn:

> Broadly and within the comparatively narrow overall limits of the conditions which have been tested, quartz forms at low temperatures, tridymite at medium temperatures, and cristobalite at high temperatures (G. Friedel).

It can thus be said that laboratory experiments have approximately confirmed the fact that the crystallization temperature of granite is lower than that of lavas.

Feldspars. The feldspars of granite should be of the so-called low temperature varieties. It has long been known that the orthoclase of granites is never of the sanidine type, so common on the contrary in lavas. This would imply that the temperature of crystallization of granite has not exceeded 900°. Microcline, which does not occur in lavas but can crystallize in sedimentary rocks, is very abundant in granites and is of the low temperature variety. The plagioclases occur, as we know today, in two series, one of low temperature and one of high temperature, distinguished on the basis of optic axis angles and lattice structures. It is the low temperature form which is present in granites.

The effects of exsolution, however, in the potash-soda feldspars suggest the possibility of an evolution of these feldspars after their crystallization. Signs of endometasomatism indicate important re-arrangements in the rock at the end of crystallization. It follows then that the thermometric indications obtained from the feldspars for the major phase of the formation of the granite may be challenged.

T. F. W. Barth (1956) has suggested an interesting thermometric method based on the ratio of the proportions of the albite molecule dissolved in the potash feldspar and the plagioclase feldspar of the rock. This method should be useful particularly in the comparison of the temperatures of formation of rocks rather than for the determination of the exact temperature of formation of a particular rock.

Mica. Muscovite forms at low temperatures in the reactions of weathering. It is not present in volcanic rocks, but is developed prom-inently in pegmatites and pneumatolytic veins. In some granites it is formed along with biotite in interlayered lamellae. Muscovite must have a temperature stability range from that of the crystallization of peg-matites (600°?) down to ordinary temperatures. Biotite seems to be stable only at fairly high temperatures; it is found in volcanic rocks. It may also form in the wall rock of hypothermal veins in which the temperatures have been estimated to have been 300–500° by W. Lindgren, but it does not form at lower temperatures. The association of the two micas which is typical of some granites thus indicates temperatures of the order of 300–600° and undoubtedly closer to the higher figure.

Corundum. Some granites have inclusions of this mineral. It is pro-duced industrially in electric furnaces by the fusion of bauxite at temperatures of several thousand degrees. It also forms, however, according to Michel-Lévy and Wyart (1946) at 500° in the presence of water vapour under pressure and calcium fluoride. It is beyond doubt that in nature its formation was similarly catalyzed at low temperatures.

Cordierite. It is sometimes found under high temperature conditions: porcelainite or sandstone calcined by basalt, in burnt-out coal mines, or in inclusions in lavas. The same holds for cordierite as for corundum, for Christophe Michel-Lévy has found it formed at 500–600° in the presence of excess water under pressure.

Conclusion

A range of the order of 900–600° is generally accepted for the overall crystallization temperatures of granites. In this respect A. Demay (1955) has provided important evidence. We have reviewed the reasons why the temperature of formation must be lower than that of lavas. The gradational connection between granites and pegmatites in which the coexistence of the two kinds of quartz suggests overlapping temperatures of crystallization around 600° should establish the lower limit of the crystallization temperature of the quartz in granite at shallow depths in the crust. This lower limit would be higher at greater depths.

R. W. Goranson has determined experimentally the curve for the temperatures of the start of solidification of molten granite as a function of the amount of water dissolved in the magma. It varies from 1100° for no water to 600° for a content of 7 per cent water. The water content of the natural environment of granitization during the process of cooling was probably several units of per cent, so that the orders of magnitude are in agreement. However, this outcome would only be completely valid for granites which had passed completely through a magmatic state.

The 900–600° range has value only as an order of magnitude. It encompasses a temperature range outside of which it is unlikely that granites will crystallize with the exception of terminal rearrangements below 600°. Nothing, however, forces us to believe that all granites have passed through the entire range between the beginnings and the end of their crystallization. For some, the entire evolution has probably taken place around 600°.

THE PHYSICAL STATE OF GRANITE BEFORE CRYSTALLIZATION

Some decades ago it was generally held that granites were the result of crystallizations from a liquid magma. This magma was not a bath of molten silicates similar to what would be produced if a piece of granite were melted in a laboratory crucible because a simple fusion of silicate minerals and silica involves much too high a temperature. For example quartz veins associated with pegmatites and often given off by granites melt in the "dry" between 1200° and 1800°. These temperatures are much higher than those that we have seen to be likely for the crystallization of granite. Therefore it can only be a matter of a liquefaction comprising a mutual solution of constituents, a liquefaction facilitated by solvents which must have been eliminated at the end of the solidification, and which were composed in particular with the presence of water vapour.

However, many objections to this "purely magmatist" concept were expressed. In particular the simple relationship between granite and volcanism which could be anticipated according to this hypothesis does not exist. The subvolcanic granite massifs, whose interpretation is ambiguous, do not provide any very precise argument in favour of magmatic granite.

A variation of this theory holds that the evolution of the granitic environment should have involved, before crystallization, mixed physical states such as crystal aggregates impregnated with liquid or suspensions of crystals, taking into account the certainly very long duration of this evolution and the overlapping crystallization of minerals. Perhaps at no one moment would the whole mass have been entirely liquid. Perhaps even the fraction *simultaneously* liquid remained constantly small. The process would thus approach that of a metamorphic recrystallization. This would also explain the microscopic corrosion textures of granitic crystals, sometimes seen, which resemble crystalloblastic textures of the metamorphic rocks.

Moreover granite being a facies of *convergence*, several evolutions or rhythms of the evolution must have produced it in different ways. As has been demonstrated throughout this book, I have particularly supported this idea of a *mixed state*, which for me represents the situation within a mobilized environment during granitization.

More recently an important number of specialists have supported the theory of the formation of granite by diffusion of chemical substances in a solid, or more correctly, crystallized environment: an environment which has been granitized by metasomatism without passing through a liquid state. Thus R. Perrin and M. Roubault (1939, 1945) have vigorously supported the idea of a granitization by the interaction of diffusions in two directions and over great distances in the heart of the crystallized material of rocks. They base their arguments on experiments on diffusions in the walls of metallurgical furnaces and upon observations made in the metamorphic aureoles. They take note at the same time of the obscurities existing in the interpretation of observations when one is forced to represent the mode of formation and emplacement in a liquid way. A similar view has been put forth by

K*

W. H. Collins (1933) based on an experiment by F. D. Adams on bricks of magnesite. This author only envisions, however, such a diffusion as one of the factors likely to be involved, the elaboration of granite in a liquid way being possible in other ways.

If the preceding opinions concern granites in general, the particular case of the rapakivi granite has been examined in a profound manner by H. G. Backlund (1938 b), who has concluded that this granite was formed in place in the solid state by metasomatism of sandstone under the effects of fluids rich in alumina, alkalis and fluorine. However only the varieties of this granite formed without an increase in volume thanks to the porosity of the sandstone would have evolved in the solid state. In contrast those for which the influx of emanations has been overwhelming would pass to a state of magma to be poured out in an effusive form, as for instance the rhyolitic porphyries observed in connection with the rapakivi granite. The study emphasized in a felicitous manner the likely proximity of evolutions either in the solid form or in a partly liquid form for neighbouring rocks under the domination of possibly very small variations in the reigning conditions. The phenomenon of this fluidification is called *rheomorphism* by Backlund.

Similarly the extruded or *diapiric* granites derived from batholiths or migmatites (p. 35, p. 200) have a homogeneous facies which suggests a transition through a more fluid state than that of the subjacent facies of anatexis. But this is not necessarily so. When masses of migmatite are displaced, relatively homogeneous bodies are very quickly produced, as can be seen in the cliffs of Finland and Greenland, according to Wegmann. Ice can be squeezed through very small openings while remaining in the crystalline state.

Let us examine in particular one of the objections which Perrin and Roubault have made concerning the transition through the liquid state: the well-known occurrence of crystals of feldspar in enallogenic inclusions and in the solid rocks of the aureole, these crystals being identical in nature and facies to those of the neighbouring granite. Whence the objection: if the granite were liquid, its feldspar would not be identical to those which developed in the solid country rock nearby. This is the fact sometimes designated under the name *the phenomena of the double enclave*, that is to say, the inclusion of granitic feldspar in an inclusion of the enclosing rocks. It is produced as commonly in the ordinary granites as in the exceptional ones such as the rapakivi granite.

For example, Ch. Barrois (1884) describes how large orthoclase twins of the porphyritic Rostrenen granite of Brittany are found near the contact disseminated through micaceous schists which are at the same time injected by large granite dykes. They are often isolated, or occasionally associated with a little granitic matrix. They sometimes adopt a singular disposition like that of beads on a more or less curvilinear rosary, kinds of discontinuous veins extending several meters from the terminations of granitic dykes injecting the rocks. These veins are called *moniliform veins* by C. Barrois.[1] Close to rapakivi granite a similar phenomenon is particularly striking, for the ovoids characteristic of this granite made up of rounded potash feldspars surrounded by envelopes of plagioclases have also emigrated in a similar way into the surrounding rocks (Sederholm, 1923; J. de Lapparent, 1932).

If there is in the facts of this genre an objection to the passage of granite through a liquid state, one can nevertheless reply that one does not know which of the physico-chemical factors determine the composition and facies of the growing crystals of feldspar. It is possible that among these factors a more or less advanced liquid state may not be essential. At the moment of the crystallization of the feldspars the granite is not liquid or is no longer liquid. From the magmatist's point of view it is at this moment "mixed" with numerous crystalline particles in suspension. Reciprocally the aureole is at the same time permeated with microsolutions. The physical state of one part or the other could not have been very different. C. N. Fenner in this regard (1933) has advanced another hypothesis, that of a pneumatolysis in the form of vapour in the aureole. He points out that if three phases, solid, liquid and gaseous are in equilibrium the deposition of crystals from the liquid must be accompanied by the deposition of similar crystals from the vapour.

In my opinion the *disagreement between the metasomatists and the magmatists is not fundamental* providing that they first admit the role of pneumatolytes and second do not regard the granitic magma in the course of solidification as a molten bath isolated in a crucible; the disagreement is then only a question of scale and proportions. More important, to my mind, is the disagreement between the "dry" and the "wet" metasomatists. The former do not admit the role of water, namely pneumatolytes. Their argument seems to be that water is not indispensable for chemical migrations and metasomatisms. It seems to me that this is a question of fact and that plenty of observations, emphasized here and there throughout this book, reveal the reality of the role of pneumatolytes. If one accepts this role the following questions provide material for discussion:

[1] From the Latin for a collar or necklace.

1. In the mobilized environment of granitization is the crystalline material bathed in the fluid of the order of magnitude of a crystal seed, a visible crystal, or an aggregate of crystals?

2. What is the proportion of fluid: great for the magmatist, small for the metasomatist, or perhaps so small that it would be restricted to ionic films and it would be nonsensical to speak of a liquid or crystalline state, but rather of more or less imperfectly-ordered states (Wegmann, 1955)?

3. Is the mobile environment a relatively closed system?

An exact and precise response to these questions is impossible because without doubt it would have to be delicately modified for each and every granite and for each and every stage in the formation of a particular granite.

I will admit that granite has passed through a *mobilized state* comparable to that of an aggregate of crystalline material bathed in a milieu which acted as much by metasomatism as by physical penetration of the interstices, and which could have been diluted by pneumatolytes at some periods of its evolution. Moreover some extreme cases are admissible in either sense depending on the particular granite. In this manner of conceiving "mixed", the arguments in favour of the metasomatists' point of view have already been presented little by little in the course of the foregoing chapters as well as the arguments for the opposing thesis. Let us summarize the essential points.

The metasomatist's point of view is based primarily on petrographic observations which disclose the kinship between the granitic texture and the metamorphic textures in the aureole, and also on the conditions of formation of bodies of granite which are rarely plainly intrusive in the manner of volcanic rocks, but which show transitions on various scales between the granite and its enclosing rock. The most imposing argument, however, is certainly the preservation within the heart of a granite of ghosts of pre-existing structures.

In support of *the magmatist's point of view* the following arguments can be assembled:

1. The relatively high temperature of formation which is sufficient to liquefy silicates in the presence of alkaline aqueous solutions.

2. Crystallization of the minerals of granite following an order reminiscent of the sequence defined by N. L. Bowen for the crystallization of various silicate melts. Bowen's laws would essentially regulate the fluid material of the mixed state of a granitic milieu. The agreement, which seems to be general and which has been put forward by his collaborators at the Geophysical Laboratory at Washington,

between the chemical composition of hololeucocratic alkaline granites and the composition of the zone in the quartz-albite-orthoclase diagram where the crystallization temperature in the presence of water is at a minimum, is a fact of considerable importance (O. F. Tuttle, 1955).

3. The importance of aqueous pneumatolytes, probably liquid or in a supercritical state in the necessary migrations of granitization, and the essential role of water (J.Wyart). In the synthesis of granitic minerals water acts in a quantitative way at least in some cases, dissolving silica and alkalis, and not simply as a catalyst efficient in trace amounts. However, as Wyart has pointed out, water is regenerated upon the crystallization of anhydrous minerals of granite and returned to liberty to serve anew during the progress of the granitization.

4. The phenomena of marginal intrusive penetration is clearly exposed at the borders of some granitic massifs. Dilational veins of aplite, pegmatite and even granite are to be observed insinuating themselves in faults, fractures, and in between the beds of the enclosing rocks with dispositions similar to those of volcanic dykes or hydrothermal quartz veinlets. This does not exclude the existence in other, probably more common, cases of more or less large metasomatic veins in which an "injection" of magma did not take place or was reduced to a subtle emanation. The two processes, however, probably often work together in granitic veins.

5. The similarity of granite and other plutonic rocks which are often related to it by transitions or differentiations: syenites, diorites and gabbros. To suppose an origin for granite purely and completely metasomatic in all cases would lead to the same hypothesis for the other rocks. Now these occur at times in bodies that are clearly intrusive, notably in laccoliths or dilational dykes.

6. Displacements of inclusions in the mobilized environment in the course of granitization suggest transportation in a fluid medium. At times small inclusions are tilted relative to one another, or splinters of the wall of a dyke are twisted and pulled away by the injection. Examples have been cited on pages 75 and 144. However, the fact is not universal, for inclusions have often remained in place; moreover observations of this kind are of doubtful validity in cases where the rocks have been folded or fractured before the formation of the granite.

7. At the contacts of granites in circumscribed massifs the sedimentary beds are often clearly cut by the granite. This does not exclude the possible existence of inclusions extended in a linear arrangement, nor the more or less accented orientation of minerals in the

granite between the alignments of inclusions. But the cleanly-cut beds belie the notion of a gradual diffusion in the solid state, particularly when they are compared with the metamorphic rocks which have recrystallized without passing through a magmatic state but under the action of incontestable diffusions. These do not show such abruptness of contacts, but transitions.

8. The structural scheme outlined by Cloosian granite tectonics is at times clearly different from the tectonic structure of the enclosing rocks and simpler. One would expect metasomatism to retain the overall plan of the structure. Of similar import are the cases of fluidity of the granite parallel to its contacts and discordant with the enclosing rocks: but the opposite case is much more common.

9. The chemical and mineralogical similarity of granite and some other families of plutonic rocks with authentic magmatic volcanic rocks. The convergence of some facies connected with granitic massifs (margins, dykes) with rhyolites.

In short, a mixed state is definitely probable because *one always observes, in the detail of the phenomena of the evolution of granite, imprecise traces suggesting an evolution in the crystalline state for some aspects and a liquid evolution for others.*

ASPECTS OF THE FORMATION OF GRANITE

Problems Posed by the Conditions of Occurrence

All the details of the structure of granites with diffuse borders or of anatectic granites in their beginning state in the migmatites bear witness to an extreme mobility. To this mechanical mobility is added a chemical mobility which is shown by a general diffusion of ichor across the fabric of the rock.

When the chemical aspect of the mobility is dominant, granites result which are capped by vast regular zones of "tranquil" migmatites. When the mechanical aspect dominates, lenticular granitized bodies result, controlled by the surface of tectonic discontinuities within the migmatites or outside of them. Upward granitic expansions are also found in the form of bells or of tongue-shaped forms recalling the mechanism of salt diapirs. These extruded granites grade into types of circumscribed granites which will be discussed below.

The two aspects of the mobility of anatectic granites, chemical and mechanical, are reflected in the two constituent elements of these granites: *an introduced material* revealed in the innumerable veinlets and leucocratic schlieren of the rock, resulting from the manifestation of siliceous alkaline solutions or from "clouds" of the same chemical elements arriving in a poorly understood ionic state; and a *fabric* or *framework* which is the pre-existing rock invaded by this material.

The introduced material, which can be called the "filtering column", "granitic emanation" or "ichor", involves a transport of material on an enormous scale, which is almost inconceivable when one tries to envisage it. How can the introduced material move through the solid? Through the interstices of individual crystals, or through zones of atomic instability represented by their surfaces of contact or disorders of their lattices? Is it maintained by reactions in this "unstable inter-granular film", as C. E. Wegmann (1935 a) has suggested?

It is more than 20 years since I defined the concept of an inter-granular film consisting of the superficial layers in crystal lattices, layers characterized by a less perfect order than in the interior of the lattice . . . The intergranular film has often been confused with the liquids filling pores, a notion due to Eskola. The concept of liquid or solid has no validity on the scale of these thin superficial lattice layers, where order is imperfect. They could be called *schedotactic* (almost-ordered) layers in contrast to the eutactic (well-ordered, the actual unity of the crystal) domains and atactic (without order) domains. The schedotactic layers probably surround the units of the lattice mosaic of the actual crystal and thus offer channels of transport; it will be difficult to prove the passage of ions through the eutactic portions. It is possible on this basis to categorize metasomatically-introduced material in the following way: (1) atomic particles which can lodge themselves in eutactic spaces by replacing other particles; (2) atomic particles which can only lodge themselves in the schedotactic spaces; their size and charge can be more variable than those of the first category. Arriving in a favourable configuration, they may form the seeds for a new lattice. Probably a major part of the trace elements lodge themselves in schedotactic domains; (3) atomic particles which can only lodge themselves in the atactic domains; they will only leave if they can make up part of an insoluble phase. In speaking of very minute domains, the use of the notion of solid and liquid states is not to be recommended, a concept which scarcely has validity on this scale; it is preferable in this case to speak of states whose orders are more or less perfect (Wegmann, 1955).

Wegmann then defines the channelways for materials on greater scales, those of veinlets and veins, either by diffusion (non-dilational veins) or by transport in the fluid state.

Countering the idea of a general transport of introduced material by means of such miniature channelways along the interstices of structure, King (1954) made the following statement: "If metasomatism depended only on a material flow of mineralizing solutions, its role in the genesis of rock would diminish with depth. But on the other hand there is strong evidence that the process is much more active at deeper levels of the crust". Contrary to this G. Fischer (1951) notes that a theory of migrating ions implies a chemical gradient which would contradict the well-known fact of the remarkable homogeneity of granitic massifs.

Whatever the mysterious mechanism of chemical migration may be, its propagation is undeniable. At the same time, however, the framework deflects and deforms the streams of material which invade it. Its movement contributes to the initiation of zones of instability by its pervasive deformation. Reciprocally the introduced material shifts on its own account in modifying as it pleases even the substance of the framework. This activity takes place in a shifting environment: it calls to mind the play of condensing fog, or wispy clouds which drift together or bank up, and whose aerial support is animated by complex movements, relative to which these vapours have a certain degree of independence. Thus the beginnings of granites in the Earth's crust seem to obey some kind of fantastic meteorology. Along the same lines, Sederholm noted another resemblance between the eddying of the myriad of injections within migmatites and the forms shown by foam on the surface of the waters in the rapids of the streams of his country as they go from one lake level to another. Strange is the mobility of anatectic granites when we must search for such comparisons.

But to what is related the chemical introduction of materials of anatexis? Are the innumerable veinlets of pegmatite, aplite and granite injecting or impregnating the pre-existing rocks emissaries of a still deeper magma? Is it necessary on the contrary to regard them as a mobilization of pre-existing substances in the solid crust itself when it is heated sufficiently? In other words, is the "filtering column" at the end of a long journey when it begins to initiate the formation of granite by reaction on the material in place; or else does it exude a small distance and almost in place in the thickness of neighbouring layers, as Holmquist (1916) and Eskola (1933) propose, and as K. R. Mehnert (1953) demonstrates for certain migmatites in the Black Forest? And is it preponderant or subordinate in quantity in the resulting granite?

What is ultimately the cause of its ascent? I believe that the answer cannot be the same for every granite massif.

The granites of the *circumscribed massifs* behave differently. Often of great volume, they are found lodged in sedimentary rocks and surrounded in a simple way by an aureole of little thickness, wherein the sedimentary rocks have undergone a metamorphic recrystallization without the formation however of more than insignificant amounts of migmatites. In themselves these granites have a special aspect and pose some particular problems. Cutting cleanly through the layers of the surrounding formations which enclose them, they give the impression of having come from elsewhere, and can by this virtue merit the denomination of intrusive granite. In the light of this "intrusion" the point of view of the mobility of granite takes on a very special interest and *a priori* a more perceptible one than in anatexis. We will return to this below. Thus it is for the assimilation of the enclosing rocks by the granite and for the metamorphic transformation initiated for some distance in the geological setting. The rather common proximity of the intrusion of granite massifs of this type close to the surface should facilitate the understanding of these phenomena.

Duration of Evolution

So far as the large massifs are concerned, granite is essentially formed in place, at least in very large part, by a recrystallization bound up with the introduction of chemical constituents. We have seen that in some migmatites the introduction of material may be reduced to very small proportions. The rise in temperature and then the gradual crystallization of the environment by cooling, require considerable time, because of the low thermal conductivity of rocks. Actually we scarcely know the order of magnitude of this conductivity. It has been calculated that an eruptive magma at 1000° will at first cool some hundreds of degrees in 10,000 years, and thereafter more and more slowly, the total evolution possibly lasting millions of years. At the same time the rocks neighbouring the magma at first heat rapidly to a maximum, then cool following a similar pattern (Schneiderhöhn, 1941). Such calculations envision very simple circumscribed cases of small dimensions. In any case the phenomena are more complicated in nature. Thermal conductivity is not the only factor: heat transfer is also effected by injections along networks of fractures. Zones of hydrothermal veins, at times occupying some square kilometers of the actual topographic surface and containing hundreds of mineralized veins, bear witness to the activity and spatial development of such phenomena.Without claiming to explain in this way the "filtering columns" assumed by Pierre Termier for the origin of granitization, it is not out of the question that an intensive fissuring sometimes plays a role and accelerated thermal exchange by hydrothermal or pneumatolytic circulation. And if the process can activate the thermic influx, it can also produce a heat loss which prolongs the evolution in the phase of heating.

Is it possible to compare these time intervals on the scale of geological time? In Chapter 13 it was seen that, if there was volcanism prior to plutonism or contemporaneous with it, there also seemed to have been a later volcanism which could be regarded as a termination to the plutonism. I envision that in this terminal phase some granites of an orogenic cycle have already consolidated, while the deeper parts of other granites of this cycle are still active and provide the energy for final volcanism. One can conceive, with the reservation already made, that the Permian volcanism of the Hercynian cycle in Europe and the Miocene volcanism of the Alpine cycle represent conclusions of the corresponding plutonism. The order of magnitude of the interval thus would embrace several geological epochs:Westphalian + Stephanian or Eocene + Oligocene. This order of magnitude, which is the same as orogeny with its successive phases of activity and repose, would represent tens of millions of years for the creation of a great granitic phenomenon comprising a succession of related granites and satellites of different types.

Alkalinization

Except for unusual varieties, sedimentary rocks contain several percentage units of alkalis, whereas granites have 8–10%. For example in a slate series which can contain 3–4% alkalis, half the quantity necessary for the formation of a granite without chemical addition would be lacking. In the case of other formations the proportions could be very different. Moreover granite is tolerant and accommodates itself indifferently to a predominance of soda or potash. Along with the alkalis there follows, in general, it would seem, a migration of alumina and of silica, the whole constituting the *ichors* of Sederholm, impregnating the domains of anatexis. In some cases an elimination of calcium, iron, magnesium and other substances seems probable (C. E.Wegmann, 1935 a; D. Reynolds, 1946). The metasomatisms developed in the aureole of granite reveal in an obvious way the effect of such migrations (chapter 6). The scale, however, is incomparably greater in general granitization.

One of the best indications of this transfer of material rests in the well-known fact that homogeneous granite massifs give rise to gravimetric deficiencies relative to their geological setting (Bollo and Goguel, 1950).

The alkaline influx may be derived in part from neighbouring eruptive rocks, formed and consolidated earlier and enclosed in the sedimentary rocks, and also possibly from tuffaceous sedimentary rocks, arkoses, or from evaporates. We have no idea of the maximum distance of this transfer: we do not even know whether it can affect the complete thickness of the crust. As we will see, the transfer undoubtedly takes place by degrees.

Another part of the alkalis of the granites may arise from a mobilization of those alkalis pre-existing in place, a mobilization connected with the mobilization of silica and accessory substances. Such a phenomenon in a state of formation is frequently encountered in crystalline schists of general metamorphism. One can see

> small lenses of quartz or of pegmatite, some tens of centimeters in length at most, which develop away from any granitic intrusion. Their composition is closely related to the composition of the facies which enclosed them: quartz lenses in mica schists, pegmatite lenses in gneiss. We shall see, in the latter case, that the feldspar is the same as that of the rock which contains it (M. Roques, 1941).

They are local exudates, identical to the creation of an ichor in place from the enclosing rock.

The cause undoubtedly resides in the hygroscopic water of the rocks and the water of the hydrated minerals such as the clays. Heated to a high temperature they dissolve alkalis and silica. This phenomenon is probably accentuated above the critical temperature of water. By cooling, small lenses of feldspar or quartz crystallize here and there, which represent the above exudations. But if the phenomenon is prolonged, it becomes more accentuated: the formation of ichor becomes ubiquitous; its corrosivity increases in proportion as the solutions develop in quantity; as they develop a greater mobility the environment becomes more permeable. Similar solutions formed far away may contribute: adding themselves and multiplying by degrees, they give rise to a more and more intense thermal transportation. Such a process has been conceived and described by P. Eskola under the name of *differential anatexis*. In these phenomena of exudation, deformations, microscopic and ultramicroscopic lamination and crushing of crystalline material probably play an effective role.

Homogenization

The homogenization of the granitic domain is a remarkable fact. For example, the Pelvoux granite, in the Alps of Oisans in Dauphiné, displays large exposures of the order of several kilometers or tens of kilometers. "In all these massifs, the rocks possess, apart from very tiny differences, the same chemical composition and the same mineralogical character. The Pelvoux granite is thus clearly a perfect entity" (Pierre Termier, 1897). Even near contacts where it becomes aplitic, there are scarcely any chemica modifications, except possibly a little more silica.

Chemical homogeneity is in fact maintained in spite of extensive variations in texture. For instance, the Vosges granites in the Epinal region are fine-grained, medium-grained or porphyritic. The effects of differentiation can be seen in them: in spots, structural banding and varying composition. There are gradations from biotite granites to granite with two micas or to ampibole granite.

Several of these granites, originating in various settings and often far removed from one another, have been analysed.[1] One might ask if certain differences of aspect and of structure correspond to sufficiently notable divergences in chemical and mineralogical composition to establish the existence of several independent granitic massifs, possibly even resulting from successive emplacements. But the similarity in chemical composition of these granites is so obvious that they certainly form a single massif, where the two-mica granites predominate and the biotite granites form a variation facies due to the decrease in the content or the absence of muscovite (E. Jérémine, 1940).

What can be the mechanism of this homogenization of granites in large domains? A brewing of magma in the liquid state has been envisioned. It is a fact that diapiric granites, seemingly extruded from a migma, are much more homogeneous than the corresponding migmatites. The granitic magma would gradually make its place in the crust by the continual sinking of blocks from its roof (xenoliths) into the heart of the melt and by their dissolution deep within the magma chamber. This is the theory of "overhead stoping" put forward by R. A. Daly. Taking into account that the molten granite may have a density of about 10% less than the crystallized granite, he calculates that blocks of most rocks would sink in the magma. H. Cloos has

[1] The author gives 14 analyses.

objected that a universal development of this process would of necessity everywhere threaten the integrity of the Earth's crust as a whole. According to C. E. Wegmann one generally finds blocks only transported upward: there are blocks tipped and toppled but they have not travelled a great distance downwards. Moreover, many observations conflict with the idea of very important displacements in the form of blocks carried by liquid currents in the course of consolidation. One often sees zones of inclusions little displaced in the granite; one also encounters in the heart of granite alignments of diorite due to endomorphism of the granite by sedimentary layers or basic volcanic rocks, or quartzose alignments due to the incomplete assimilation of sandstone by the granite. These alignments are the same as those of the corresponding layers before granitization.

The slight fluidity or flow structure which one observes in granite is not randomly distributed, as one might expect in a continually stirred-up viscous environment. It is fairly uniformly arranged in relation to the general shape of the granite massif, as Cloos has shown. If there is a sinking of xenoliths from the roof of the granite, it can only be in very limited quantity and amplitude, and is probably braked by the viscosity of the melt. More effectively, in my opinion, the homogenization of the mobilized environment must start even with the spreading of the alkaline emanations, when the environment is in that state of which the migmatites give us a view.

It is striking to compare the homogeneity of granite and the distribution by superposed layers in very differentiated zones that one encounters in the basic or hyperalkaline massifs. For instance, the structure of the gigantic Bushveld norite body in South Africa exhibits, as we have seen (p. 261) veritable beds, well-stratified, of thicknesses of some meters, which can be traced for tens of kilometers, beds sometimes of anorthosite, sometimes of norite of different facies, or again beds enriched in chromite or in magnetite. The metasomatic theory of S. van Biljon would explain this structure. In a similar way the Lovozero alkaline massif on the Kola peninsula has been affected by a differentiation to form stratiform horizons.

The thickness of these horizons varies from some meters to several tens of meters. The three principal minerals constituting this massif (nepheline, microline and aegirine) form different combinations in the qualitative framework and in this way create different categories of rocks: foyaïte with a predominance of feldspar, lujaurite with a predominance of aegirine and urtites formed almost entirely of nepheline. The three rocks are distributed in the massif in a very regular manner, forming beds with three horizons which alternate rhythmically several tens of times within a total thickness of more than a thousand meters (K. A. Vlassov, 1955).

In these two cases, the calmness and regularity of the phenomenon is remarkable, regardless of whether it is a question of either metamorphic or metasomatic differentiation, or a rhythmic magmatic differentiation. In contrast the result of the propagation of "filtering columns" of the granitic ichor in the heart of migmatites exhibits a very different aspect. It indicates an extensive *chemical brewing* taking place during the mobilization of the "mixed environment" or migma.

The preceding considerations do not exclude the possibility of granites produced by differentiation of basic magmas (as at Sudbury?) or by the individualization of rheomorphic massifs. But these magmatic granites seem only to play a subordinate role compared to that of the great massifs.

HYPOTHESES ON THE MECHANISMS OF THE EMPLACEMENT OF GRANITE

We will consider successively the mobility of the granitic environment, the metamorphic transformation of the enclosing rocks, and the assimilation of the enclosing rocks by the granite. These three classes of phenomena would seem *a priori* to be sufficient to explain the emplacement of granite. We will see that this is not so. After mentioning other factors which have sometimes been suggested without greater success, we will finally return to the problem of the individualization of granite.

Mobility of Granite

In several of the foregoing chapters the mechanical effects of the mobility of the environment in the course of granitization have been reviewed, and the importance of the intimate deformation in structural details has been stressed: shear planes, stretched inclusions, schlieren and other local heterogeneities of the granite and the hornfelses of the aureole. Perhaps these deformations play a major role in granitization among the factors contributing to the mineralogical and structural transformations of the environment. It is a case of a mobility on a small scale which shows up in the little deformations distributed throughout the mass.

Can these add up to produce mobility on a grand scale, capable of putting a granite massif in place *in the manner of an intrusion in the true sense*?

According to the hypothesis of an original granitic magma, intrusion is quite possible. The formation of granite by differentiation of a basic magma, although not held too widely, remains a possible interpretation. Apart from the Sudbury lopolith (p. 262), R. A. Daly cites several examples of granites differentiated from gabbros. This phenomenon should be even more common beneath the crust, if the sima could create granitic magma by assimilation and differentiation, according to Daly's theory (1933).

But in the crust the displacement of granite in great bulk is not conceivable apart from diapiric intrusions in a probably non-magmatic state, that is to say, a mixed state of the mobilized environment. The geometry and the kinematics of homogeneous granite stocks or massifs at the periphery of migmatite domains often indicate diapirism; these granites give the impression of having been ejected in bulk from the migma. On a smaller scale signs of rheomorphism are often striking.

For example, F. F. Grout (1933 b) has shown that the Saganaga batholith in Minnesota and Ontario, tilted by tectonic movements, is exposed over an extent corresponding originally to a vertical depth of 25 miles. It ends downwards in a gneissic environment in a number of relatively narrow columns analogous to roots. From these the granite seems to have risen, coming together and blossoming as it reached upwards.

However, the kinematic "diapiric" indications must be interpreted with caution, and within the framework of as complete and exact a structural analysis of the geological environment as possible. It is conceivable that the so-called diapiric character of certain massifs reflects only the mechanical state of the environment and a general tendency to movement, perhaps a movement of restrained amplitude: it may rather give an *illusion* of movement than the actual stamp of progression *en masse* over a great distance.

Apart from the case of authentic diapiric massifs, one finds oneself in the great majority of cases, and for the great massifs, in the presence of a formation of granite nearly in place, of which we have seen many indications in the foregoing chapters. This formation "in place" evidently signifies "without massive displacement relative to the framework of the enclosing formations".When the enclosing formations are affected by orogenic movements contemporaneously with the granitization, one may find stratiform synkinematic granites which represent an intermediate case. But the character "nearly in place" applies to the majority of cases, such that the mobility of granite would not seem to me to resolve by itself the problem of emplacement relative to the framework of the enclosing formations.

Metamorphism

Contact metamorphism, studied in chapter 6, covers the assemblage of phenomena affecting the environment where the granite forms, phenomena revealing several aspects of the process of granitization.

The evolution of the rocks in the aureole is due above all to release of pneumatolytes radiating from the granite. They react on the rocks and initiate the formation of feldspar, mica, amphibole, tourmaline, garnet and various other minerals, in amounts progressively decreasing with distance. They fix in the rock some new chemical elements, or facilitate the recrystallization of pre-existing chemical elements in new forms. Recall that among the pneumatolytic elements, water is considered as the most important. Its role in granitization is also confirmed by concrete observations. In a completed granite, analysis discloses a content of water in the order of 1%. This water is partly in the form of liquid inclusions in microscopic cavities in quartz crystals. S. J. Shand (1927) indicates that in the Cornwall granite, the cavities of quartz form up to 5% by volume of the quartz and the included water 1% of this volume, which means 0·2% by weight of the granite for water retained in the natural state. He notes that this water could not have been introduced after the crystallization of the quartz, which is compact and without cracks. If a completed granite can retain 1% of water free or combined, a large part of the water must have been released before the end of crystallization. Evidence for this exists in the swarm of hydro-thermal veins often present in the peripheries of granite massifs and in fillings of fissures containing hydrated minerals.

Certain metamorphic crystallizations are chemical rearrangements in new mineralogical form achieved by chemical diffusions over short distances: feeding of crystals, collective crystallization, exchanges in both directions of material of inclusions of particular composition. They resemble crystallizations in the solid state and in the "dry" by ionic diffusion, such as seen in metallurgical processes as R. Perrin and M. Roubault have emphasized. Without denying the possibility of diffusion in rocks in the solid state, one is obliged to take into account the existence of microsolutions present everywhere in the interstices of crystals of most rocks in Nature, and above all in the sedimentary series. The peculiarly small dimensions of the channels in which such micro-solutions infiltrate is confirmed by observations of the minerals in metalliferous veins, where metasomatism has been produced by micro-solutions emanated from fissures sometimes visible, but sometimes completely invisible even under the microscope.

However contact metamorphism is often irregular, being very pronounced at one point on the border of a granite and almost nonexistent at another, following the caprice of the mineralizers which are given off here and there, or which are very irregularly distributed. Granite often appears almost without an aureole, "all or nothing", at least locally. The aureole is thus not necessary for the emplacement of granite.

Assimilation

The assimilation of rocks by granite is a striking phenomenon at the border of many massifs. Blocks separated from the surrounding rocks appear swamped in the granite, which has more or less impregnated them or modified them. In the layers of the neighbouring enclosing rocks, a penetration of granitic veinlets splits and fragments the beds, preparing them for incorporation in the granite in the form of inclusions. Although assimilation touches upon the fact of granitization itself, it must be realized that its mechanism remains obscure.

If one melts an appropriate mixture of shales, sandstones, and lime-stones of a sedimentary series, as well as the intercalated eruptive rocks, one can obviously obtain the chemical composition of a granite. But assimilation on a large scale, *by a magma of molten silicates*, clashes with the objections which N. L. Bowen (1928) has specified. In order to dissolve silicates, the essential constituent of rocks in a magma, great absorption of heat is required. The "superheating" of the magma, i.e., the excess of its temperature over that where it begins to crystallize, must be very strong. Now even if it is true that volcanic flows are often very hot because of the exothermic reactions of their gases, and that they can often vitrefy their inclusions or develop minerals stable at high temperature (tridymite, etc.), it is still not the same for granite. It is scarcely probable that it could arise at temperatures over 1000° in the beds where we observe it. And it has crystallized at temperatures of the order of 800–600°. The superheating can only have been weak. As there is a great disparity between the small specific

292 FORMATION AND EMPLACEMENT OF GRANITE

heat of molten silicates and the very high heat of fusion of solid silicates, it follows that the small amount of heat available probably would be quickly consumed by the fusion of a few inclusions. Assimilation by superheated granitic magma is thus hard to accept.

But as Bowen shows, some assimilation without superheat is not impossible. In the consolidation of a magma the crystals precipitate in a given order, forming definite series. At every moment the magma is oversaturated relative to substances which correspond to members in the series which have already precipitated, and is not saturated with members not yet precipitated. If inclusions are introduced into the melt, they are chemically comparable to one or another of the members in the foregoing series; the magma, saturated or not in regard to them, treats them as ordinary products of its normal crystallization. Let us assume the inclusion is similar to a member of the series already precipitated: it cannot be dissolved, the magma will react on it with a tendency to transform it into a more evolved member of the series. If it is similar to a member not yet precipitated, the magma dissolves it and at the same time precipitates crystals of the member with which it is presently in equilibrium. Bowen shows that in the first case the reaction is weakly exothermic, and that in the second there is a balance between heat absorbed and released. However, in any case, the course of fractional crystallization of the magma is not considerably modified. The proportions of the normal mineralogical constituents in the rock can be changed and the quantity of granite increased. But it is not increased in a limitless manner; for in the course of cooling the chemical evolution always takes place in the same direction with the tendency for the final phase fairly well fixed beforehand, and the potentialities of assimilation of the magma decrease at the same time. The necessity of bringing the inclusions, at first cold, to the temperature of the magma moreover accelerates the cooling. Thus assimilation must necessarily be limited, even if one can conceive that it could operate by dissolution in a magma.

On the other hand many observations indicate the metasomatic effects in assimilation (chapter 5). Instead of regarding it as a dissolution in a magma, one could envision a process controlled by an interaction of the basic and the alkaline fronts; an extreme degree of metamorphism. But this does not explain the "leap" from the rock of the aureole to the pure granite, and a fortiori from a country rock almost without an aureole to a granite. It does not explain the individualization of granite, to which we will return.

Other Suggested Factors

The preceding factors, mobility, metamorphism, assimilation, do not seem adequate to explain the magnitude of the phenomenon of granitization. Contact metamorphism is not essential, since it can amount to very little. Assimilation in the magmatic sense is by itself soon limited; or conceived in the metasomatic sense it brings us back to metamorphism. Mobility, whose traces we can possibly pick up, does not exclude the regular and quiet formation in place of many granitic massifs. It is tempting to invoke unknown factors.

Alb. Michel-Lévy (1939) has suggested the possibility of chemical reactions under similar conditions to those of explosions, in other words, under very high pressures and temperatures. Nuclear reactions, releasing enormous quantities of thermal energy, offer perhaps some prospects (J. Noetzlin, 1940). G. Choubert (1952) has developed this hypothesis and introduces the possibility of atomic transmutations. However, no distinct basis bolsters such concepts. L. Glangeaud (1946) has proposed the hypothesis that crystallized material at very high pressures may achieve an unstable state which he calls an "oligophase state" and that then it would be susceptible to much stronger transformations. He cites as an example quartz, which allows some metallic oxides to penetrate it when it is in transition between its two phases, because of the disorder affecting its lattice during the unstable configuration.

Such hypothetical factors could only arise for the granites of very deep zones. Now some granites of vast extent are formed at shallow depth, in the order of 1–2 km for instance. They fall within the category of disharmonic granites of M. Walton (1955), in other words granite not in metamorphic equilibrium with their settings. Walton is inclined to regard such granites as clearly magmatic and intrusive in the strict sense. Nevertheless we have seen that some appear to be formed almost in place although formed near the surface. This is the case for the Quérigut granite of the Ariègeois Pyrenees, for example (Lacroix, 1899 and 1900). Whatever the physical state was that can be assumed for these granites during their formation, one cannot envision what mysterious factors to invoke outside the classic factors of metamorphism and assimilation.

There is also the problem of the *influx of the necessary heat*, taking into account the temperature of crystallization of granite. M. Lugeon (1930) thought that the mechanical effects of great orogeny could be transformed into heat and cause a fusion generating granitic magma.

H. Stille also envisages the fusion of the roots of the orogens. Some calculations of J. Goguel (1948) indicate, however, that elevations of temperature during orogeny are of a very low order of magnitude, only some tens of degrees. These calculations nonetheless are based on the assumption that the heat is diffused throughout the rock mass. If the rise in temperature were possibly concentrated along certain layers or certain tectonic surfaces, the temperature could obviously rise much higher locally. The pseudo-tachylites or mechanically-melted zones within mylonites can be cited as examples. I definitely believe that the transfer of ichors upwards is the most probable source of heat, whatever the difficulties may be to conceive of this transfer.

Individualization of Granite

We have established homogenization, which expresses the development of granite in a particular volume of the crust formerly heterogeneous. But why and how do the many and delicate chemical and physical processes revealed in granitization bring about the formation of a granite massif, sometimes of gigantic size, having a chemical composition lying within the fixed limits of granitic compositions?

Of course a magmatic intrusion, formed either by differentiation of a basic magma or by ascent of a problematic granitic magma would resolve the question for the most part. But we have seen how unlikely an intrusion is, in the immense majority of cases, and notably in all the cases where the formation of granite in place, or nearly in place, is affirmed for the great part of its material or almost all of it.

Pierre Termier (1910) has visualized the formation of a eutectic mixture: in the regions of the crust where the chemical composition attains, through the action of "filtering columns", that of such a eutectic mixture, the assemblage melts rapidly and a granitic magma is formed. The different plutonic families would correspond to different eutectic mixtures.

This concept raises difficulties. On one hand, observations of migmatites and anatectic granite indicate a progressive fusion, if there is a fusion, contradicting the idea of a rapid eutectic fusion. On the other hand, a melt of eutectic composition and temperature would have no way to dissolve the neighbouring rock, and it would have no activity. In cooling it would form a mass without any order of crystallization for its mineral constituents, the eutectic points being characterized by a simultaneous crystallization of the constituents. The eutectic state would only be an end, the outcome of Bowen's crystallization series, as Wegmann has pointed out to me.

One could reply to these objections: that it would not be a question of simple eutectic phenomena, but of effects of this type, localized and overlapping in time during the evolution of the mobilized environment. We are far from the grandiose simplicity of Termier's view. However some results merit consideration. G. Fischer (1951) statistically analyzed 190 granites and shows that in a triangular quartz-feldspar-mica diagram, the granites are clearly grouped about the point Q = 30, F = 63·5 and M = 7·5. "Granite", he writes, "thus has a eutectoid composition which is close to the quartz-feldspar eutectic of Vogt". And: "It is not excluded in the course of the evolution of magma that the eutectic lines or surfaces are attained where the solution is simultaneously oversaturated with two or more components". In the migmatites of the Black Forest, K. R. Mehnert (1953) found that the light-coloured zones are exudation veinlets and have a eutectic quartz-feldspar composition. These views approach those of Eskola concerning differential anatexis. As we have already mentioned, O. F. Tuttle (1955) indicates the concordance of the chemical compositions of numerous leucocratic alkaline granites with that of the ternary mixture orthoclase-albite-quartz which has the lowest crystallization temperature.

It is however scarcely possible to define in simple terms a granitic magma that is a eutectic mixture apart from this ternary mixture. If we wish to visualize the individualization of the granitic environment and also stay within the domain of observations, we could describe it in the following way. In order to be formed as homogeneous, that is with a sufficient mobility, the granitic environment requires a minimum content of ichor, as the spectacle of anatexis shows. When this amount is attained, the granitization proceeds progressively. As the influx of alkalis, water and other mineralizers continues, these surplus products pass easily through the mobilized mass producing granitization farther out, or else they remain in the form of more or less ghost-like local heterogeneities in the heart of the granite. During the very long crystallization period, they remain more mobile than the normal granitic environment, and there is every chance of their being peripherally eliminated because of tectonic or other acts which affect the domain during the long evolution. The residuates which have remained here and there in the granite consolidate in the form of pegmatites, but they become abundant only at the border of the massif. According to this point of view there would be *a chemical composition containing a minimum amount of the alkalis necessary for complete mobilization, and an almost complete elimination of the very mobile residual components.* Such would be the translation, in the language of the field geologist, of the eutectic aspect suggested by Pierre Termier and the present-day authors mentioned above, for the explanation of granitization.

We should remember, however, that for us "mobility" means just that, and not necessarily liquefaction.

This process seems to apply better to granites with diffuse borders than to the circumscribed granites, where the abruptness of the contacts is surprising. In these the mobility of the ichor seems to be less great, apart from that of subtle emanations which have left their traces in the aureole. The phenomenon is more localized and is present on an "all or nothing" basis. In the formation of granites with diffuse borders, the chemical evolution with partial homogenization *during the mobilization* would dominate. In the circumscribed granites, homogenization *after the mobilization* seems to take precedence. Since in this case the process takes place in an almost closed container, phenomena of differentiation will appear. If the ichors are less mobile, marginal pegmatite bodies become more important. Finally if the mobilized environment is obviously distinct from the surrounding rigid rocks, rheomorphic intrusions in the manner of ordinary eruptive rocks may result, if the enclosing rocks are fractured.

Whatever the ways may be, however, of the formation of different types of granites, *the essential points remain obscure.* Why do the alkalis and other mineralizers enriching the ichor diffuse incessantly during the enormous period of a granitization process, and why at a particular moment do they stop, leaving the resulting granitic environment to evolve and consolidate slowly? What is the origin of the heat flow? For the solutions to these problems, one is inevitably driven to search in the depths, and to assume sources of energy in the regions below the terrestrial crust. In the absence of actual documentation on the interior of the earth, however, all the hypotheses of this kind seem to me vain.

CONCLUSION

The geology of granite is still in an elementary stage, as is proved by the fact that of all the questions raised we have found few exact answers. Nonetheless they are of great interest. I have the feeling that they have a common base with other important branches of the geological sciences, orogeny and the geochemistry of the crust, that it must by degrees reveal something of the evolution of the terrestrial globe in its deeper zones. Geologists have had to decipher many features of the

"Face of the Earth", in other words, they have been able to reconstruct in certain measure the external evolution of the globe: tectonics, sedimentation and erosion. If one day we have access to an understanding of the deeper parts, thanks to the granites, we will probably discover at the same time the explanation for many pages of this external evolution, and furthermore our knowledge will increase upon the Earth as a planet. For, if the outermost aspects of cosmic space will be deciphered, vastly expanding our universe, the depths of our planet, much more close at hand, remain enigmatic. Progress in the geology of granite will enlarge the domain of the geological sciences, until now much too confined to the surface of the Earth.

BIBLIOGRAPHY

AHLFELD, F. and MUNOZ REYES, J., 1939: *Die Bodenschätze Boliviens.* 1 vol., Berlin.

ALLEN HOWE, J., 1902: *The Geology of the Building Stones.* 1 vol., London.

ARNOULD, M., 1961: Etude géologique des migmatites et des granites précambriens du N.E. de la Côte d'Ivoire. *Mém. Bur. Rech. Géol. Min.,* No. 3. 174 p.

AVIAS, J., 1955: Relations minéralogiques et géochimiques entre les serpentines et péridotites de Nouvelle-Calédonie, leurs inclusions, leurs enclaves et les roches encaissantes. *Sciences de la Terre,* Nancy, numéro hors série (Les échanges de matières au cours de la genèse des roches grenues acides et basiques), pp. 213–325.

BACKLUND, H. G., 1937: Die Umgrenzung der Svecofenniden. *Bull. geol. Institute, Upsala,* XXVII, S. 219–269.

BACKLUND, H. G., 1938: (*a*) Zur Granitisationstheorie. *Geol. Föreningens Stockholm.* Bd. 60, H. 2, S. 177–200.

BACKLUND, H. G., 1938: (*b*) The Problems of the Rapakiwi Granites. *Journal of Geology.* XLVI, No. 3, pp. 339–396.

BALK, R., 1937: Structural Behavior of Igneous Rocks. *Geol. Soc. of America,* Memoir 5.

BARROIS, CH., 1884: Le granite de Rostrenen, ses apophyses et ses contacts. *Annales Soc. géol. Nord,* XII.

BARROIS, CH., 1894: Le Bassin du Menez-Bélair. *Idem,* XXII, p. 181.

BARROIS, CH., 1927: Discours présidentiel. *C. R. Acad. Sciences,* Paris, 185, p. 1333.

BARROIS, CH., 1930: Les grandes lignes de la Bretagne. *Livre Jubilaire du Centenaire de la Soc. géol. France,* t. I, p. 83.

BARROIS, CH., 1934: Le gisement des staurotides en Bretagne et leur genèse. *Annales Soc. géol. Nord,* LIX, p. 29.

BARTH, T. F. W., 1956: Studies in Gneiss and Granites. *Norske Vid. Akad.,* Oslo, Mat.-Naturv. Kl., No. 1, 35 p.

BEARTH, P., 1933. Ueber Gangmylonite der Silvretta. *Schweiz. Min. Petr. Mitt.,* XIII, S. 347–355.

BEDERKE, E., 1948. Grundfragen des Vulkanismus. *Geol. Rundschau.* B. 35, S. 127–133.

BEMMELEN, R. W. VAN, 1936: The Undation Theory of the Development of the Earth's Crust. *Proc. XVIth Intern. geol. Congress, Washington* 1933. vol. II, pp. 965–982.

BERTHOIS, L., 1938: Massif dioritique de Brée-Néau, Mayenne. *Bull. Soc. française Minéralogie,* LXI, p. 214.

BERTHOIS, L., 1939: Contribution à l'étude des roches éruptives de la Feuille de Mayenne. *Bull. Services Carte géol. France,* XL, p. 379.

L

BIANCHI, A., and DAL PIAZ, G. B., 1937: Il Settore Meridionale des Massiccio dell' Adamello. *Bol. R. Ufficio geol. Italia*, LXII, No. 15.

BILJON, S. VAN, 1949: The Transformation of the Upper Part of the Pretoria Series in the Bushveld Igneous Complex. *Trans. geol. Soc. South Africa*. Vol. LII, 163 p.

BODIN, L., 1951: Contribution à l'étude des granites birrimiens dans le Précambrien de l'A. O. F. *Bull. Direction des Mines A. O. F.*, No. 12, Dakar.

BOLLO, R. and GOGUEL, J., 1950: Mesures gravimétriques en Bretagne. *Public. Bureau de Recherches Géol. et Géophysiques*, No. 8, Paris.

BORN, A., 1936: Zur Tektonik des Harznordrandes. *Zeit. deutsch. geol. Gesellsch.* S. 449–497.

BOTT, M. H. P. and MASSON-SMITH, D., 1956: The geological Interpretation of a Gravity Survey of the Alston Block and Durham Coalfield. *Proc. geol. Soc. London*, No. 1535, 16.4.56.

BOURCART, J., and JÉRÉMINE, E., 1938: Fuerteventura. *Bull. volcanologique*, série II, t. IV, p. 51.

BOWEN, N. L., 1928: *The Evolution of the Igneous Rocks*. 1 vol., Princeton, New Jersey.

BOWEN, N. L., 1933: The broader Story of magmatic Differenciation. In: *Lindgren Volume*, published by *Amer. Inst. of Min. and Metallurg. Engineers*, New York, p. 106.

BRUNN, J. H., 1952: Les éruptions ophiolitiques dans le NW de la Grèce. *XIXe Congrès géol. Internat.*, Alger, section XV, fasc. XVIII, pp. 19–27.

BUBNOFF, S. VON, 1922: Die Methode der Granitmessung und ihre bisherigen Ergebnisse. *Geol. Rundschau*, XIII, p. 151.

BUDDINGTON, A. F., 1933: Correlation of Kinds of Igneous Rocks with Kinds of Mineralization. In: *Lindgren Volume*, published by *Amer. Inst. of Min. and Metallurg. Engineers*, New York. p. 350.

BUGGE, J., 1945: The geological Importance of Diffusion in the solid State. *Norske Vid. Akad.* Oslo. Mat.-Naturv. Kl., No. 13.

CAILLEUX, A., 1946: Disposition des enclaves du granite et granitisation. *Bull. Soc. géol. France*, t. 46, pp. 471–476.

CAMERON, E. N., JAHNS, R. H., MACNAIR, A. H. and PAGE, L. R., 1949: Internal Structure of Granitic Pegmatites. *Econ. Geol.* Monograph 2.

CARRETTE, G., 1946: Relations entre la minéralisation et les venues éruptives du massif des Montmins, Allier. *Bull. Soc. franç. Minéralogie*, t. 69, p. 21.

CHOUBERT, G., 1952: L'origine des granites et la physique nucléaire. *Notes et Mémoires. Service géol. Maroc*, No. 95, t. IV, pp. 167–214.

CHOUBERT, G., FAUVELET, E., and HINDERMEYER, J., 1952: Note sur les granites précambriens d'âge tardif de l'Anti-Atlas. *XIXe Congrès géol. Internat.*, Alger, section I, fasc. I, pp. 73–80.

CLAR, E., 1953: Ueber die Herkunft der Ostalpinen Vererzung. *Geol. Rundschau*, 42, S. 107–127.

CLOOS, E., 1933: Structure of the Sierra Nevada Batholith. *XVIth Internat. geol. Congress, Washington*. Guidebook 16, p. 40.

CLOOS, H., 1929: Zur Mechanik der Randzonen von Gletschern, Schollen und Plutonen. *Geol. Rundschau*, B. 20, S. 66.

CLOOS, H., 1933: Plutone und ihre Stellung in Rahmen der Krustenbewegungen. *XVIth Intern. geol. Congress, Washington*. Vol. I, 1936, p. 235.

CLOOS, H., 1947: *Gespräch mit der Erde*. 1 vol., 410 S., München.

CLOOS, H. and CHUDOBA, K., 1931: Der Brandberg. *Neues Jahrbuch für Miner., Geol. und Pal.*, Stuttgart, 66. Beilage Bd., Abt. B, 130 S.

CLOOS, H. and RITTMAN, A., 1939: Zur Einteilung und Benennung der Plutone. *Geol. Rundschau*, 30, S. 600–608.

CLOUGH, C. T., MAUFE, H. B. and BAILEY, E. B., 1909: The Cauldron Subsidence of Glen Coe and the associated Igneous Phenomena. *Quart. Journal Geol. Soc.*, LXV, p. 611.

COGNÉ, J., 1950: Observations au sujet d'enclaves déplacées dans un granite près de Saint-Nazaire, Loire-Inférieure. *C.R. Acad. Sciences*, Paris, 231, p. 1076.

COGNÉ, J., 1953: Schistes cristallins et granites en Bretagne Méridionale. *Bull. Soc. géol. France*, 6ᵉ série, III, pp. 785–806.

COLLOMB, P., 1951: A propos d'un phénomène de croissance secondaire des feldspaths potassiques dans une microgranulite filonienne. *Idem*, 6ᵉ série, I, p. 621.

COLLOMB, P., 1952: Observations sur les roches filoniennes de Villefranche-de-Rouergue. *XIXᵉ Congrès géol. Intern.*, Alger, section VI, fasc. VI, pp. 23–27.

COMPTON, R. R., 1955: Trondhjemite Batholith near Bidwell Bar, California. *Bull. geol. Soc. America*, 66, pp. 9–44.

COPPENS, R., 1950: Etude de la radioactivité de quelques roches par l'émulsion photographique. *Bull. Soc. française Minéralogie*, 73, pp. 217–321.

DAL PIAZ, G. B., 1937: Atlante geologico-petrografico dell' Adamello Meridionale. *R. Universita di Padova.*

DALY, R. A., 1914: *Igneous Rocks and their Origin.* I vol., New York.

DALY, R. A., 1933: *Igneous Rocks and the Depths of the Earth.* I vol., New York.

DEICHA, G., 1955: *Les lacunes des cristaux et leurs inclusions fluides.* 1 vol., 126 p., Paris.

DEMAY, A., 1942: Microtectonique et tectonique profonde. *Mém. pour servir à l'Explication de la Carte géol. détaillée de la France.* I vol., 260 p., Paris.

DEMAY, A., 1952: Sur la structure et la genèse de quelques types de microgranites, d'aplites et de granites présentant quelques caractères microgranitiques. *XIXᵉ Congrès géol. Internat.*, Alger, section VI, fasc. VI, pp. 139–151.

DEMAY, A., 1955: Sur les conditions physiques des déplacements de matière et des cristallisations qui aboutissent à la formation d'un massif granitique. *Sciences de la Terre*, Nancy, numéro hors série. (Les échanges de matière au cours de la genèse des roches grenues acides et basiques), pp. 249–271.

DENNIS, J. G., 1952: Remplacement Dykes in the Brandberg Area, S. W. Africa. *XIXᵉ Congrès géol. Internat.*, Alger, section VI, fasc. VI, pp. 73–75.

DESPUJOLS, P. and TERMIER, H., 1946: Introduction à l'étude de la métallogénie et à la prospection minière. *Notes et Mémoires, Service géol. Maroc*, No. 66, 177 p.

DESTOMBES, J. P. and RAGUIN, E., 1955: Etude de la partie occidentale du massif de l'Aston, Ariège. *Bull. Soc. géol. France*, 6ᵉ série, V, pp. 101–113.

DIDIER, J. and ROQUES, M., 1960: Nature des enclaves dans les différents types de granites du Massif Central français. *XXIth Intern. geol. Congress*, Copenhagen. Reports, Part XIV, pp. 194–206.

DRESCHER-KADEN, F. K., 1948: *Die Feldspat-Quartz Reaktionsgefüge des Granites und Gneiss.* I vol., 259 S., Heidelberg.

DUBERTRET, L., 1953: Géologie des roches vertes du N.-O. de la Syrie et du Hatay. *Notes et Mémoires Moyen-Orient* (Muséum d'Histoire Naturelle, Paris), t. VI, 179 p.

DUHOUX, V., 1949: La pétrogénèse et la métallogénèse du domaine minier de Kilo-Moto. *Ann. Soc. géol. Belgique.* LXXIII, pp. M 171–243.

ELLENBERGER, F., 1954: Migmatites d'âge permien dans la zone houillère briançonnaise, Alpes occidentales. *Bull. Soc. géol. France*, 6ᵉ serie, IV, C. R. somm., pp. 64–66.

EMMONS, W. H., 1933: On the Mechanism of the Deposition of certain metalliferous Lode System associated with granitic Batholiths. *Lindgren Volume*, published by *Amer. Inst. of Min. and Metallurg. Engineers*, New York, pp. 327–349.

ESKOLA, P., 1933: On the Differential Anatexis of Rocks. *C. R. Soc. géol. Finlande*, No. 7, pp. 12–25.

ESKOLA, P., 1938: On the esboïtic Crystallization of Orbicular Rocks. *Journal Geology*, 46, pp. 448–485.

ESKOLA, P., 1954: Lamprophyrgang in Helsinki und die Lamprophyrprobleme. *Tschermaks Min. Petr. Mitteilungen*. B. 4, S. 329–337.

EXNER, C., 1948: Tektonik, Feldspatausbildungen und deren gegenseitige Beziehungen in den östlichen Hohen Tauern. *Idem*. B. 1, S. 197–284.

EXNER, C., 1951: Mikroklinporphyroblasten mit helizitischen Einschlusszügen bei Badgastein. *Idem*, B. II, 1950, S. 355–374.

FAUVELET, E. and HINDERMEYER, J., 1952: Note préliminaire sur les granites associés à des coulées rhyolitiques précambriennes au Sud d'Ouarzazate, Anti-Atlas central, et dans le Sarrho. *C. R. Acad. Sciences*, Paris, 234, p. 2626.

FENNER, C. N.,1933: Pneumatolytic Processes in the formation of Minerals and Ores. *Lindgren Volume*, published by *Amer. Inst. of Min. and Metallurg. Engineers*, New York, p. 58.

FERSMAN, A. E., 1931: (*a*) Les pegmatites. *Mém. Acad. Sciences U.R.S.S.* (Traduction en langue française, Louvain 1951).

FERSMAN, A. E., 1931: (*b*) Sur la classification géochimique génétique des pegmatites granitiques. *Min. Petr. Mitteilungen*, XLI.

FISCHER, G., 1951: Granit und Sial. *Geol. Rundschau*, 39, S. 32–77.

FRASL, G., 1954: Anzeichen schmelzflüssigen und hochtemperierten Wachstums an den grossen Kalifeldspaten einiger Porphyrgranite, Porphyrgranitgneise und Augengneise Osterreichs. *Jahrbuch Geol. Bundesanstalt*, XCVII, S. 71–131.

FRIEDEL, G., 1926: *Leçons de Cristallographie*. 1 vol., Paris.

GEOFFROY, J., 1955: Minéralogie et Métallogénie des Gisements d'Uranium et de Thorium dans le monde. *Congrès Centenaire Soc. Industrie Minérale, Paris*. In: *Revue Ind. Minérale*. Numéro Spécial 1R. January 1956, pp. 177–188.

GLANGEAUD, L., 1946: Introduction à l'étude thermodynamique de la pétrogénèse profonde. *Bull. Soc. géol. France*. 5e série, XVI, p. 563.

GLEDITSCH, C., 1950: Sur la formation de gneiss oeillés et de granites d'anatexie d'après des observations dans des zones orogéniques de différentes époques. *Idem*, XX, pp. 345–352.

GOGUEL, J., 1945: Sur l'origine mécanique de la schistosité. *Idem*, XV, pp. 509–522.

GOGUEL, J., 1948: Introduction à l'étude mécanique des déformations de l'écorce terrestre (2nd édition). *Mém. pour servir à l'Explication de la Carte géol. détaillée de la France*. 1 vol., 530 p.

GOGUEL, J., 1952: *Traité de Tectonique*. 1 vol., Paris, 383 p.

GORAI, M., 1950: Proposal of Twin Method for the Study of the Granite Problem. *Geol. Soc. of Japan Journal*, 56, No. 655, pp. 149–156.

GRANDJEAN, F., 1910: Le feldspath néogène des terrains sédimentaires non métamorphiques. *Bull. Soc. française Minéralogie*, 32, p. 103, et 33, p. 92.

GROUT, F. F., 1933: (*a*) Duluth Rocks and Structures. *XVIth Intern. geol. Congress, Washington*, Guidebook 27, p. 67.

GROUT, F. F., 1933: (*b*) Structural Features of the Saganaga Granite. *Idem*, Report, p. 2551.

GROVES, A. W., 1935: The Charnockite Series of Uganda. British East Africa. *Quart. Journal geol. Soc. London*, XCI, pp. 150–207.

GRUBENMANN, U., 1906: *Die Kristallinen Schiefer*. 1 vol., Berlin.

GRUBENMANN, U. and NIGGLI, P., 1924: *Die Gesteinsmetamorphose*. 1 vol. Berlin.

GUIMARAES, D., 1949: Geoquimismo magmatico e origem dos batolitos graniticos. *Estado de Minas Geraes, Inst. Tecnol. Industr.*, Bol. 9.

GUITARD, G., 1953: (a) Sur la présence d'amas gabbro-dioritiques en bordure des migmatites du versant S.O. du Canigou, Pyrénées-Orientales. *Bull. Soc. géol. France*, 6e série, III, pp. 43–57.

GUITARD, G., 1953: (b) La structure du massif du Canigou, *Idem*, III, pp. 907–924.

GUITARD, G. and RAGUIN, E., 1961: Sur les roches ultrabasiques (cortlandites) du Paléozoïque inférieur de la partie orientale des Pyrénées. *C. R. Acad. Sciences*, Paris. 252, p. 3606–3608.

HALL, A. L. and MOLENGRAAFF, G. A., 1925: The Vredefort Mountain Land. *Verhand. Konink. Akad. Wetenschappen Amsterdam*, XXIV, 3.

HALLER, J., 1955: Der zentrale metamorphe Komplex von NE Groenland. Teil I. *Meddelelser om Gronland*, Bd. 73, No. 3.

HAMMER, W., 1914: Das Gebiet der Bündner Schiefer im Tirolischen Oberinntal. *Jahrbuch K. K. Geol. Reichsanstalt*, Bd. 64, S. 555–562.

HARKER, A., 1902: *Pétrographie*. 1 vol., Paris.

HARKER, A., 1952: *Metamorphism*. 3rd edition (reprinted). 1 vol., London.

HAUG, E., 1911: *Traité de Géologie*. 3 vols., Paris, 1908–1911.

HESS, F. L., 1933: The Pegmatites of the Western States. *Lindgren Volume*, published by *Amer. Inst. Min. and Metallug. Engineers*, New York, p. 526–536.

HIETANEN, A., 1947: Archean Geology of the Turku District in Southwestern Finland. *Bull. geol. Soc. America*, 58, pp. 1019–1084.

HOLMQVIST, P. J., 1916: Swedish Archean Structures and their Meaning. *Bull. geol. Inst. of Upsala*, XV.

HOLMQVIST, P. J., 1926: Zur Morphologie der Gesteinsquartz. *Geol. Föreningens Förhandlingar*, 48, H. 3, p. 410.

HOLTEDAHL, O., 1943: Studies on the Igneous Rock Complex of the Oslo Region. *Videnskaps Akademi Oslo*, I, Mat.-Naturv. Klasse, No. 2, 71 p.

HUPÉ, P., 1948: Observations sur le batholite granitique hercynien du Néouvielle, Hautes-Pyrénées. *Bull. Soc. Géol. France*, 5e série, XVIII, *C. R. somm.*, p. 46.

HUPÉ, P., 1949: Sur l'existence du Gothlandien sous le granite du Néouvielle, Hautes-Pyrénées. *Idem*, XIX, *C. R. somm.*, p. 59.

HUPÉ, P., 1951: Sur un type nouveau d'enclaves du granite. *Idem*, 6e série, I., *C. R. somm.*, pp. 59–61.

JACOBSON, R. R. E., 1952: Observation à la communication de P. Lapadu-Hargues (Étude pétrographique du massif antécambrien des Eglab). *C. R. XIXe Congrès géol. intern. Alger*, fasc. I, section I, p. 103.

JAEGER, J., 1951: Remarques au sujet de critères géométriques qui permettraient d'établir le mode de formation de certains filons. *Bull. Soc. Géol. France*, 6e série, I, pp. 611–620.

JAMOTTE, A., 1944: Sur un principe de mobilité de l'émanation et de l'intrusion granitique. *Mém. Comité Spécial du Katanga*.

JEDWAB, J., 1956: Caractérisation spectrochimique des granites. *Bull. Soc. belge Géologie*, LXIV, pp. 526–534.

JÉRÉMINE, E., 1940: Sur quelques granites des Vosges. *C. R. Acad. Sciences*, Paris, 210, p. 571.

JÉRÉMINE, E., LELUBRE, M., and SANDRÉA, A., 1951: Sur une pegmatite à amazonite du Tibesti. *Bull. Soc. géol. France*, 6e série, I, pp. 243–250.

JOHNSTON, W. D. Jr., 1945: Beryl Tantalite Pegmatites of N.E. Brazil. *Bull. Geol. Soc. America*, 56, pp. 1015–1069.

JUNG, J., 1928: Contribution à la géologie des Vosges hercyniennes d'Alsace. *Mém. Service Carte géol. Alsace et Lorraine*, Strasbourg, No. 2, 481 p.

JUNG, J., 1949: Les gneiss œillés de Bort-les-Orgues, Corrèze. *Annales Hébert et Haug*, Paris, VII, pp. 223–238.

JUNG, J., 1958: *Précis de Pétrographie*, Paris.

JUNG, J. and ROQUES, M., 1936: Les zones d'isométamorphisme dans les terrains cristallophylliens du Massif Central français. *Revue Sciences Naturelles Auvergne*, I, fasc. 4, pp. 1–50.

JUNG, J. and ROQUES, M., 1938: Les schistes cristallins du Massif Central. *Bull. Serv. Carte géol. France*, XXXIX, pp. 284–312.

JUNG, J. and ROQUES, M., 1952: Introduction à l'étude zonéographique des formations cristallophylliennes. *Idem*, L. pp. 1–62.

JUNG, J., CHICHERY, M. and VACHIAS, O., 1939: Contribution à l'étude stratigraphique, magmatique et tectonique de la Montagne Bourbonnaise et du Forez. *Mém. Soc. géol. France*, No. 38, t. XVI-XVII.

KAITARO, S. S., 1952: On the lamprophyric Dikes in the Ava Area, The Aland Islands. *XIXe Congrès géol. Internat. Alger*, section VI, fasc. VI, p. 171.

KARL, F., 1959: Vergleichende petrographische Studien an den Tonalitgraniten der Hohe Tauern und den Tonalit-Graniten einiger periadriatischer Intrusivmassive. *Jahrb. Geol. Bundesanstalt*, 102. B., H.I., 192 p.

KATO, IWAO, 1955: Petrogenetic Considerations of the Green Tuffs found in the lower part of the Neogene developed in the Yokote Basin and the Shinjo Basin. *Science Reports of the Tohoku University*. 3rd Series, V, No. 1, Sendaï.

KING, B. C., 1948: The Form and Structural Features of aplite and pegmatite Dikes and Veins in the Osi Area of the Northern Nigeria. *Journ. Geol.*, 56, No. 5, pp. 459–475.

KING, B. C., 1952: Structure and Igneous Activity in the Creag Strollamus Area of Skye. *Trans. Royal Soc. Edinburgh*, LXII, Part II, pp. 357–402.

KING, B. C., 1954: Geology: Metasomatism in Petrogenesis. *Science Progress*, No. 167, London.

KING, B. C. and SWARDT, A. M. J. DE, 1949: The Geology of the Osi Area, Ilorin Province. *Geol. Survey of Nigeria*, Bull. No. 20.

KING, B. C. and RAST, N. 1955: Tectonic Styles in the Dalradian and Moines of parts of the Central Highlands of Scotland. *Proc. Geologist's Association*. Vol. 66, Part 3, pp. 243–269.

KLÜPFEL, W., 1941: Ueber die Altvulkane und die Neuvulkane und ihre Abstammung. *Forschungen und Fortschritte*. 17. *Jahrgang*, No. 16–17, p. 191. (Même titre: *Zentralblatt für Mineralogie*, Abt. B. Nos. 8, 9, 10, 11).

KÖHLER, A., 1941: Die Abhängigkeit der Plagioklasoptik vom vorangegangenen Wärmeverhalten. *Zeitschr. Kristallogr. Min. Petr. Mitt.*, Bd. 53, S. 24–49.

KÖHLER, A., 1950: *Ibidem* (N. Folge), Bd. I, S. 51.

KORN, H. and MARTIN, H., 1954: The Messum Igneous Complex in South-West Africa. *Trans. geol. Soc. South Africa*, LVII, pp. 83–124.

KROKSTRÖM, T., 1932: The Brefven doleritic dike. *Bull. geol. Inst. Upsala*, XXVIII, pp. 242–330.

LACROIX, A., 1899: Le granite des Pyrénées et ses phénomènes de contact. Premier Mémoire. *Bull. Serv. Carte géol. France*, X, p. 241.

LACROIX, A., 1900: Le granite des Pyrénées et ses phénomènes de contact. Deuxième Mémoire. *Idem*, XI, p. 50.

LACROIX, A., 1907: *Produits silicatés de l'éruption de Vésuve.* 1 vol., Paris.

LACROIX, A., 1893–1913: *Minéralogie de la France.* 5 vols., Paris.

LACROIX, A., 1923: *Minéralogie de Madagascar.* 3 vols., Paris.

LACROIX, A., 1933: Contribution à la connaissance des roches éruptives de l'Indochine. *Bull. Service géol. de l'Indochine*, XX, No. 3.

LACROIX, A., 1934: Les minéraux d'étain et de tungstène. *In:* les Ressources de la France d'Outremer, t. II. *Publications Bureau d'Etudes géol. et minières coloniales.* 1 vol., Paris.

LAPADU-HARGUES, P., 1945: Sur l'existence et la nature de l'apport chimique dans certaines séries cristallophylliennes. *Bull. Soc. géol. France*, 5e série, XV, pp. 255–310.

LAPPARENT, J. DE, 1923: *Leçons de Pétrographie.* 1 vol., Paris.

LAPPARENT, J. DE, 1932: Courses géologiques en Finlande. *Bull. Soc. géol. France*, 5e série, II, p. 145.

LAPPARENT, J. DE, 1935: Rythmes du métamorphisme dans les Highlands. *Idem*, V, p. 281.

LAUNAY, L. DE, 1901: Les roches éruptives carbonifères de la Creuse. *Bull. Serv. Carte géol. France*, XII, p. 185.

LEGOUX, P., 1939: Le massif de Man, Côte d'Ivoire. *Bull. Serv. Mines A. O. F.*, Dakar.

LEMOINE, M., 1955: Note préliminaire sur le mode de gisement de certaines ophiolites des Schistes lustrés du Queyras, Hautes-Alpes. *Bull. Soc. géol. France*, 6e série, V, *C. R. somm.*, p. 94.

LINDGREN, W., 1933: Differentiation and Ore Deposition, Cordilleran Region of the U.S. *Lindgren Volume*, published by *Amer. Inst. Min. and Metallurg. Engineers*, New York, p. 152.

LINDGREN, W. and BASTIN, E. S., 1935: The Braden Copper Deposit, Rancagua, Chile. *XVIth Intern. geol. Congress. Copper Resources of the World.* Washington, p. 459.

LJUNGGREN, P., 1954: *The Region of Halia in Dalecarlia, Sweden.* (Thèse). Göteborg. 1 vol., 112 p.

LOVERING, T. S., 1933: Geology of Colorado. In: *XVIth Intern. geol. Congress.* Guidebook 19, Washington.

LUCAS, G., 1942: Description géologique des Monts de Ghar-Rouban. *Bull. Serv. Carte géol. Algérie*, 2e série, No. 16.

LUGEON, M., 1930: Sur l'origine du granite. *C. R. Acad. Sciences*, Paris, 190, p. 1096.

MACKENZIE, W. S. and SMITH, J. V., 1955: The Alkali Feldspars. I. Orthoclase microperthite. *Amer. Mineralogist*, 40, pp. 707–732.

MAGNUSSON, N. H., 1950: Zinc and Lead Deposits of Central Sweden. *XVIIIth Intern. geol. Congress. London 1948.* Part VII, pp. 371–379.

MARTIN, N. R., 1952: The Structure of the Granite Massif of Flamanville, Manche, N.W. France. *Quart. Jour. geol. Soc. London.* CVIII, No. 432, p. 311.

MEHNERT, K. R., 1953: Zur Abfolge der Gesteinsmobilisation im tiefen Grundgebirge ohne Zufuhr. *Geol. Rundschau*, 42, S. 4–11.

MEHNERT, K. R. and WILLGALLIS, A., 1961: Die Alkaliverteilung im Malsburger Granit, Schwarzwald, *Jahrb. Geol. Landesanstalt Baden-Württemberg*, 5, pp. 117–139.

MICHEL, R., 1953: Les schistes cristallins des massifs du Grand-Paradis et de Sesia-Lanzo, Alpes franco-italiennes. *Sciences de la Terre*, Nancy. t. I, No. 3–4, 287 p.

MICHEL-LÉVY, ALB., 1908: Les terrains primaires du Morvan et de la Loire. *Bull. Serv. Carte géol. France*, XVIII, 1907–1908, p. 193.

MICHEL-LÉVY, ALB., 1929: Les éruptions dacitiques et rhyolitiques de la fin des temps primaires dans le Morvan. *Bull. volcanologique*, VIe année, No. 19–22.

MICHEL-LÉVY, ALB., 1930: Quelques observations sur les formations primaires du Morvan. *Livre Jubilaire, Centenaire de la Société géologique de France*, t. II, p. 513.

MICHEL-LÉVY, ALB., 1937: Notice de la Feuille de Château-Chinon. *Carte géol. détaillée de la France au 80,000e*.

MICHEL-LÉVY, ALB., 1939: Synthèse de minéraux par la détonation d'explosifs brisants et par pneumatolyse. *Bull. Soc. géol. France*, 5e série, IX, p. 105.

MICHEL-LÉVY, ALB. and WYART, J., 1946: Reproduction synthétique de la topaze, de la cryolite et du corindon. *Bull. Soc. franç. Minéralogie*, 69, pp. 156–161.

MICHEL-LÉVY, ALB. and WYART, J., 1947: Reproduction artificielle des minéraux silicatés à haute pression. *Mém. Soc. géol. France*, t. XXVI, No. 55.

MICHEL-LÉVY, AUGUSTE, 1889: *Structure et classification des roches éruptives*. 1 vol., Paris.

MICHOT, P., 1948: L'équilibre minéralogique dans les roches éruptives et le cadre géologique. *Acad. Royale Belgique, Bull. Classe des Sciences*, 5e série, 34, pp. 167–187. — Essai d'une classification naturelle des roches granitiques. *Idem*, pp. 449–458.

MICHOT, P., 1955: L'anatexie leuconoritique. *Idem*, 5e série, 41, pp. 374–385.

MORIN, PH., 1952: Mica et béryl, pp. 337–346. *In:* Géologie des Gites minéraux marocains. *Notes et Mémoires Service géol. Maroc*, No. 87.

MUCHEMBLÉ, G., 1943: Sur la radioactivité élevée des roches marines du terrain houiller du Nord de la France. *C. R. Acad. Sciences*, Paris, 216, p. 270.

MUIR, I. D., 1953: A local potassic modification of the Ballachulish Granodiorite. *Geol. Mag.*, XC, No. 3, pp. 182–192.

NIEUWENBURG, C. J. VAN and ZON, VAN, 1935: *Recueil Trav. Chim.*, Pays-Bas, 54, pp. 129–132.

NIEUWENKAMP, W., 1949: De Oorsprong der Materie bij Endogene Gesteente vorming. *Geologie en Mijnbouw*, pp. 289–300.

NIGGLI, E., 1952: Zur Entstehung der Aplit-Pegmatitgänge im Kontakthof des Godolphin-Granites, Cornwall, England. *XIXe Congrès géol. Intern. Alger*, section VI, fasc. VI, pp. 35–41.

NIGGLI, E., 1953: Zur Stereometrie und Entstehung der Aplit-Granit-und Pegmatitgänge im Gebiete von Sept-Laux, Belledonne-Massiv. *Leidse Geologische Mededelingen*, XVII, pp. 215–236.

NIGGLI, P., 1929: *Ore Deposits of Magmatic Origin*. 1 vol., London.

NOE-NYGAARD, A. and BERTHELSEN, A., 1952: On the Structure of a High-Metamorphic Gneiss Complex in West-Greenland. *Meddelelser Dansk Geologisk Forening*, B.12, H. 2, S. 250–265.

NOETZLIN, J., 1940: Volcanisme et chimie nucléaire. *Journal Physique et Radium*, Paris, série 8, t. I, No. 3–4.

PAIGE, S., 1933: The Region around Santa-Rita and Hanover, New Mexico. *XVIth Intern. geol. Congress, Washington*. Guidebook 14, p. 23.

PERRIN, R., 1934: Extrapolation à la géologie de données métallurgiques. *Ann. des Mines*, 13e série, VI, p. 135.

PERRIN, R. and ROUBAULT, M., 1939: Le granite et les réactions à l'état solide. *Bull. Service Carte géol. Algerie*, 5e série, No. 4, 180 p.

PERRIN, R. and ROUBAULT, M., 1945: A propos de la note de M. Lapadu-Hargues sur les schistes cristallins. *Bull. Soc. géol. France*. 5e série, XV, *C. R. somm.*, p. 122.

PERRIN, R. and ROUBAULT, M., 1949: Des critères permettant de déterminer le mode de formation des filons à bords parallèles: injection ou remplacement. *Idem.*, XIX, pp. 641–656.

PERRIN, R. and ROUBAULT, M., 1951: (*a*) Réflexions et discussions à la suite de récents travaux sur les feldspaths. *Idem*, 6e série, I, pp. 105–117.

PERRIN, R. and ROUBAULT, M., 1951: (*b*) La révolution moderne des idées en Pétrographie. *Revue Scientifique*, Paris, No. 3310, pp. 101–109.

PERRIN, R. and ROUBAULT, M., 1955: Granites à enclaves dites déplacées et naissance *in situ* de schistosités discordantes ou contournées. *Sciences de la Terre*, Nancy, numéro hors série (Les échanges de matières au cours de la genèse des roches grenues acides et basiques), pp. 105–118.

PETRASCHECK, W. E. Jr., 1953: Magmatismus und Metallogenese in Südosteuropa. *Geol. Rundschau*, 42, S. 128–143.

PITCHER, W. S., 1953: The Rosses granitic Ring-Complex. County Donegal, Eire. *Proc. Geologist's Association*, London. 64, Part 3, pp. 153–182.

RAGUIN, E., 1927: Contribution à l'étude de la tectonique dans la région ouest du Massif Central français. *Bull. Serv. Carte géol. France*, XXX, p. 419.

RAGUIN, E., 1930: Haute-Tarentaise et Haute-Maurienne, Alpes de Savoie. *Mém. pour servir à l'explication de la Carte géol. détaillée de la France*. 1 vol., 107 p.

RAGUIN, E., 1934: (*a*) Le granite du Lys dans la Haute-Garonne. *Bull. Soc. géol. France*, 5e série, IV, p. 421.

RAGUIN, E., 1934: (*b*) Observations sur les gîtes métallifères de contact. *Idem*, IV, p. 563.

RAGUIN, E., 1949: (*a*) Sur l'évolution du granite de Quérigut, Ariège. *Idem*, XIX, pp. 181–188.

RAGUIN, E., 1949: (*b*) Métallogénie hydrothermale et failles vivantes. *Idem*. XIX, pp. 415–426.

RAGUIN, E., 1950: Observations nouvelles sur le granite de Quérigut, Ariège. *Bull. Soc. Hist. Nat. Toulouse*, t. 85.

RAGUIN, E., 1953: Front de migmatites et métallogénie pyrénéenne. *Geol. Rundschau*, 42, S. 59–62.

RAGUIN, E., 1955: Texture originelle et migrations chimiques dans la gneissification d'un poudingue pyrénéen. *Sciences de la Terre*, Nancy, numéro hors série (Les échanges de matières au cours de la genèse des roches grenues acides et basiques), pp. 17–24.

RAMDOHR, P., 1955: Neue Beobachtungen an Erzen des Witwatersrands in Südafrika. *Abhandl. Deutschen Akad. Wissensch. Berlin* (Kl. Mathematik), Jahrgang 1954, No. 5, 43 S.

RANKAMA, K., 1946: On the geochemical Differentiation in the Earth's Crust. *Bull. Comm. géol. Finlande*, No. 137.

RANKAMA, K. and SAHAMA, T. G., 1950: *Geochemistry*. 1 vol., 912 p. University of Chicago Press.

READ, H. H., 1944: Meditations on Granite (Part 2). *Proc. geol. Assoc.*, LV, 2, pp. 45–94.

READ, H. H., 1948: *In:* Origin of Granite. *Geol. Survey of U.S.A.*, Mem. 28.

READ, H. H., 1949: A Contemplation of Time in Plutonism. *Quart. Journal geol. Soc. London*, CV, Part 1, No. 147, pp. 101–156.

READ, H. H., 1953: Observations à la suite de la communication de Pitcher, W. S. 1953: The migmatitic older Granodiorite of Thorr District, Co. Donegal. *Idem*. CVIII, No. 432, p. 413.

REIN, G., 1951: Die quantitativ-mineralogische Analyse des Malsburger Granitplutons und ihre Anwedung auf Intrusionsform und Differentiationsverlauf. *Jahrb. Geol. Landesanstalt Baden-Württemberg*, 5, pp. 53–115.

REINHARD, M., 1935: Ueber die Gesteinsmetamorphose in den Alpen. *Jaarb. Mijnbouwk. Vereeniging*, Delft, p. 39.

REYNOLDS, D., 1946: The Sequence of Geochemical Changes leading to Granitization. *Quart. Jour. Geol. Soc. London*, CII, p. 389.

RICHEY, J. E., 1948: Scotland. The Tertiary volcanic District. *The Regional Geology of Great Britain* (Geol. Survey and Museum, Edinburgh), 105 p.

RINNE, F., 1949: *La Science des Roches*, 4e édition, 693 p., Paris.

RITTMANN, A., 1936: *Vulkane und ihre Tätigkeit*. 1 vol., Stuttgart.

ROMEU, A. DE, 1907: Les roches filoniennes paléozoïques non granitiques des Pyrénées. *Bull. Soc. Franç. Minéralogie*, 30, p. 110.

ROQUES, M., 1941: Les schistes cristallins de la partie SO du Massif Central français. *Mém. pour servir à l'Explication de la Carte géol. détaillée de la France*. 1 vol., 527 p.

ROQUES, M., 1948: Le Précambrien de l'Afrique Occidentale française. *Bull. Soc. géol. France*, XVIII, pp. 589–628.

ROQUES, M., 1955. Étude quantitative des myrmékites. *Sciences de la Terre*, Nancy, numéro hors série (Les échanges de matières au cours de la genèse des roches grenues et basiques), pp. 189–195.

ROSENBUSCH, H., 1877: Die Steiger Schiefer und ihre Kontaktzone an den Graniten von Barr-Andlau und Hohwald. *Abhandl. geol. Landesanstalt Elsass-Lothringen*, I.

ROSENBUSCH, H., 1910: *Elemente der Gesteinslehre*, 3. Auflage. Stuttgart, 692 S.

ROUBAULT, M., 1934: La Kabylie de Collo. *Bull. Service Carte géol. Algérie*, 2e série, No. 10, 272 p.

ROUBAULT, M., LENOBLE, A. and GANGLOFF, A., 1952: Nouvelles observations sur les pegmatites de Madagascar, *XIXe Congrès Geol. Intern. Alger*, section VI, fasc. VI, pp. 180–199.

SAFIANNIKOFF, A., 1954: Classification des pegmatites du Congo belge et du Ruanda-Urundi. *Ann. Soc. géol. Belgique*, LXXVIII, p. 57.

SANDER, B., 1930: *Gefügekunde der Gesteine*, Wien.

SANDER, B., 1950: *Einführung in die Gefügekunde der geologischen Körper*, Wien.

SAN MIGUEL ARRIBAS, A., 1952: Observations pétrologiques sur les roches lamprophyriques de la Costa Brava Catalana. *XIXe Congrès géol. Intern., Alger*, section VI, fasc. VI, pp. 77–99.

SAN MIGUEL ARRIBAS, A., 1955: Les caractéristiques structurales du granite de la Costa Brava et leur signification pétrogénétique. *Sciences de la Terre*, Nancy, numéro hors série (Les échanges de matières au cours de la genèse des roches grenues acides et basiques), pp. 37–60.

SCHALLER, W. T., 1933: Pegmatites. *Lindgren Volume*, published by *Amer. Inst. Min. and Metallurg. Engineers*, New York, p. 144.

SCHERMERHORN, L. J. G., 1956: Petrogenesis of a Porphyritic Granite East of Oporto, Portugal. *Tschermaks Min. Petr. Mitt.*, VI, H. 1–2, S. 73–115.

SCHEUMANN, K. H., 1952: Die Bedeutung der lamprophyrischen Differenziation für die Herkunft granitischer Plutonite. *XIXe Congrès géol. Intern. Alger*, section VI, fasc. VI, pp. 163–168.

SCHMIDT, W., 1932: *Tektonik und Verformungslehre*, Berlin.

SCHNEIDERHÖHN, H., 1941: *Lehrbuch der Erzlagerstättenkunde*, I. Band, Jena.

SCHNEIDERHÖHN, H., 1952: Genetische Lagerstättengliederung auf geotektonischer Grundlage. *Neues Jahrbuch für Mineralogie*, S. 47–89.

SCHÜLLER, A., 1951: Petrographie und tektonische Stellung des metamorphen Granites von Dessau. *Neues Jahrbuch für Mineralogie (Abhandlungen)*, Bd. 82, H. 1–2, S. 121–142.

SCRIVENOR, J. B., 1928: *The Geology of Malayan Ore Deposits*, 216 pp., London.

SEDERHOLM, J. J., 1891: Studien über archäische Eruptivgesteine aus dem Südwestlichen Finnland. *Tschermaks Min. Petr. Mitt.*, XII, S. 134–141.

SEDERHOLM, J. J., 1916: On synantetic Minerals. *Bull. Comm. géol. Finlande*, No. 48.

SEDERHOLM, J. J., 1923: On Migmatites and associated Precambrian Rocks of Southwestern Finland, Part I. *Idem*, No. 58.

SEDERHOLM, J. J., 1926: On Migmatites and associated Precambrian Rocks of Southwestern Finland, Part II. *Idem*, No. 77.

SEDERHOLM, J. J., 1928: On orbicular Granites. *Idem*, No. 83.

SHAND, S. J., 1917: The Pseudotachylit of Parijs, Orange Free State. *Quart. Journal Geol. Soc. London*, 72, No. 287, pp. 198–221.

SHAND, S. J., 1927: *Eruptive Rocks*, London.

SIMONEN, A., 1940: Orbicular Rocks in Kemijärvi and Esbo. *C. R. Soc. géol. Finlande*, XIV, pp. 107–142.

SIMONEN, A., 1950: Three new Boulders of Orbicular Rocks in Finland. *Idem*. XXIII, pp. 31–38.

SITTER, L. U. DE and SITTER-KOOMANS, C. M. DE, 1949: The Geology of the Bergamasc Alps. *Leidse Geologische Mededelingen*, Deel XIV B.

SPURR, J. E., 1923: *The Ore Magma*, New York.

STEWART, D. B., 1956: Rapakivi granite from Eastern Penobscot Bay, Maine. *XXth Intern. geol. Congress, Mexico*. Reports. Section XI A, pp. 293–320.

SUESS, E., 1921: *La Face de la Terre* (Trad. E. de Margerie), 3 vols., Paris.

SUESS, F. E., 1926: *Intrusionstektonik und Wandertektonik im Variszischen Grundgebirge*. 1 vol., Berlin.

SULLIVAN, C. J., 1948: Ore and Granitization. *Econ. Geol*, XLIII, pp. 471–498.

TERMIER, H. and G., 1945: Le massif du Tischka. *Bull. Soc. Géol. France*, 5e série, XV, *C. R. somm.*, pp. 35, 45, 65.

TERMIER, H. and G., 1953: Géologie et Pétrogénèse. *Publications Service Carte géol. Algérie*, nouvelle série, Bull. No. 2.

TERMIER, P., 1897: Sur le granite du Pelvoux. *C. R. Acad. Sciences*, Paris. 124. p. 317.

TERMIER, P., 1898: Sur l'élimination de la chaux par métasomatose dans les roches éruptives basiques de la région du Pelvoux. *Bull. Soc. géol. France*, 3e série, XXVI, p. 165.

TERMIER, P., 1899: Microgranites de la vallée de la Guisanne, bord nord du massif du Pelvoux. *Idem*, XXVII, p. 399.

TERMIER, P., 1910: Sur la genèse des terrains cristallophylliens. *XIe Congrès géol. International, Stockholm*.

TERMIER, P., 1932: Un article de dictionnaire. In: *Mélanges*, 1 vol., Paris.

TERMIER, H., OWODENKO, B., and AGARD, J., 1950: Les gîtes d'étain de la région d'Oulmès. *Service géol. du Maroc. Notes et Mémoires*, No. 82, 328 p.

THIÉBAUT, J., 1951: Étude géologique des terrains métamorphiques de la Grande-Kabylie. *Bull. Serv. Carte géol. Algérie*, 5e série, Pétrographie, No. 6.

THOMAS, H. H. and CAMPBELL-SMITH, W., 1932: Xenoliths of igneous origin in the Trégastel-Ploumanach Granite. *Quart. Jour. geol. Soc. London*, LXXXVIII, pp. 274–296.

TILLEY, C. E., 1949: An alkali facies of Granite at Granite-Dolomite Contacts in Skye. *Geol. Mag.*, 86, pp. 81–93.

TILLEY, C. E., 1951: The zoned Contact Skarns of the Broadford Area, Skye. *Mineralog. Magazine*, London, 29, pp. 621–666.

TOPKAYA, M., 1950: *Recherches sur les silicates authigènes dans les roches sèdimentaires* (Thèse). Lausanne, 132 p.

TURNER, F. J., 1951: Observations on Twinning of Plagioclases in Metamorphic Rocks. *Amer. Mineralogist*, 36, pp. 581–589.

TURNER, F. J. and VERHOOGEN, J., 1951: *Igneous and metamorphic Petrology*, New York, 602 p.

TUTTLE, O. F., 1952: (a) Optical Studies on Alkali Feldspars. *Amer. Jour. Science* (Bowen Volume), pp. 553–567.

TUTTLE, O. F., 1952: (b) Origin of the contrasting Mineralogy of extrusive and plutonic salic Rocks. *Jour. of Geology*, 60, No. 2, pp. 107–124.

TUTTLE, O. F., 1955: L'origine et la classification des granites à la lumière des études expérimentales. *Sciences de la Terre*, Nancy, numéro hors série (Les échanges de matières au cours de la genèse des roches grenues, acides et basiques), pp. 299–309.

TUTTLE, O. F., 1955: Degré géothermique et magmas granitiques. *Sciences de la Terre*, Nancy, No. hors-série, p. 87–100.

TUTTLE, O. F. and BOWEN, N. L., 1958: Origin of Granite in the Light of Experimental Studies in the System $NaAlSi_3O_8$—$KAl Si_3O_8$—SiO_2—H_2O. *G.S.A. Memoir* 74, 154 p.

VANDERNOTTE, L., 1913: *Contribution à l'étude géologique des roches éruptives de la bordure SE du Massif Armoricain*, 1 vol., Paris.

VARLAMOFF, N., 1946: La répartition de la minéralisation d'après la clef géochimique de Fersman. *Ann. Soc. Géol. Belgique*, LXX, No. 3, pp. B 108–138.

VARLAMOFF, N., 1948: Gisements de cassitérite de la région de Kalima, Maniema, Congo Belge. *Idem*, LXXI, No. 7, pp. B 194–237.

VARLAMOFF, N., 1949: Granites et minéralisation au Maniema. *Idem*, LXXIII, pp. M 111–169.

VARLAMOFF, N., 1954: (a) Transitions entre les aplites et les pegmatites dans les zones de contact des massifs granitiques du Maniema. *Idem*, LXXVII, pp. B. 101–116.

VARLAMOFF, N., 1954: (b) Tendances actuelles dans l'étude des pegmatites. *Idem*, LXXVII, pp. B 245–267.

VARLAMOFF, N., 1956: Matériaux pour l'étude des pegmatites du Congo Belge et du Ruanda-Urundi. *Idem*, LXXIX, pp. B 385–403.

VERNADSKY, W., 1924: *La Géochimie*. 1 vol., Paris.

VLASSOV, K. A., 1955. Les différenciations par émanation et par cristallisation comme facteurs de concentration des éléments rares. *Sciences de la Terre*, Nancy, numéro hors série (Les échanges de matières au cours de la genèse des roches grenues acides et basiques), pp. 197–212.

WAARD, D. DE, 1949: Tectonics of the Mont Aigoual Pluton in the Southeastern Cévennes, France. *Proc. Kon. Nederlandsche Akademie van Wetenschappen*, LII, No. 43, pp. 389–403.

WAHL, W. A., 1937: The Granites of the Finnish Part of the Svecofennian Archaean Mountain Chain. *Bull. Comm. géol. Finlande*, 115, pp. 489–505.

WALTON, M. S., 1952: In: *XIXe Congrès géol. Internat. Alger. C. R. des Excursions au Maroc* (Granite de Skoura). Une Brochure, 92 pp., Rabat, 1954.

WALTON, M. S., 1955: The Emplacement of Granite. *Amer. Jour. Science*. Vol. 253, pp. 1–18.

WEGMANN, C. E., 1930: Ueber Diapirismus. *C. R. Soc. géol. Finlande*, No. 3, pp. 1–19.

WEGMANN, C. E., 1931: (*a*) Uebersicht über die Geologie des Felsgrundes im Küstengebiete zwischen Helsingfors und Onas. *Bull. Comm. Géol. Finlande*, No. 89, pp. 1–65.

WEGMANN, C. E., 1931: (*b*) Ueber einige Deformations- und Bewegungstypen Kristalliner Schiefer. *Idem*. No. 93, pp. 40–54.

WEGMANN, C. E., 1932: Note sur le boudinage. *Bull. Soc. géol. France*. 5e série, II, p. 477.

WEGMANN, C. E., 1935: (*a*) Zur Deutung der Migmatite. *Geol. Rundschau*, 26, p. 305.

WEGMANN, C. E., 1935: (*b*) Ueber einige Fragen der Tiefentektonik. *Idem*. 26, p. 448.

WEGMANN, C. E., 1935: (*c*) Preliminary Report on the Caledonian Orogeny in Christian X Land (N.E. Greenland). *Meddelelser om Gronland*, 103, No. 3.

WEGMANN, C. E., 1938: Geological Investigations in Southern Greenland. *Idem*, 113, No. 2.

WEGMANN, C. E., 1947: Note sur quelques problèmes de la Tectonique superposée. *C. R. Soc. géol. Finlande*, XX, pp. 223–238.

WEGMANN, C. E., 1955: Les ordres de grandeur dans les phénomènes métasomatiques des roches. *Sciences de la Terre*, Nancy, numéro hors série (Les échanges de matières au cours de la genèse des roches grenues acides et basiques) pp. 169–176.

WEGMAN, C. E. and KRANKE, E. H., 1931: Beiträge zur Kenntnis der Svecofenniden in Finland. *Bull. Comm. géol. Finlande*, No. 89.

WENK, E., 1953: Prinzipielles zur geologisch-tektonischen Gliederung des Penninikums in zentralen Tessin. *Eclog. Geol. Helvetiae*, 46, pp. 9–21.

WEPP, M., 1950: Contribution à l'étude des gîtes de tungstène français. *Géologie Appliquée et Prospection Minière*, Nancy, III, No. 1–2–3.

WESTERWELD, J., 1936: The Granites of the Malayan Tin-Belt compared with Tin-Granites from other Regions. *Proc. Kon. Akad. Wetenschappen Amsterdam*, 39, No. 10, p. 1199.

WESTERWELD, J., 1941: Mineralisatie op de Tineilanden. *Jaarboek der Mijnbouwkundige Studenten te Delft*, 1938–41, p. 187.

WHITTEN, E. H. T., 1960: Quantitative evidence of palimpsestic ghost-stratigraphy from modal analysis of a granitic complex. *XXIst Intern. geol. Congress, Copenhagen*, Reports. Part XIV, pp. 182–193.

WINKLER, H. G. F., 1960: La genèse du granite et des migmatites par anatexie expérimentale, *Rev. Géogr. phys. Géol. dynam.*, Paris, No. 3, p. 67–76.

WINKLER, H. G. F. and PLATEN, H. v., 1957–1960: Experimentelle Gesteinsmetamorphose. *Geochim. Cosmochim. Acta*, 13, 1957, p. 42–59; 15, 1958, p. 91–112.

WRIGHT, F. E., 1906: Schistosity by Cristallisation. *Amer. Jour. Science*, XXII.

WYART, J., 1945: Action de l'eau et de solutions potassiques agissant sous pression sur les différentes formes de silice. *C. R. Acad. Sciences*, Paris, 220, p. 830.

WYART, J., 1947: Solubilité de la potasse dans la vapeur d'eau et cristallisation de la silice amorphe. *Bull Soc. française Minéralogie*, 70, p. 38.

WYART, J. and SABATIER, G., 1959: Transformation des sédiments pélitiques à 800° et granitisation. *Bull. Soc. Fr. Minér. Crist.*, 82, p. 201–210.

ZAVARITSKY, A., 1947: Les pegmatites, formations intermédiaires entre les roches éruptives et les filons hydrothermaux. *Mém. Soc. russe de Minéralogie*, 76, No. 1, p. 37.

GLOSSARY OF TERMS

The numbers indicate the pages on which the terms are defined.

Agmatites 47
Alaskite 139
Allotriomorphic (texture) 1
Anatexis 45
Anatexites 47
Antecedent (veins) 108
Aplites 139
Arterites 47
Assimilation 59
Asthenolith 201
Aureole 86
Automorphic 1
Autopneumatolysis 164
Baregiennes 106
Barylites 28
Batholith 30
Blastesis 19
Boudinage 106
Catazone 189
Chemical front 94
Charnokite 57
Chonolith 38
Cloosian (tectonic) 116
Contact (metamorphism) 86
Coupholites 28
Crystalloblastesis (*see* Blastesis) 19
Crystalloblastic (texture) 90
Cryptoperthite 11
Diablastic (texture) 93
Diaphthoresis 190
Dictyonite 198
Differential anatexis 55, 285
Differentiation 125
Dilational (veins) 144
Dissogenite 83
Ectinite 174

Embrechite 47
Enallogenic (inclusion) 72
Enclave, inclusion 72
Endometasomatism 22
Endomorphism 80
Endopolygenic (inclusion) 72
Epibolite 47
Epimetamorphism 189
Epizone 188
Filtering column 281
Fissures 116
Granitization 7
Granoblastic (texture) 93
Granophyre 138
Granulite 14
Greisen 103
Homoeogenic (inclusion) 72, 128
Hornfels 88
Hypidiomorphic (texture) 16
Ichor 47
Idiomorphic 1
Juvenile 231
Lamprophyre 153
Lepidoblastic (texture) 93
Leptynolite 88
Lithophyse 2
Lithosphere 258
Lopolith 261
Magma 7
Mesostase 2
Mesozone 189
Metamorphism 173
Metasomatism 6
Miarolitic 18
Micropegmatite 13
Migma 49

Migmatite 45
Mineralizers 141
Mylonite 165
Myrmekite 13, 23
Nebulite 47
Nematoblastic (texture) 93
Ophthalmite 47
Orbicular (structure) 18
Orthogneiss 175
Palingenesis 54
Paragenesis 97
Paragneiss 175
Pegmatite 139
Perthite 11
Phacolith 38
Phasmatoclasic (inclusion) 77
Phenoblast 90
Phlebite 47
Plagidiomorphic (texture) 16
Pluton 30
Plutonic 1
Pneumatogenic (inclusion) 128
Pneumatolysis 87, 98, 139
Pneumatolytes 87, 141
Poecilitic (texture) 90
Poeciloblastic (texture) 93
Porphyroblast 90

Porphyritic (granite) 17
Protoclasis 170
Pseudotachylite 169
Ptymatic (folds) 196
Pyrosphere 257
Rapakiwi 69
Retromorphosis 190
Rheomorphism 6
Saussuritization 164
Schillerization 12
Schlieren (facies of variation in streaks)
Septum 48
Sial 259
Sima 259
Skarn (metalliferous pyroxene hornfels)
Stock 30
Stress 177
Stromatite 47
Structure 15
Sutured texture (*structure engrenée*) 16
Symmigmatic (folds) 47
Tactite 88
Texture 15
Variation (facies of) 127
Venites 47
Xenoliths 72